LONGMAN

HOMEWORK HANDBOOKS

KEY STAGE 3

SCIENCE

Christine Millican
Keith Palfreyman and Elaine Wilson

LONGMAN

HOMEWORK HANDBOOKS

Series editors:

Geoff Black and Stuart Wall

Other titles in this series:

ENGLISH
FRENCH
GERMAN
MATHEMATICS

Addison Wesley Longman Ltd.
Edinburgh Gate, Harlow
Essex CM20 2JE
England
and Associated Companies throughout the world.

First Published 1996

ISBN 0582 29328-6

British Library Cataloguing in Publication Data
A catalogue record for this title is available from the British Library

Set in 9.5/11 pt Stone by 30

Printed in Great Britain by Henry Ling Ltd. at the Dorset Press, Dorchester, Dorset

CONTENTS

ACKNOWLEDGEMENTS

I would like to express my thanks to my family for all the help that they have given me during the writing of my section of this book, especially to my wife for yet more patience and my sons for reading and checking material. The pupils of Pope Pius School have been helpful as always – sometimes without being aware of it!! – and the other two authors have been most co-operative in making the process as smooth as possible.

Keith Palfreyman

Clive Hurford for advice and support while writing the book. Angela Bullard for typing the manuscript. Neil Ellis of Ogwr DASH for advice and information on drugs and health.

Christine Millican

USING THIS BOOK

You will find in this book entries, arranged in alphabetical order, on a variety of terms and topics relevant to Key Stage 3 Science, including:

- definitions of scientific materials such as metals, chemicals, parts of the body, plants and animals;
- examples of experiments such as photosynthesis and fractional distillation;
- topical issues such as drugs, food and diet;
- accounts of leading scientists and their work;

All three Science subjects, Biology, Chemistry and Physics are covered.

Where reference is made to another entry in the book, bold italic lettering in the second colour is used, as in the following example:

ACID RAIN

Rain normally has a ***pH*** of 5.6, but acid rain has a pH less than this. This is because rain becomes contaminated by pollutant gases, such as sulphur dioxide from coal and oil fired power stations and nitrogen dioxide from car exhausts. These pollutant gases of sulphur dioxide and nitrogen dioxide then react in the ***atmosphere*** to form sulphuric acid and nitric acid. Both of these are ***strong acids***, which lower the pH of the rain to below 5.6.

Acid rain has many negative effects:

- It causes corrosion in buildings and metal structures.
- It is also linked with a number of illnesses involving respiration, such as asthma.
- It kills off wildlife by making streams and lakes too acidic to support life.
- It removes vital ***elements***, such as magnesium from the soil and so interferes with plant growth.

This indicates that there is a separate entry on ***PH***, ***atmosphere***, ***strong acids*** and ***elements*** else where in the book, which you might find helpful to refer to when thinking about the topic acid rain.

In addition, at the end of some entries you will find a list of other entries which you might also find useful. The entry on ***alternating current (ac)***, for example, ends with the following:

Current, Direct current, Earth, Frequency

Again, it may be useful for you to look at these entries when thinking about ***alternating current***

Throughout the book there are also checkpoint exercises to help you practice what you have just learnt. The answers to these can be found at the back of the book.

At the end of the book there are also two appendices. The first gives a detailed account of how to approach an investigation. The second gives the National Curriculum Programmes of Study for Science (see also p.xi). Please read these carefully to give you a better understanding of what will be expected of you when studying Key Stage 3 Science.

SCIENCE AT KEY STAGE 3

In order to assess Science, the National Curriculum divides Science in four sections, called Attainment Targets (AT's).

AT 1 Experimental and Investigative Science (Teacher Assessed)
AT 2 Life Processes and Living Things (mainly Biology)
AT 3 Materials and their Properties (mainly Chemistry)
AT 4 Physical Processes (mainly Physics)

Appendix 2 at the end of the book provides a brief outline of what you should know under each of the topic headings for Key Stage 3, called the *Programmes of Study*. The alphabetical arrangement of entries in this book cover these Programmes of Study, which are the basis for the National Tests at Key Stage 3.

HOW TO APPROACH HOMEWORK

This book is one of a series of Homework Handbooks books on different Key Stage 3 subjects. They are called Homework Handbooks because they contain information and advice which should be useful to you when you are studying and working at home. You will find information on important topics and exercises to help you measure your own progress. There is also a section helping you to write up your practical investigations. In this introductory section we shall first look at homework itself, asking WHY, WHERE, WHEN and HOW:

WHY? – What is homework for?
WHERE? – Where should you do homework?
WHEN? – When should you do homework?
HOW? – How should you do homework?

WHAT IS HOMEWORK FOR?

There is a tendency for pupils to think of homework as an unnecessary burden imposed on them by teachers who simply want to see them suffer! In fact, however, homework is an essential part of your Science course, as there are many necessary and relevant tasks that cannot be completed at school, either because there is not enough time in the school day or because school is not an appropriate environment for the tasks concerned.

Some of the main uses and advantages of homework are listed below.

- It enables you to undertake longer pieces of work (such as projects) for which there is insufficient time at school. Such assignments sometimes require you to carry out *research*, often of a kind which cannot easily be conducted in school. You may need to consult books in a library or speak to your family or friends.
- Homework can be used to prepare for activities which are to take place during lesson time. If your class is to have a discussion on a topical issue, for example, homework time can be used to find out more about the subject and to prepare what you are going to say.
- Homework enables you to improve and develop your skills in the subject. The old saying 'Practice makes perfect' is relevant here. The more investigations that you write about, numerical problems that you solve and material that you read and learn, the more your understanding of science will improve.
- Homework gives you time to learn equations and check that you understand the principles behind your current work.
- Homework also helps to develop attitudes and qualities which will serve you well in later life. It encourages self-discipline, concentration and the ability to work independently.

WHERE SHOULD YOU DO HOMEWORK?

The obvious answer to this question is 'at home', and it is of course here that most of your homework is likely to be done. Occasionally, however, you might be able to make use of other locations. These include:

School

There might be certain times in the week when you are able to work on your homework at school, perhaps in the library. Some schools provide a room for a homework club.

Libraries

As a school student, you should make full use of your school library and your local public library. The books and other resources contained in a library can help you not just with your Science work, but with your other subjects as well. You will also find many books that you can read for pleasure or interest.

In this section we shall explain how libararies are organized and suggest how you can get the most out of the libraries available to you.

Types of library

- **School libraries**. Your school library is likely to have books on each of the subjects you are studying and books that are especially suitable for your age group. You should make sure you have a good working knowledge of your school library. The following points are especially important:
  - What is the general layout of the library? Where is the reference section? (This contains encyclopaedias, etc. which are permanently available for reference and cannot be borrowed.) Where are magazines and newspapers kept? Are there quiet areas for private study?
  - Where on the shelves are the books most likely to be of interest to you? This includes books on the subjects you are studying and books relating to your hobbies and interests.
  - Find out where the libarary's cataloguing system is and how to use it. Are details of the books in the library listed on computer, or are there card indexes or printed catalogues? (For more on this, see 'Finding what you want' below.)

- Find out what newspapers and magazines are stocked. Are there any that might be of particular interest to you? Are any back issues stored in the library?
- Ask if there are any special collections of books or other materials (e.g. project packs) relevant to your subjects. Often these are stored behind the library counter.
- Find out about the borrowing arrangements – how many books can you take out, and for how long?
- What are the opening hours?
- Are there photocopying facilities?
- Find out how to order books. If the library does not have a book you want, it may be willing to buy the book for you. Alternatively, there may be an inter-library loan system, which means that if another school library in the area has the book, your library can get it for you. If the book you want is out on loan to another pupil, you should be able to reserve it.
- Don't be afraid to ask the library staff about any of these points.

● **Public libraries**. Most of the above applies to public libraries as well. Familiarize yourself with your local library and with the books, magazines, and reference materials and so on that it contains. Public libraries are usually bigger than school libraries and stock a wider range of books. Local libraries are especially useful for obtaining information about your local area.

Finding what you want

In order to find what you want in a library, you need to know how the library's stock of books is arranged. The system used by the majority of libraries for organizing books is the *Dewey decimal system*. This numbers books according to the following main categories:

0 – General Works
100 – Philosophy
200 – Religion
300 – Society
400 – Languages
500 – Science
600 – Technology
700 – Arts
800 – Literature
900 – History

Each of these main categories is then broken down further into smaller divisions and subsections. Science, for example, includes Medicine (610), Physics (350) and Botany (580). A subsection of Medicine is Diseases (616) and a subsection of Diseases is Diseases of the digestive system (616.3).

The books in most libraries are arranged on the shelves in number order, using this system. Finding the book or books that you need is relatively straightforward provided you know one of two things:

- the classification number of the subject you are interested in; or
- if you are searching for a particular book and know the title and author, the classification number of that particular book.

In both cases the relevant number can be found by consulting the library indexes and catalogues. These are of four main kinds:

● **Subject index**. Here subjects are arranged in alphabetical order and the classification number for each subject is given. For any one assignment you may need to look up several different subjects. For an assignment on pollution, for example, you might look up such terms as 'pollution', 'environment' and 'ozone layer'. If you cannot find the subject index, try to think of a word with a similar or closely related meaning. If you are writing an assignment on cigarette smoking, for instance, you might not find 'cigarettes' listed, but might have better luck with 'tobacco' or 'smoking'.

After consulting the subject index, you may find when you go to the shelves that there are a large number of books on the subject and that you are not sure where to start. In this situation it is best to spend some time glancing along the titles on the shelves, taking out any books that look as if they might be of use and skimming through the contents or index pages to check what they cover.

● **Classified catalogue**. This lists the books in the library in number order. This means that if you know the Dewey number of the subject you are interested in, you can check which books the library has on that subject. This catalogue includes books which are not on the shelves because they are out on loan, and in the case of the public libraries often also lists books which can be found in other libraries within the same area.

● **Author index**. This lists authors' names alphabetically, and gives the titles of books by each author together with their classification number. If you are searching for a particular book and know the author's name, this is the index to use.

● **Title index**. Here books are listed alphabetically according to their titles. For each title the index identifies the authors and the classification number.

These indexes and catalogues come in various forms. Usually they are stored on computer, but there may also be card indexes, printed catalogues or microfiche indexes (these are sheets of acetate which are placed on a viewer for scanning).

Sources of information in a library

Of course, the books that you can borrow are the most obvious source of the information in a library. However, you should not overlook the following:

- **The reference section**. The reference section of any library contains *encyclopaedias*, *dictionaries* and other reference books which cannot be taken out on loan. The great advantage of a reference section is that the books and other material contained within it should always be available for you to use. When you go to a reference section to carry out research for an assignment, take with you a list of the main topics your assignment covers. Always make a careful note of the source of any information that you find, as this may need to be included in your assignment.
- **Newspapers and magazines**. Public libraries in particular usually carry a large stock of these, and often keep back issues of some publications. For some newspapers there are indexes to help you locate articles on a particular subject.
- **Information on computer**. Much information can be accessed by computer. Many libraries make use of CD-ROM, which stands for Compact Disc – Read Only Memory. These are discs which are capable of storing massive amounts of information and which can be read on a computer screen. Many complete books, including encyclopaedias and dictionaries, and back issues of magazines and newspapers are now available on computer disc.

Note, however, that public libraries are often quite busy places and it can be difficult to concentrate if you want to work there.

Friends' houses

Some homework activities lend themselves to a group approach, and helping each other with homework tasks can be a useful way for you and your friends to learn. You can also prepare for tests by asking each other questions on relevant topics. Remember, however, that if your teacher expects an assignment to be your own work, it should be that and not something that you have simply copied from someone else. Remember also that it is easy to be distracted if you are in the company of your friends – avoid the temptation to spend the whole time watching television or playing computer games.

Working at home

As far as working at **home** is concerned, here are a few pieces of advice:

- Try to work at a desk or table. This makes writing easier and sitting upright at a desk encourages a focused, workmanlike attitude. The desk should be as free of clutter as possible.
- Although unnecessary items should be cleared from the desk, make sure that when you sit down to work your pens, pencils, paper, a ruler and anything else you might need are near at hand. Getting up to look for things in the middle of a piece of work breaks your concentration.
- The surroundings in which you work should be as quiet as possible. If you have your own room this will usually be the best place to go. Pupils who say they work best with the television on or music playing in the background are usually fooling themselves: noise generally interferes with concentration and you will almost certainly work more efficiently if there are no distractions.

WHEN SHOULD YOU DO HOMEWORK?

If homework is left to the last minute, this is likely to mean that the work concerned is either rushed (in which case what you produce will not do justice to your ability) or not done at all. To avoid this you need to *organize* your time. The easiest way to do this is to have a *timetable*.

You will already have a timetable for each school day, in which different periods of time are allocated to different subjects. A homework timetable simply extends this system into the hours outside school. At its simplest, a blank homework timetable for a particular day might look like this:

	4–5 pm	*5–6 pm*	*6–7 pm*	*7–8 pm*	*8–9 pm*
Monday					

You then fill in the blank spaces, allocating different time periods to each subject you are studying. Of course not all of the hours will be occupied by homework. You need free time for meals and activities such as sport, watching favourite television programmes and general relaxation. It is worth writing any regular recreational activities into the timetable as well, as it shows you the amount of spare time that is available for homework. Try to have some periods of time during the week that are completely free (Sunday mornings, for example). Such times are then available when needed for homework activities that take longer than usual (such as revising for tests).

Often your school will provide you with some form of homework schedule, so that you know when in the week particular homeworks will be set, and how much time you need to allocate to each subject. If so you need to estimate how much time to allot to the different subjects you are studying. Try to divide the time fairly equally, though it makes sense to give a bit of extra time to subjects you find especially difficult.

If at any time you feel you are in danger of being swamped by homework, try to remain calm and re-organize your time accordingly. Write down a list of all that you have to do, and work out when each item in the list can be done. For longer pieces of work it helps in any case to have an *Action Plan*, in which the assignment is broken down into a series of short, manageable tasks. If what you need to do really does seem to be impossible in the time available to you, speak to a teacher or one of your parents about it.

How should you do homework?

Assuming you have decided when and where you are going to do your homework, here is some final advice on *how* you should do it:

- Just as your overall homework schedule needs to be organized, so too do the individual tasks and assignments within it. Tasks become easier if they are broken down into smaller steps. Make a list of things that you need to do and arrange them in a sensible order. Approach your work in a methodical, organized way.
- If you find work difficult, try not to lose heart too easily. If you can't find what you are looking for in one book, try another.
- It can help to talk and work with others. Talking to parents and friends might give you fresh ideas on how to approach a particular topic and increase your confidence.
- Try not to be afraid to approach teachers for information and advice. They will usually be happy to help you.
- Try to be serious and businesslike in your approach to homework and once you have started on a task, stick with it. Do not continually break off to watch television, eat biscuits and so on. At the same time, do not overdo things. If you start to feel tired, irritated or bad-tempered, take a break – or go to bed!
- Don't try to do revision in long sections of time, especially not at the last minute. It will always be easier to revise if you include it in your timetable as regular shorter sessions. You can then concentrate better and learn more efficiently. Make sure that you know what you need to *learn* rather than *understand*. Try to *do* something such as writing down key words or very short notes instead of just reading the work. This will help you to keep your concentration.
- Finding information. You will probably find the help or information that you need in the alphabetic section of this book and there is a short list of cross references at the end of each section to lead you to more material. If you do not find what you want, do try other sources, especially other books in your library, and don't be afraid to use the encyclopaedias. You may also find a lot of useful science on the computer C.D. rom's that contain a modern electronic encylopaedia.
- Action Plans. You will probably find it useful to make an action plan, especially for longer pieces of work, so that you know what you are going to do and when you are going to do it. Try to be realistic about the time that you decide to spend. The following example may help.

DATE	TASK	TIME	COMMENTS
Mon. 2 Feb./ Tues. 3 Feb. (lunchtimes)	Refer to encyclopaedias/other books in school library. Make notes.	30 mins x 2	Ask librarian for advice on where to find information
Mon. 2 Feb. (after school)	Visit local library – look for useful books to borrow	30 mins	As above
Tues. 3 Feb. (Eve.)	Make notes from library books	1 hr	
Weds. 4 Feb. (Eve.)	Write plan	30 mins	
Sat. 7 Feb. (a.m.)	Write first draft	1 hr	Finish Sun. a.m. if necessary
Sun. 8 Feb. (p.m.)	Check through first draft, note improvements, copy out finished version		

Action plan

ABDOMEN

In humans, this is the part of the body below the ***diaphragm***, containing the stomach and intestines, liver, kidneys, and the reproductive organs. In *insects*, this is the third section of the body.

ABSOLUTE ZERO

This is the lowest possible ***temperature*** and is used as the zero of the ***Kelvin*** temperature scale.

When you heat up a material, the particles that it is made from move faster. If you cool it down, the particles move slower. We notice this as a change in temperature. If you cool the material enough its particles will stop and you cannot make it any colder. The temperature when this happens is called absolute zero. Absolute zero is –273°C.

Kelvin, Kinetic theory, Temperature, Temperature scale

ABSORPTION

This is when small food molecules move through the gut wall into the ***blood***. Most foods, e.g. ***proteins***, ***carbohydrates*** and ***fats***, have to be digested before they can be absorbed, but some are already small and do not need to be digested, e.g. ***vitamins***, ***minerals*** and some sugars.

Absorption occurs in the ileum (small intestine). The walls of the ileum are covered with villi to increase the surface area, so absorption is very efficient. Food is absorbed into the blood, then it is taken directly to the ***liver*** to be processed.

ACCELERATION

When ***speed***, or ***velocity***, changes there is an acceleration. Acceleration measures *how fast* the speed is changing.

The units will be m/s^2 (because they are velocity units per second = m per s per s = m/s^2).

You can find acceleration from:

$$\text{Acceleration} = \frac{\text{Change in velocity}}{\text{Time taken}}$$

If the answer to your calculation is a negative number it means that the body is slowing down rather than speeding up – it is *decelerating*. The acceleration is a ***vector*** because it takes place in a particular direction.

For example:

1. A car moving at 2m/s accelerates to 11m/s in 12 s. What is its acceleration?

$$\text{Acceleration} = \frac{\text{Change in velocity}}{\text{Time taken}} = \frac{11-2}{12} = \frac{9}{12} = 0.75 \text{ m/s}^2$$

2. The driver of a train, moving at 20m/s, brakes until the velocity becomes 5m/s. If the braking takes 30s what is the deceleration?

$$\text{Change in velocity} = v-u = 5-20 = -15 \text{ m/s}$$

$$\text{Acceleration} = \frac{\text{Change in velocity}}{\text{Time taken}} = \frac{-15}{30} = -0.5 \text{ m/s}^2$$

You should remember that the negative sign means that it is slowing down.

Remember: It will need a force to produce an acceleration.

CHECKPOINT

A change of speed is an ____________, which would be measured in _____.
To make something ___________ always needs a f ____ .

Write down the equation you learned in this section.

Force, Vector, Velocity

Acid rain

Rain normally has a ***pH*** of 5.6, but acid rain has a pH less than this. This is because rain becomes contaminated by pollutant gases, such as sulphur dioxide from coal and oil fired power stations and nitrogen dioxide from car exhausts. These pollutant gases of sulphur dioxide and nitrogen dioxide then react in the ***atmosphere*** to form sulphuric acid and nitric acid. Both of these are ***strong acids***, which lower the pH of the rain to below 5.6.

Acid rain has many negative effects:

- It causes corrosion in buildings and metal structures.
- It is also linked with a number of illnesses involving respiration, such as asthma.
- It kills off wildlife by making streams and lakes too acidic to support life.
- It removes vital ***elements***, such as magnesium from the soil and so interferes with plant growth.

Acids

An acid is a substance which:

- has a sour taste
- will change the colour of plant dyes (***indicators***)
- will neutralize ***bases***
- will react with metals to form salts
- contains hydrogen ***ions*** when dissolved in water.

We can recognize the sharp or sour taste in fruits or in vinegar, though it would be unwise to taste some acids! Vinegar is also called ***ethanoic acid*** and is a ***weak acid***. Hydrocholoric acid, which is found in your stomach, is a ***strong acid***.

Acids can also be corrosive, they can dissolve many substances such as metals and some rocks. This can be very useful but can also be a nuisance, as with the corrosion of iron and buildings by acids in the atmosphere, e.g. ***acid rain***.

Acids only behave as acids when they are dissolved in water. So we can only really meet them as solutions in water. The reason for this is that, in water, the acid produces hydrogen ions (H^+). All acids contain hydrogen ions in water.

Acids change the colour of some dyes, which we call indicators. Acid will turn litmus indicator red. Strong acids have a low pH number and will turn universal indicator red, whereas weak acids will turn universal indicator yellow.

Adaptations to the environment

Each ***habitat*** has its own particular set of environmental conditions. In order to be successful, i.e., to survive and breed, an organism must be suitable (adapted) for its habitat – we call this adaptation to the environment.

There are thousands of examples of organisms (plants and animals) which are successfully adapted to their habitats. In order to understand how this works, you need to know two things:

- what are the conditions in that habitat?
- what features do organisms have that help them to survive?

Example 1: Desert habitat

Conditions: very dry
hot during the day, cold at night
sand is blown around by wind.

Cactus

Cacti can collect and store whatever water is available. They have spines to avoid being eaten. They usually reproduce asexually.

Thick waxy covering prevents damage by wind-blown sand and prevents excessive water loss
Small spiny leaves help to reduce water loss (by transpiration) and stop the plant being eaten by herbivores
Thick, fleshy stem stores water and can photosynthesise to make sugar
Long, deep roots, which spread out sideways to collect all available water

Camel

Camels can survive for a long time without water. They have thick fur to keep them warm at night.

Thick fur helps to keep it warm at night
Hump with stored fat which provides water when it is broken down in respiration
Very efficient kidneys which produce small amounts of very concentrated urine
Can survive for up to three weeks without drinking

Example 2 : Woodland habitat

Conditions: temperature varies throughout the year amount of light varies (in summer the sunlight is strong but most of it is absorbed by the leaf canopy, so the woodland floor is quite dark).

Bluebell

Bluebells grow from bulbs. They grow and flower early in the year (April to May) before the trees grow their leaves. This means that the bluebells have enough light to ***photosynthesise*** properly. After they have flowered and made ***seeds***, they die back and spend the rest of the year dormant as a bulb again.

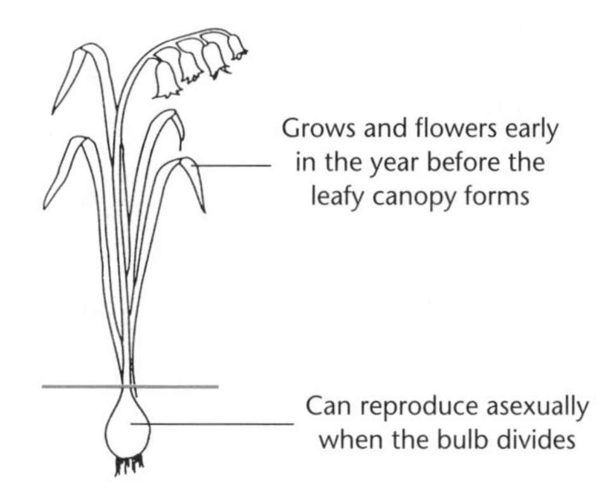
Grows and flowers early in the year before the leafy canopy forms
Can reproduce asexually when the bulb divides

Dormouse

Dormice spend the cold winter hibernating. They become active in spring and feed on flowers and fruits. They feed at night to avoid predators, e.g. owls. In autumn they eat hazelnuts.

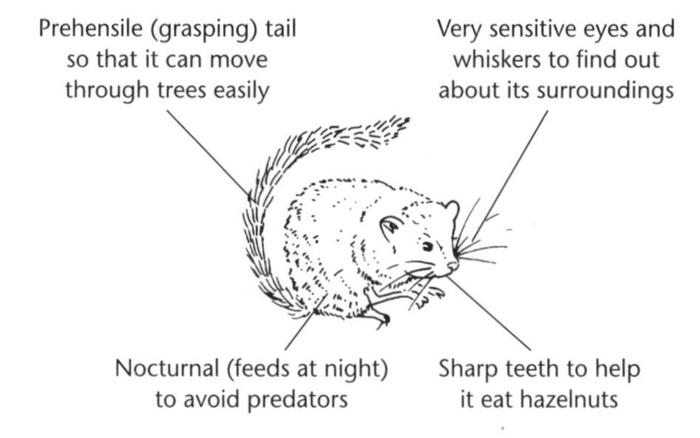
Prehensile (grasping) tail so that it can move through trees easily
Very sensitive eyes and whiskers to find out about its surroundings
Nocturnal (feeds at night) to avoid predators
Sharp teeth to help it eat hazelnuts

Example 3 : Pond habitat

Conditions: temperature varies throughout the year amount of light varies throughout the year amount of water varies throughout the year (the pond will become shallower in summer when there is less rainfall and water evaporates due to the heat).

Water lily

Roots anchor the plant to the bottom of the pond. There are smaller underwater leaves to absorb water and minerals.

The large, flat leaves have air spaces to make them float. The stomata are on the upper surface, so that gas exchange is more efficient.

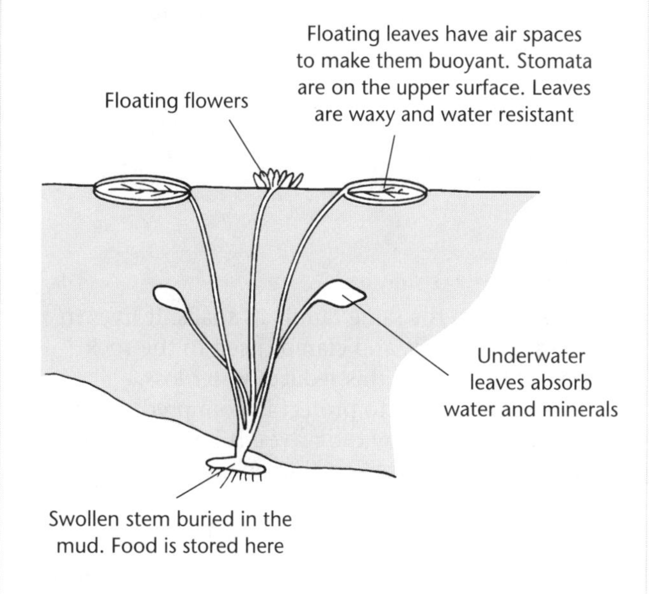
Floating flowers
Floating leaves have air spaces to make them buoyant. Stomata are on the upper surface. Leaves are waxy and water resistant
Underwater leaves absorb water and minerals
Swollen stem buried in the mud. Food is stored here

Water boatman

This small insect can swim quickly through ponds. It has a streamlined shape, and powerful back legs with hairs to increase the area in contact with the water. It is a carnivore, so it has poisonous saliva to kill its prey.

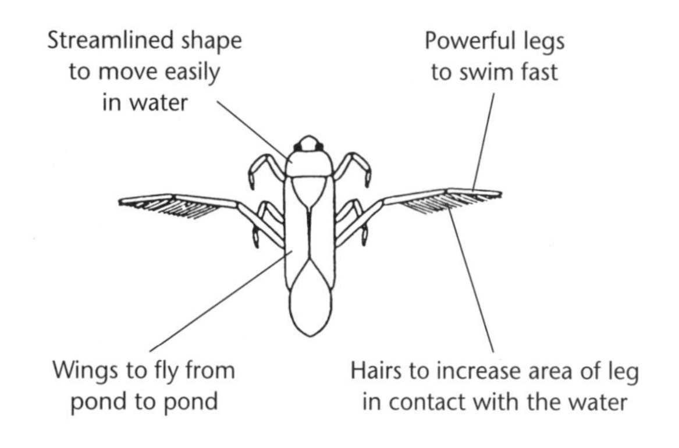
Streamlined shape to move easily in water
Powerful legs to swim fast
Wings to fly from pond to pond
Hairs to increase area of leg in contact with the water

Example 4 : Rocky shore habitat

Conditions: tides mean that the shore is covered and uncovered twice a day large changes in temperature, availability of water and light for the organisms that live there.

Seaweed (Ulva)

This is a small, green seaweed. It has a holdfast to anchor it firmly to the rocks.

It is found on the upper shore, and can cope with being exposed to the air for hours without drying out too much.

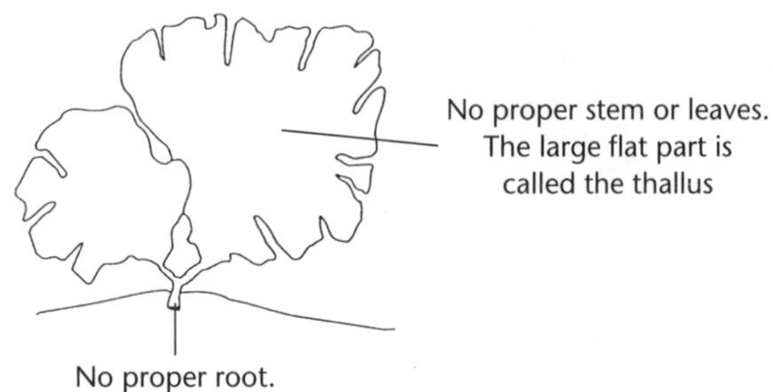
No proper stem or leaves. The large flat part is called the thallus
No proper root. A holdfast sticks it onto the rock

Periwinkle

This belongs to the same family as snails. It lives in crevices in the rock, and clamps itself to the rock when the tide is out; this reduces water loss.

It has a thick shell to protect it from predators, and being damaged by the waves. It has a rasping tongue to feed on algae on the rocks (it scrapes them off).

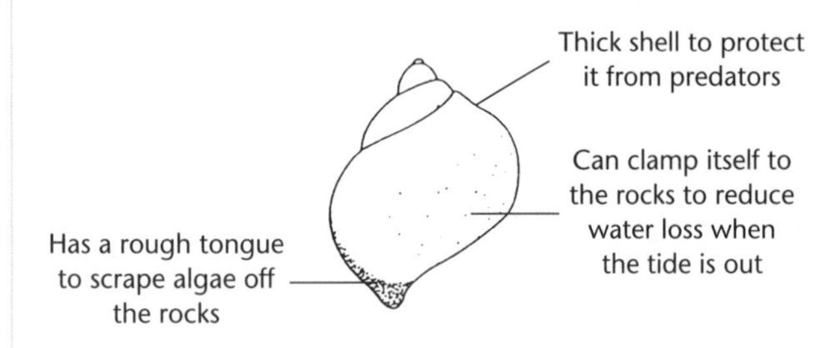
Thick shell to protect it from predators
Can clamp itself to the rocks to reduce water loss when the tide is out
Has a rough tongue to scrape algae off the rocks

Organisms can solve the problem of surviving in a particular environment in several ways; there is not one 'ideal solution'. For example:

- limpets, mussels, fish, sea anemones, barnacles, shrimps, starfish } all live in the sea
- earthworms, snails, woodlice, spiders, ants, butterflies, crows, squirrels } all live in woods

If organisms live in different parts of the habitat, or behave in different ways, e.g. have different food supplies, or feed at different times, it helps them to be successful because they are not competing for the same resources.

Competition for resources, Ecosystem, Environment

ADDICTION

This means that a person is dependent on something, and feels that he or she cannot cope without it.

Many **drugs** are addictive, for example:

nicotine (in cigarettes)
caffeine (in tea, coffee, coke)
alcohol
tranquilizers, e.g. Temazepam, valium
LSD
heroin

Some drugs are *physically addictive* – the body needs the drug to work normally, and the person gets unpleasant withdrawal symptoms if they do not have it. Some drugs are *psychologically addictive* – the person wants to take the drug, and feels that they must have it to feel better, or to cope with daily life.

Once a person gets used to a particular drug, *tolerance* often develops. This means that the person needs more of the drug in order to get the same effect from it.

If a person is dependent on a drug, it can affect the whole family:

- the person's behaviour may change, e.g. become more aggressive, or moody and withdrawn.
- the person needs money to buy drugs, so he or she may neglect the needs of others in the family, or steal from them.

AIDS

This is an **infectious disease** caused by the HIV virus (human immuno-deficiency virus). There are three main ways it can be caught:

1. through sexual intercourse with an infected person.
2. by sharing needles, e.g. for injecting drugs, with an infected person.
3. it can pass from a mother to her baby across the placenta before birth.

The virus infects and damages **white blood cells** involved in the production of **antibodies**, so the person's **immune system** does not work efficiently. This means that they are more likely to catch and become ill with other types of infectious diseases, and may die from them.

At the moment there is no vaccine against HIV and no cure for people who have the disease.

AIR

Air is important for most living things and is vital for humans. If you have not done anything today you will have breathed in about 15,000 litres of air. The footballer, Ryan Giggs, will have breathed considerably more in only 90 minutes during a football match. Air is a **mixture** of gases, as shown in the following table and the figure overleaf.

Air separation

Composition of air	
Gas	*% by volume*
Nitrogen	78.030
Oxygen	20.990
Argon	0.930
Other noble gases	0.002
Carbon dioxide	0.030
Hydrogen	0.001
Other	0.017

The gases in the air are very useful. For example, oxygen is used during ***respiration*** to convert food into energy and nitrogen is essential for the formation of proteins in all living organisms.

The gases in air can be separated by an important industrial process, called ***fractional distillation*** of liquid air.

ALCOHOL

This is a legal depressant drug. It is made by ***yeasts*** feeding on sugar in anaerobic conditions; the process is called ***fermentation***.

The type of alcoholic drink depends on the plant material added to the yeast, for example:

barley is used to make beer or lager,
grapes are used to make wine.

Alcohol has been used by humans for thousands of years. It is drunk mixed with water or other soft drinks. The amount of alcohol in drinks varies, for example:

beer is about 5 per cent alcohol,
wine is about 10 per cent alcohol,
spirits are about 50 per cent alcohol.

Alcohol is normally measured in *units*. One unit is the amount of alcohol in:

- half a pint of beer, lager or cider,
- one glass of wine or sherry,
- one measure of spirits.

The effects of alcohol start about ten minutes after it is drunk and last for several hours. They include:

- feeling more relaxed, and losing your inhibitions,
- loss of judgement, i.e., you are less capable of making sensible decisions,
- loss of muscle co-ordination, e.g. slurred speech, double vision, staggering,
- sedative effect; the person feels sleepy and may become unconscious.

What are the dangers of alcohol?

These can be divided into two groups: short-term dangers and long-term dangers.

Short-term dangers, i.e., from drinking a lot of alcohol at one time, include:

- being sick (and the person may choke on vomit),
- lack of co-ordination, so the person is more likely to have an accident and injure him- or herself (particularly if driving),
- becoming unconscious.

Long-term dangers, i.e., from drinking alcohol regularly over months or years, include:

- liver damage (cirrhosis),
- heart disease,
- brain damage,
- stomach ulcers and damage to the pancreas,
- addiction.

Doctors, as from 1996, recommend that men should drink less than 28 units of alcohol per week and women should drink less than 21 units of alcohol per week.

Addiction, Drugs

Alkali

An alkali is a substance that:

- is a soluble ***base***
- will neutralize ***acids***
- will change the colour of ***indicators***
- contains hydroxide ***ions***.

In the same way that there are ***strong*** and ***weak acids*** so there are ***strong*** and ***weak alkalis***. Strong alkalis provide a lot of free hydroxide ions in solution. Sodium and potassium hydroxides are strong alkalis, whereas ammonium hydroxide and calcium hydroxide are weak alkalis.

Alkalis turn litmus indicator blue, and will turn universal indicator blue or violet depending on their strength; violet indicates strong alkalis with a high ***pH*** number.

pH scale

Alloy

An alloy is a mixture of two or more ***metals***. Alloys are made by mixing molten metals. Alloys are used because a mixture of metals often has better overall properties than the individual metals themselves.

For example, stainless steel is shown in the table over as an alloy of iron, chromium and nickel. Stainless steel is more resistant to corrosion than the individual metals themselves, and is widely used in making cutlery and surgical instruments.

Common alloys

Name of alloy	*Metals mixed together*
Bronze	Copper 90% + Tin 10%
Brass	Copper 70% + Zinc 30%
Solder	Tin 50% + Lead 50%
Stainless steel	Iron 70% + Chromium 20% + Nickel 10%
Cast iron	Iron 97% + Carbon 3%
Silver coins	Copper 75% + Nickel 25%
Copper coins	Copper 97% + Zinc 2.5% + Tin 0.5%

Alternating current (ac)

Alternating ***current*** will go first in one direction round a circuit and then in the opposite direction. This process is repeated many times per second – 'mains' supply has a ***frequency*** of 50 Hz, so it changes direction 100 times per second. (Because it goes one way *and* the opposite way 50 times!)

Current, Direct current, Earth, Frequency

Alternative energy sources

These are sources of energy that do not use ***fossil fuels*** such as coal, gas or oil.

Sources of energy

Alveolus

In each ***lung*** there are millions of tiny alveoli or air sacs where ***gas exchange*** takes place. Alveoli are adapted (suitable) for gas exchange because:

- there are lots of them, so they provide a large surface area for gas exchange to occur,
- they have very thin walls (only one cell thick), so gases can pass through them easily,
- they are very close to ***capillaries***, so gases can easily be exchanged between the alveoli and the blood.

AMMETER

An ammeter is the meter that you use to measure electric ***current***. The current that you want to measure must go through it, so it is connected in ***series*** in the circuit.

You connect the meter so that its + terminal is closest to the + of the supply to get the current going through it in the correct direction.

Some meters are used to measure very small currents in milliamps (1mA = 1/1000TA) and are called milliammeters (or sometimes galvanometers).

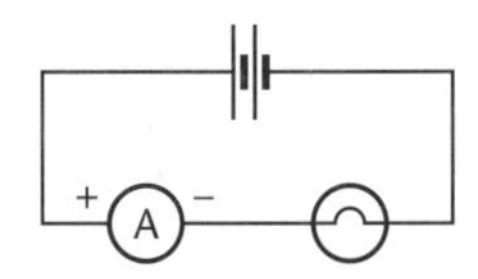

Measuring the current through a bulb with an ammeter

Remember: The current that you measure must go through the meter.

An ammeter should have the smallest possible ***resistance*** so that it does not make the current smaller when you put it into the circuit.

> *CHECKPOINT*
>
> Draw a simple circuit to show how to measure the current flowing through a motor.

Ampere, Circuit, Current, Series

AMNION

This is a bag of fluid surrounding the developing ***foetus***. It helps to cushion it from bumps during pregnancy. It usually bursts during labour as the ***uterus*** contracts ('breaking of the waters').

Reproduction

AMPERE (AMP)

The ampere (or 'amp') is the unit that you use when you measure electric ***current***. To do the measuring you use an ***ammeter***. The symbol for an amp is A.

Ammeter, Current

AMPLITUDE

This is the maximum distance that a particle moves from rest when a ***wave*** passes by.

A wave with a bigger amplitude will carry more ***energy***.

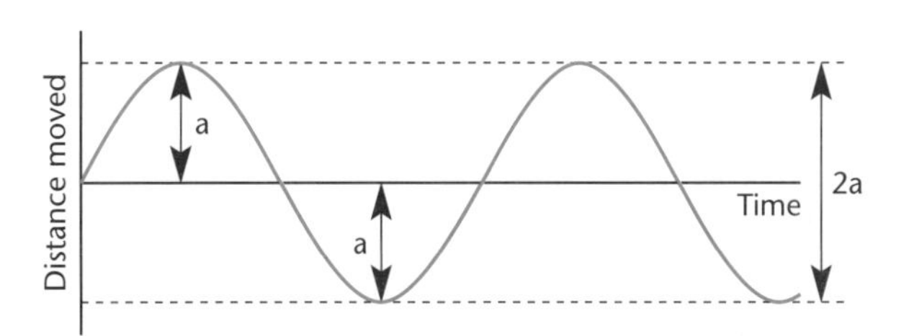

Amplitude

*Remember: The distance from the top of a peak to the bottom of a trough will be **two** amplitudes.*

A ***sound*** wave that has a bigger amplitude will be louder. A quieter sound will have a smaller amplitude.

A bigger vibration will send out a sound wave with a bigger amplitude so that it carries more energy and is louder. An amplifier makes the vibration of a loudspeaker larger so that the sound is louder. Many musical instruments are designed to make the vibration larger.

A ***light*** wave that has a bigger amplitude will be brighter.

Frequency, Light, Loudness, Sound, Wave

ANIMALS

All animals have two things in common:

1. their cells do not have a cell wall
2. they feed on other organisms (animals or plants).

Animals are normally classified into two main groups, ***vertebrates*** and ***invertebrates***. Most of the information in this book is about humans (so it applies to most other *mammals*).

Classification

ANODE

The name given to a *positive electrode*, either in an ***electrolysis*** cell or in an electrical cell (***battery***).

Antacid

Antacids are substances that ***neutralize*** excessive acid in the stomach and help to relieve indigestion. They usually contain calcium carbonate, magnesium hydroxide or aluminium hydroxide. Common brand names include Rennies, Settlers, etc.

Antagonistic muscle pair

This is a pair of muscles that have opposite effects to each other, e.g. biceps and triceps.

Joints, Muscles

Antibiotics

These are drugs that are used to kill ***bacteria*** inside the body. The first antibiotic to be discovered was penicillin, by Alexander Fleming in 1928.

Antibiotics are naturally made by ***fungi***, but now most are made synthetically by chemists working in a laboratory. There are many different types, e.g. ampicillin, tetracycline.

Remember: Antibiotics will only kill bacteria, not viruses or fungi.

Disease, Drugs

Antibodies

These are chemicals made by white blood cells inside the body, which help to fight disease.

They are produced when we are infected by ***bacteria*** or ***viruses***, and they attack and destroy the microbes.

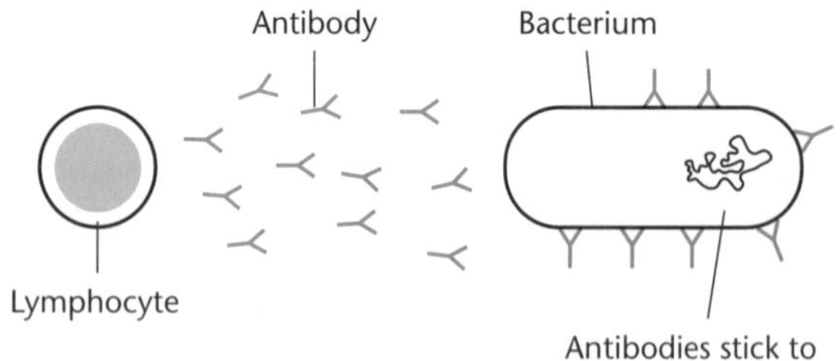

Lymphocytes (white blood cells) make antibodies

Once antibodies have been made to attack a particular type of microbe they can quickly be made again, so we are protected against that microbe in the future. This process is called ***immunity***, and white blood cells are part of the ***immune system***.

Defence against disease

Apparent depth

The depth of a transparent material like glass or water often looks less than it really is. The apparent depth that it seems to have is less than the real depth. This is caused by the light changing direction at the surface. The change of direction is called ***refraction***.

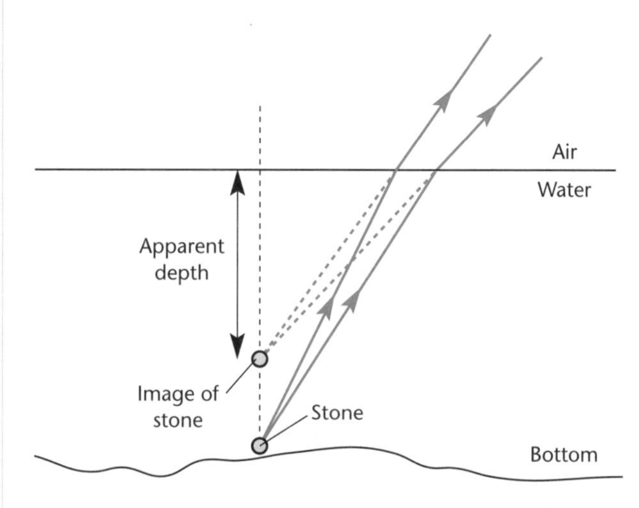

The apparent depth of a pond

The diagram shows the light from the bottom of the pond. As the light is refracted, it seems to come from a point directly above the original place but nearer to the surface. This is why swimming pools can look shallower, fish seem nearer to the surface of water, and sticks or fishing rods that are pushed into the water may look bent at the surface.

Refraction

Arteries

This type of ***blood vessel*** carries blood away from the ***heart***. They have strong, thick walls because the blood is travelling fast and at high pressure.

The main artery of the body is called the aorta. It carries blood out of the left side of the heart, and branches of the aorta carry blood to all body organs.

You can feel a pulse in arteries that run close to the skin surface, e.g. at the wrist, in the neck. Counting the ***pulse rate*** is an easy way of measuring a person's heart rate.

Artificial selection

This is another name for ***selective breeding***. It means that humans choose which parents breed together to get offspring of a particular type.

Asexual reproduction

This type of reproduction involves only one parent and produces a ***clone*** of identical offspring.

Reproduction

Asthma

People who have asthma sometimes find it very difficult to breathe. The small tubes in the ***lungs (bronchioles)*** become narrower, so not enough air gets into the ***alveoli*** for ***gas exchange*** to occur efficiently. During an asthma attack, a person may use an inhaler or nebulizer that contains drugs to keep their bronchioles open.

There are now lots more people suffering from asthma than there were 30 years ago. Scientists do not know why about ten per cent of the British population now have asthma, but some factors are known to increase the chances of an asthma attack in people who are affected, e.g. pollution, cold weather, exercise, pollen and animal fur.

Atmosphere

The atmosphere is what we usually call ***air***. In fact, it is a layer of gases, about 300 kilometres thick, surrounding the Earth. It makes up only a tiny fraction (about 0.00001 per cent) of the mass of the whole ***Earth***. Three billion years ago, when the Earth was quite young, there was no oxygen in the atmosphere. We owe the fact that oxygen is now in the atmosphere to the appearance of plants.

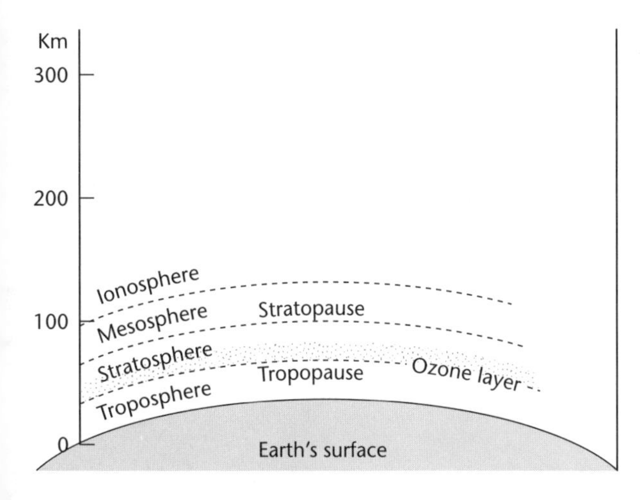

The layers of the atmosphere

The atmosphere can be divided into a number of layers (see figure below). Changes that take place in the troposphere cause our weather conditions. The ozone layer protects the Earth from harmful cosmic and ultra violet rays coming from outer space.

The atmosphere also acts as a 'blanket', keeping the Earth warm and preventing the temperature changing too drastically between day and night. The Moon, which is the same distance from the Sun as the Earth, has no atmosphere. On the surface of the Moon the temperature changes from as high as 100°C in the sunlight to as low as –150°C at night.

Acid rain, Greenhouse effect, Ozone

Atom

An atom is the smallest part of an ***element*** that can exist, and yet has all the properties of an element. Another way of trying to visualize this is to imagine being in a desert where you can see nothing but sand. When you look more closely, you can see that the sand is made up of much smaller sand grains. Here, the sand in the desert represents the elements, and the individual sand grains represent the atoms.

In the nineteenth century, after many years of research, Ernest Rutherford devised a model which is still used to explain how atoms behave. His model shows that the atoms themselves are made from still smaller particles called protons, electrons and neutrons. The atoms are arranged rather like the ***solar system***. The ***protons*** and ***neutrons*** are close together in the ***nucleus***, and represent the Sun. The ***electrons*** orbit around the nucleus, rather like the planets orbit around the Sun.

Atoms can join together in different ways to produce all the materials that are around you.

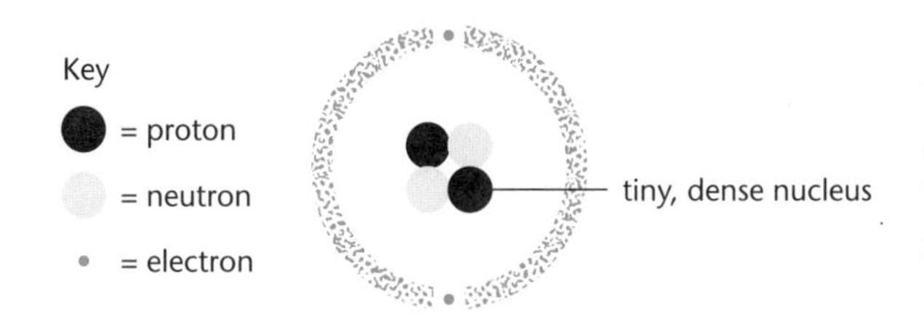

Rutherford's model of the helium atom

Atomic mass number

This is the number above the ***element*** symbol in the ***periodic table***. It tells you how many ***protons*** and neutrons there are in the ***nucleus***.

$$^{4}_{2}\text{He}$$

Atomic Mass Number 4
Atomic Number 2

Helium

✦ ***Atom***

Atomic number

This is the number below the ***element*** symbol (see the figure of helium above) in the ***periodic table***. It tells you how many ***protons*** there are in the ***nucleus***.

Bacteria

Bacteria are microscopic organisms, which are in the classification kingdom ***Monera***.

Each bacterium is a single cell, usually about a thousandth of a millimetre long (0.001mm). It has a strong cell wall to protect it, with cytoplasm and DNA inside. Bacteria do *not* have a nucleus.

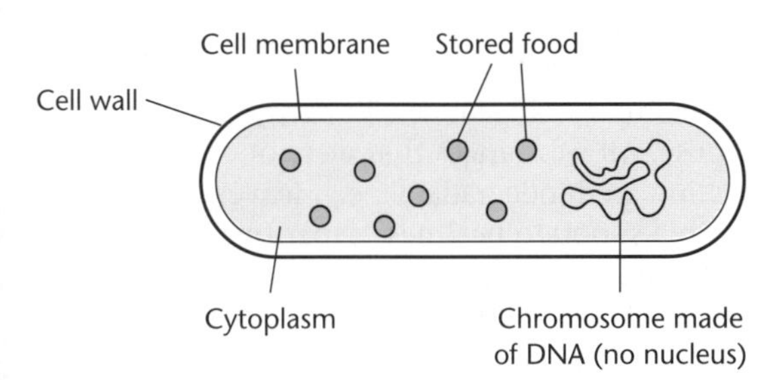

A typical bacterium

Some bacteria are useful to humans, and some are harmful.

Useful bacteria

- ***decomposers,*** which make dead material rot. These help to get rid of dead material, and to release useful substances so they can be re-used.
- bacteria used in sewage treatment (these are decomposers).
- bacteria used in food manufacturing, e.g. to make yoghurt, cheese, vinegar.
- bacteria used in genetic engineering, to make products useful to humans, e.g. insulin to treat diabetics.

Harmful bacteria

- bacteria that cause disease in humans, e.g. typhoid, cholera, TB, scarlet fever, tetanus.
- bacteria that cause disease in other animals or in plants.
- bacteria that make food go off, and can cause food poisoning, e.g. salmonella.

Bacteria inside the body can be killed by ***antibiotics***. Bacteria outside the body can be killed by chemicals, e.g. disinfectant, or by high temperatures.

Bacteria reproduce ***asexually***, to form a ***clone***. In ideal conditions, they can double their numbers every 30 minutes.

Balance

This is an instrument that measures ***mass***.

There are quite a lot of different types of balance and many work because objects that have mass on Earth will also have ***weight***. The weight can be used to balance a lever against a known weight or push down against a spring like in bathroom scales. In these cases, more mass gives more weight, which moves the pointer along the scale. Many modern balances, including the ones used to 'weigh' the cooking ingredients in kitchens, are electronic. All you have to do is switch on, wait for a zero reading, put the object on the balance and read its mass. Take care *not* to put too large a mass on a small balance or you could damage it permanently. *Do* use a balance with a suitable scale – there is no point in measuring 100 g to the nearest 10 g or in measuring 2000 g to the nearest 0.01 g!

You should be able to see that a balance which works by the force produced on a spring would give the wrong answer for mass anywhere except on the surface of the Earth (the force is a weight and the force of gravity would be different in other places!).

 ***Mass***

Balanced diet

Our diet is everything that we eat. A balanced diet contains the right *amounts* of the right *types* of food. There are six main food groups, and our diet should be roughly one-sixth fat, one-sixth protein and four-sixths carbohydrate.

Table to show the main food groups in a balanced diet

Food group	*Needed to ...*	*Found in ...*
Carbohydrate	give us energy (acts as a fuel in respiration)	sugary foods, e.g. sweets, soft drinks drinks starch foods, e.g., bread, potatoes, rice, pasta
Protein	make new cells e.g. for growth and repair	meat, fish, eggs, milk, cheese, beans, nuts
Fat	give us energy (acts as a fuel in respiration)	fried foods, e.g. chips, crisps butter, margarine, cheese, nuts, chocolate, red meat

Vitamins	keep the body healthy	
e.g. vitamin C	healthy skin and gums	oranges, blackcurrants, potatoes, green vegetables
e.g. vitamin D	healthy bones and teeth	fish, egg, liver, and made in the skin in sunlight
Minerals	keep the body healthy	
e.g. iron	making red blood cells	red meat, green vegetables, cocoa
e.g. calcium	healthy bones and teeth	milk, cheese, fish
Fibre (roughage)	keep the gut healthy and to avoid constipation	wholemeal bread and pasta, brown rice, fruit, vegetables

If the diet is not balanced, the person may be unhealthy. For example:

too much ***fat*** causes ***obesity*** and can lead to heart disease
too much sugar causes ***tooth decay*** (dental caries)
too little vitamin C causes scurvy
too little iron causes anaemia
} these are called ***deficiency diseases***.

✦ ***Malnutrition, Water***

BASE

Bases are the chemical opposite of ***acids***. They react with (neutralize) acids to form a ***salt*** and water. Most bases do not dissolve (i.e., are insoluble) in water. Those bases that do dissolve include alkalis, such as metal hydroxides (e.g. sodium hydroxide).

BATTERY

A battery is two or more electric ***cells*** connected in ***series***. Their ***voltages*** will add together.

Remember: Voltages in series add.

Different ways to show batteries

✦ ***Circuit, emf***

BAUXITE

This is the ***ore*** of aluminium, the most common element in the ***Earth's*** crust. It consists of aluminium oxide with iron impurities and is found mainly in tropical countries.

BIMETALLIC STRIP

This is a strip of two different metals fastened together so that the strip bends when its temperature changes.

✦ ***Expansion***

BIODEGRADABLE

This means that a substance will ***decay*** or decompose. All substances that were once part of a living thing are biodegradable, e.g. leaves from trees, dead animals, potato peelings, paper (made from wood), faeces, fingernails, etc.

Substances that will not decay are described as non-biodegradable, e.g. metal, most plastics, concrete.

It is useful to know which substances are biodegradable if you are making ***compost***.

✦ ***Decomposer***

BIOMASS

This is the amount of matter present in living things e.g. the biomass of plants in a field is the total mass of all the plants.

It is sometimes used when we are looking at ***food chains***, and considering transfer of ***energy***. It involves using the energy in sunlight to grow plants with a high energy content, usually in sugars. The energy is then extracted from the chemicals produced by the plants. In Brazil, sugar is extracted from plants and ***fermented*** to produce alcohol. This can then be used to power engines in cars instead of petrol.

✦ ***Pyramid of biomass, Sources of energy***

BIRTH

In humans, this occurs after about nine months of ***pregnancy***. There are three stages: labour, delivery and afterbirth.

Labour

The muscles in the walls of the ***uterus*** contract and the cervix gets wider (dilates). The ***amnion*** usually breaks at some stage during labour.

Labour continues until the cervix is open wide enough for the baby's head to pass through.

Delivery

This is when the baby is pushed out through the cervix and vagina, normally head first. It is pushed out by contractions of the muscle in the uterus wall. Once it is outside the mother's body, it will start to breathe, and the ***umbilical cord*** can be clamped and cut.

Afterbirth

The uterus wall contracts again to push out the ***placenta*** and the rest of the umbilical cord. The birth is now over.

Sometimes babies cannot be born like this, and a *Caesarian* operation has to be carried out. This involves cutting through the mother's skin and uterus wall to lift the baby out.

If babies are born *prematurely*, i.e., before nine months of pregnancy, they will be smaller and may need special care to help them to survive, e.g. being kept in an incubator to stay warm, being fed special food through a tube directly to their stomach.

Reproduction

BLADDER

This is where ***urine*** is stored before it passes out of the body. It is a hollow, muscular bag which can hold about 400ml of urine. Urine is forced out through a tube called the urethra when muscles in the wall of the bladder contract.

Excretion, Kidneys

BLAST FURNACE

Iron is produced in large amounts in blast furnaces from iron ore. The furnace is huge, about four times the height of the average house.

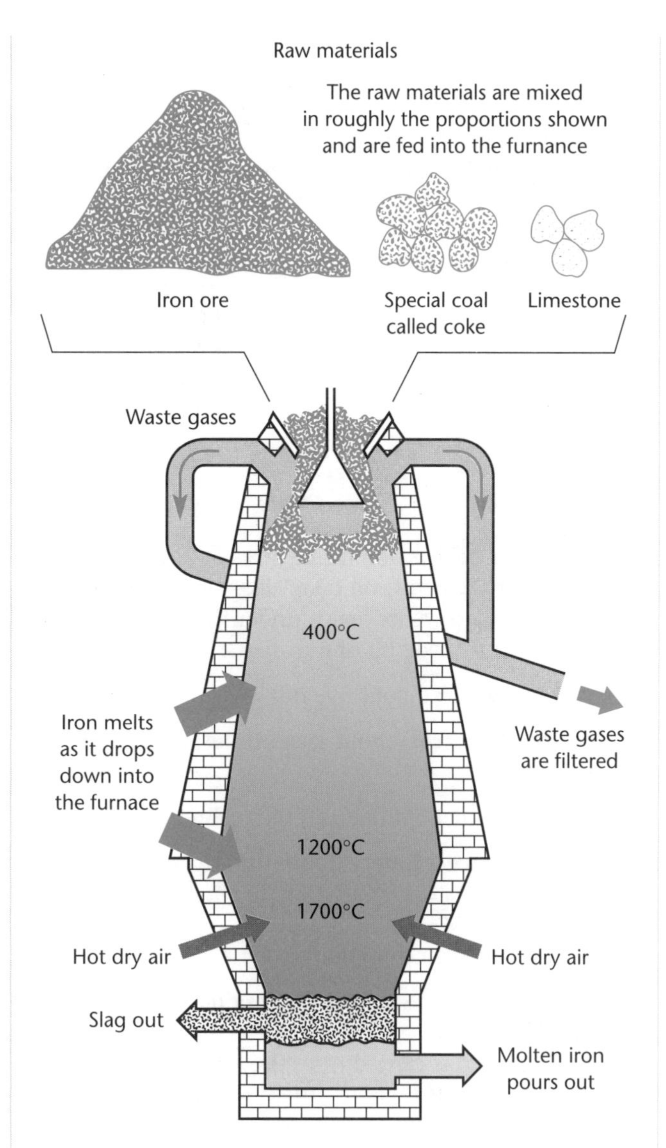

The blast furnace

Inside the furnace the iron oxide is ***reduced*** to iron metal. The carbon in the coke takes hold of the oxygen from the iron oxide, leaving iron metal. This is removed at the bottom of the furnace as *molten* iron.

This is a word equation for the reaction:

Carbon + Iron Oxide ⟶ Iron + Carbon Dioxide

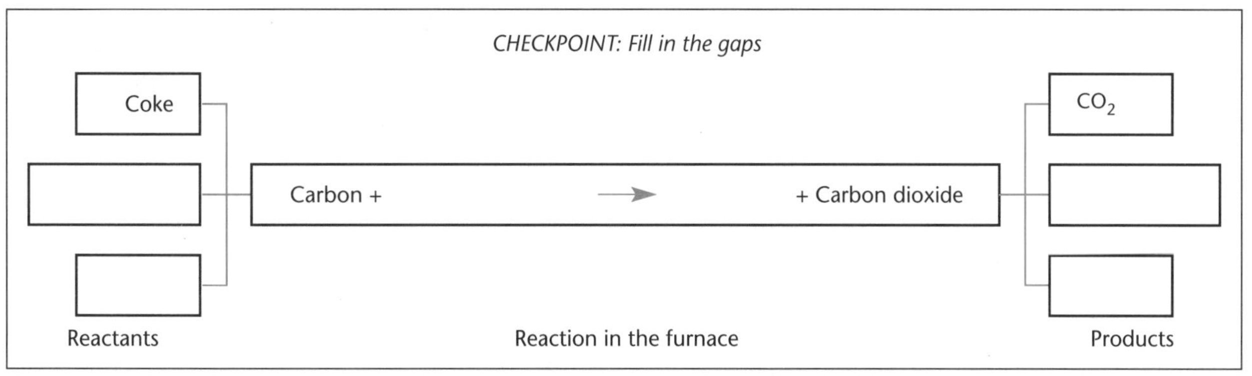

Checkpoint

Limestone is used to mop up all the impurities that are found in the iron ore. The limestone reacts with the impurities (e.g. silica) to produce a glassy material, called *slag*. The slag is less dense than the iron ore, so it floats on the molten iron. It is tapped off from the higher hole at the bottom of the blast furnace as a waste product.

The iron that comes out at the bottom of the furnace is called *pig iron*. This type of iron is used to make *cast iron*. Cast iron is brittle because it contains carbon impurities. ***Steel*** making involves getting rid of these impurities by making a new ***alloy*** with different metals.

Blood

An adult human has about five litres of blood – the exact amount depends on body size. Blood is a red liquid, but when we look at it under the ***microscope***, we can see it is made up of four parts:

1. ***red blood cells***, about five million per ml of blood
2. ***white blood cells***, about seven thousand per ml of blood
3. ***platelets***, huge numbers of tiny cell fragments
4. ***plasma***, a pale, watery liquid that the cells are carried in.

Blood has two main functions:

1. *to carry substances from one part of the body to another*
   e.g. ***oxygen*** is carried from the lungs to all body cells ***urea*** is carried from the liver to the kidneys

   carbon dioxide, food substances, waste products, hormones, drugs } are all carried in the blood

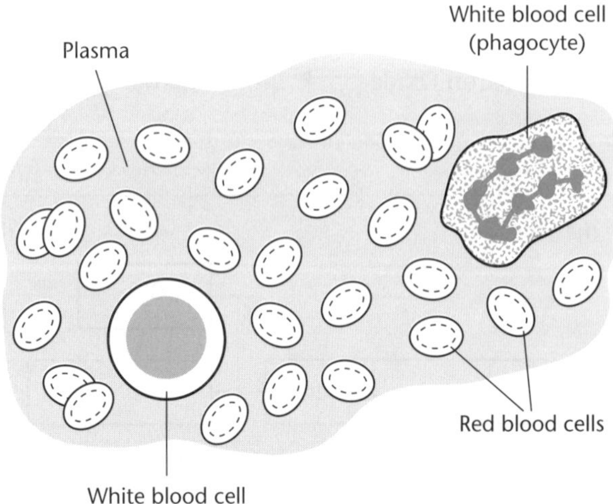

Looking at blood under the microscope (platelets are too small to be seen using most microscopes)

2. *to defend the body against disease*
   white blood cells destroy bacteria and viruses that get into the body
   platelets help the blood to clot if we cut ourselves, so that germs cannot get into the wound.

Blood vessels

These are tubes that carry blood around the body: they form part of the ***circulatory system***. There are three types of blood vessels: ***arteries***, ***capillaries*** and ***veins***.

Table to compare blood vessels

Arteries	*Capillaries*	*Veins*
outer coat; muscle layer	wall one cell thick	outer coat
have a thick wall containing muscle	have a very thin wall (one cell thick)	have a thin wall with no muscle
have a narrow lumen	have a very narrow lumen	have a wide lumen
have no valves	have no valves	have valves to stop blood flowing the wrong way
carry blood away from the heart	carry blood through body organs	carry blood towards the heart
blood is travelling fast	blood is slowing down	blood is travelling slowly
substances are *not* exchanged between blood and body cells	substances are exchanged between blood and body cells	substances are not exchanged between blood and body cells

Remember: Arteries carry blood Away from the heart

Boiling

When a ***liquid*** is heated, the particles are given more energy and move faster and faster. Eventually the faster ones break away completely from each other.

The liquid is then becoming a ***gas***. Turning a liquid to gas needs ***energy*** to reduce the forces holding the ***particles*** together. When bubbles of gas escape from a liquid, it is said to be boiling.

✦ *Changing state*

Boiling point

When liquid water is heated, it turns to steam at 100°C. The water is said to be ***boiling*** and this temperature is known as the boiling point of water. Adding impurities or altering atmospheric pressure alters the boiling point.

Bones

Bones contain living cells surrounded by a hard, mineral framework (mainly calcium and phosphate). We know that bones are living because they can grow, and can heal themselves when they are broken.

Bones are partly hollow, so that they are lighter and they contain bone marrow where new blood cells are made. Bones are moved by ***muscles***

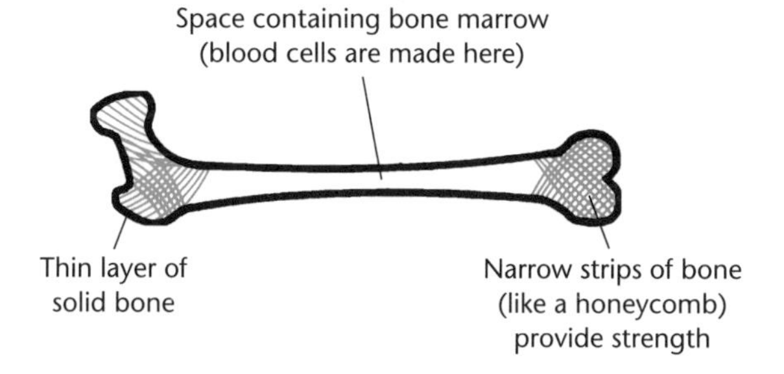

Inside a typical bone (femur)

Brain

This is a very important organ in humans, it weighs about 1.5kg and is made up of nerve tissue. It is protected by the skull. The brain has four main functions:

1. to receive information from our sense organs about our surroundings,
2. to think, decide and remember,
3. to send nerve impulses to our muscles, so that we can move,
4. to control other body organs, e.g. heart and heartrate; lungs and breathing rate.

Brass

This is an ***alloy*** made from 70 per cent copper and 30 per cent zinc.

Breathing

This is an important process in humans because it allows ***gas exchange*** to occur. When we breathe in, air containing lots of ***oxygen*** is drawn down into our ***lungs***, and some of this oxygen passes into the blood. ***Carbon dioxide*** passes out of the blood, and when we breathe out, this waste gas is released into the air.

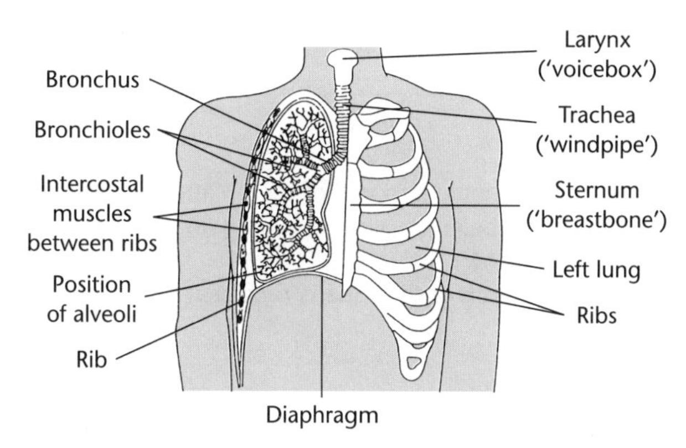

The breathing system

How do we breathe in and out?

When we breathe in, the lungs *expand*, so air is sucked into them. This happens in two ways:

1. the ***diaphragm*** flattens,
2. the ***ribs*** move up and out (when the muscles between them contract).

There is now more space inside the lungs (the lung volume has *increased*), so air is drawn in.

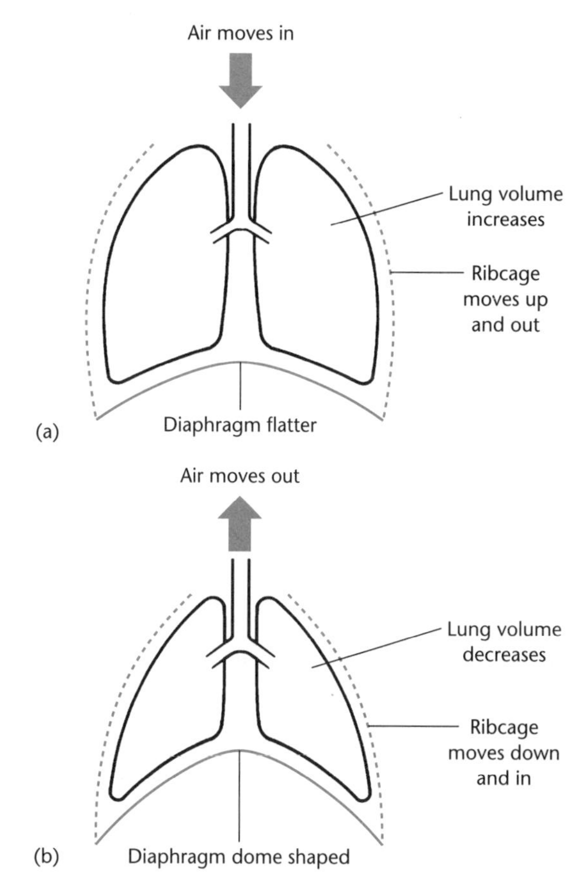

a) Breathing in b) Breathing out

When we breathe out, the lungs get *smaller*, so air is pushed out of them. This happens in two ways:

1. the diaphragm becomes more curved,
2. the ribs move down and in (when the muscles between them relax).

There is now less space inside the lungs (the lung volume has *decreased*), so air is pushed out.

CHECKPOINT

You may be shown a model of the breathing system made from a bell-jar, balloons, tubing and rubber sheet (see below).
What do each of these parts represent?

bell jar?
balloons?
tubing?
rubber sheet?

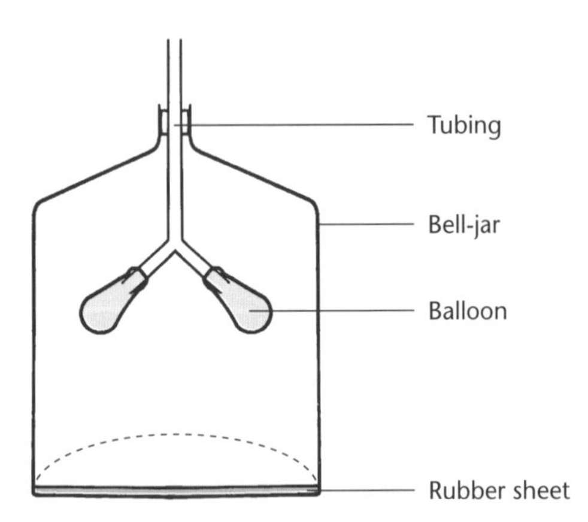

What would happen to the balloons if you pushed the rubber sheet upwards (shown by the dotted line)?
Can you explain why?

When you are sitting quietly, it is mainly movements of the diaphragm that move air in and out of your lungs.

When you take deep breaths, or you have been exercising a lot, your ribs will move to get more air in and out of your lungs. You can feel your ribs moving when you do this – try it!

Remember: Breathing is **not** *the same as respiration.*
Breathing *only occurs in animals, and it means getting gases in and out of the body.*
Respiration *is a chemical reaction happening inside all cells to make energy.*

Breathing in is sometimes called inhaling or inspiration.

Breathing out is sometimes called exhaling or expiration.

BREEDS

These are produced by ***selective breeding***. They are still members of the same ***species***, but they have very different characteristics. For example:

- all dogs are the same species, but different varieties include dalmatian, poodle, sheepdog, labrador, husky.
- all potatoes are the same species, but different varieties include King Edwards, Cara, Jersey royals, Desirée.

Breeds are sometimes called ***varieties***.

Variation

BRINE

This is a ***solution*** of sodium chloride dissolved in water. It is produced when salt deposits underground are extracted by ***solution mining***. The brine is pumped up to the surface and used as the *raw material* for an important industry called the ***chloro-alkali industry***.

Brine has long been an important raw material, and is used in the production of disinfectants, soaps, margarine, various fuels and in certain processes such as water purification and steel 'pickling'.

BRONCHI AND BRONCHIOLES

These are tubes or air passages within the ***lungs***. One bronchus leads into each lung, then divides repeatedly to form hundreds of tiny bronchioles. These lead directly to the ***alveoli*** where ***gas exchange*** occurs.

Bronchi are lined with ***ciliated cells*** to trap dust and dirt.

Bronchioles are much smaller, and have muscle in their walls. During an ***asthma*** attack the bronchioles become narrower, making breathing difficult.

BRONZE

This is an ***alloy*** made from 90 per cent copper and 10 per cent tin. It is one of the earliest known alloys. It is hard, resistant to ***corrosion*** and is used for making bells and metal sculptures.

BURNING

Combustion

CANCER

This is not one disease, but it is the name given to a large group of similar diseases.

Cancer occurs when ***cells*** somewhere in the body start to grow out of control. This results in a lump or *tumour*. Sometimes cells can break off from this tumour and spread to other parts of the body, where they will grow and form secondary tumours. Tumours are harmful because they can squash important body organs, or they can prevent them from carrying out their function properly.

How can cancer be treated?

There are three main ways to treat cancer:

1. *Surgery*: the tumour is cut out.
2. *Chemotherapy*: very strong chemicals are used to kill the cancerous cells. Sometimes these chemicals cause unpleasant side effects, e.g. feeling sick, hair falling out, because some normal cells are affected.
3. *Radiotherapy*: invisible rays are used to kill the cancerous cells (a bit like X-rays, but much more powerful). These can also cause unpleasant side effects in some people.

What causes cancer?

No one really knows why cells start to grow out of control and a tumour forms. However, scientists do know that some things increase the risk of this happening; for example:

smoking increases the risk of lung cancer
too much UV light (sunbathing or sunbeds) increases the risk of skin cancer.

✣ ***Diseases***

CAPILLARIES

These are the smallest ***blood vessels*** in the body. There are millions of them carrying blood through the organs of the body, close to all the cells.

They have thin walls (only one cell thick), so substances can easily move in and out of capillaries, i.e., material is exchanged between blood and body cells in the capillaries.

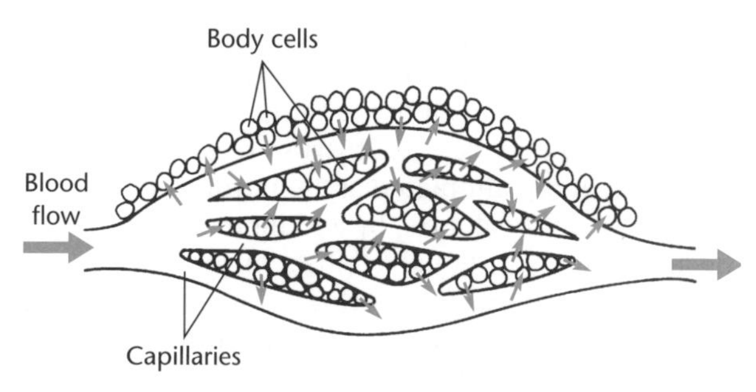

Exchange of materials in the capillaries

✣ ***Circulatory system***

CARBOHYDRATE

This is one of the main food groups making up a ***balanced diet***. Carbohydrate is found in two main forms:

Sugar: found naturally in fruits and added to lots of processed foods, e.g. sweets, cakes, soft drinks, jam.

Starch: found in bread, pasta, rice, potatoes, cereals, cakes and pastry.

Carbohydrate is an important part of a healthy diet because it gives us energy, but too much can cause problems.

Too much sugar can lead to ***tooth decay***, when acid made from the sugar damages the outer layer of the tooth.

Too much sugar or starch can lead to ***obesity*** (being overweight), because excess carbohydrate is changed into ***fat*** and stored in the body.

✣ ***Energy in food***

CARBON (C)

Carbon is an ***element*** that contains only one type of ***atom***. It has two crystalline forms:

- diamond – one of the hardest substances known
- graphite – in this form carbon will conduct electricity.

CARBON DIOXIDE (CO_2)

Carbon dioxide is:

- colourless
- odourless (no smell)
- more dense than air
- dissolves slightly in water to produce a weakly acidic solution.

The air around us is made up of 0.03 per cent carbon dioxide. Plants use carbon dioxide when they ***photosynthesise***, and all living things release carbon dioxide when they ***respire***. It is also released when ***fossil fuels*** and plant materials are burnt. Indeed, the ***combustion*** of fossil fuels, by adding more CO_2 to the atmosphere, is thought to be a major factor behind the ***greenhouse effect***.

CO_2 reacts in ***limewater*** to form a white ***precipitate*** of calcium carbonate. The limewater then goes cloudy. The test for CO_2 is as follows:

Test for carbon dioxide

Carbon dioxide + Limewater ⟶ Calcium carbonate

limewater turns cloudy

✢ *Limestone*

CARNIVORE

This is an animal that eats other animals. It is the third organism in a ***food chain*** (and any organism after this is also a carnivore).

Some ***invertebrates*** are carnivores, e.g. spiders, ladybirds, crabs.

Some *mammals* are carnivores, e.g. foxes, stoats, seals.

The first carnivore in a food chain is called a secondary ***consumer***. The last carnivore in a food chain is called a top carnivore.

Most carnivores are ***predators*** (kill their own prey), but some are ***scavengers*** (feed on dead animal remains).

CARPEL

This is the female reproductive organ in plants. A ***flower*** may contain a single carpel, e.g. tulip, or may contain lots of carpels, e.g. buttercup.

The carpel consists of three main parts:

- the stigma. This is where the pollen grain is transferred during ***pollination***. It produces a sticky liquid so that the pollen tube will grow.
- the style.
- the ovary. This contains the ***ovule*** (female gamete). After ***fertilization*** has occurred, the ovule will develop into a ***seed***, and the ovary will develop into the ***fruit***

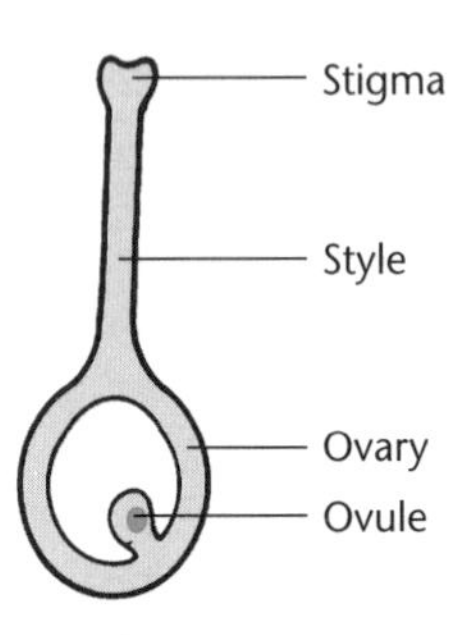

Carpel

CARTILAGE

This is a very smooth substance covering the ends of ***bones*** inside a ***joint***. It helps to reduce friction, so that bones can move easily and without pain. As people get older, their cartilage may be worn away, so the ends of the bones rub together and become damaged. This can restrict movement and be very painful, so it may be necessary to have an artificial joint fitted.

CATALYST

This is a substance which alters the ***rate of a chemical reaction*** without being used up itself. It can be removed at the end of the reaction and re-used. Usually a catalyst helps to *speed up* a reaction. For example, vanadium oxide is used as a catalyst when sulphuric acid is made. Sometimes a catalyst can *slow down* a reaction, as when food additives prevent food going bad. ***Enzymes*** are biological catalysts.

CATALYTIC CONVERTER

These are fitted to all new car exhausts to reduce the emission of polluting gases. If you cut a slice through the converter, you would see a honeycomb-shaped ***ceramic*** material coated with the precious metals, platinum and rhodium. The honeycomb shape increases the surface area that the gases come into contact with, and helps to make sure that all the gases react as they pass through. The precious metals are the ***catalysts***. They help in the reactions by which the polluting gases of ***sulphur dioxide*** and nitrogen dioxide are broken down into harmless gases, such as nitrogen and water vapour.

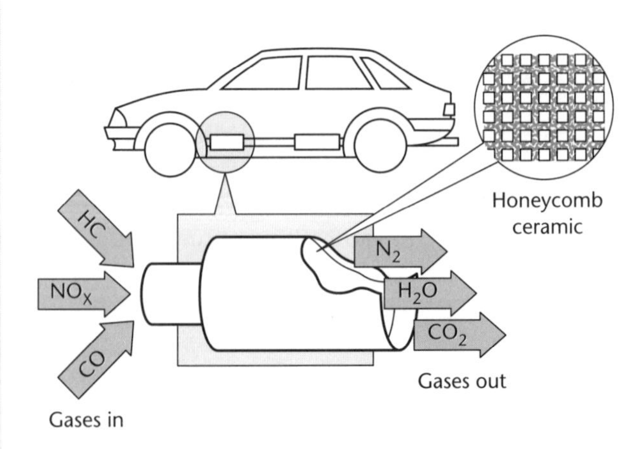

Catalytic converter

CATHODE

The name given to a *negative electrode*, either in an ***electrolysis*** cell or in an electrical cell (***battery***).

Cell (electrical)

An electric cell produces an electric ***current*** from a chemical reaction inside it. It is often called a ***battery***. A battery is really two or more cells joined in ***series***. There are two main types of cell: primary cells and secondary cells.

Primary cells

Primary cells cannot be recharged. They produce a current by a chemical reaction that cannot be reversed. When one of the chemicals is used up, the reaction will stop and the cell produces no more current, e.g. simple cell, dry cell.

A *simple cell* will be made from two different metals put into a dilute acid (copper and magnesium in a lemon will run a small motor!). The ***voltage*** will be bigger if the metals are further apart in the activity series.

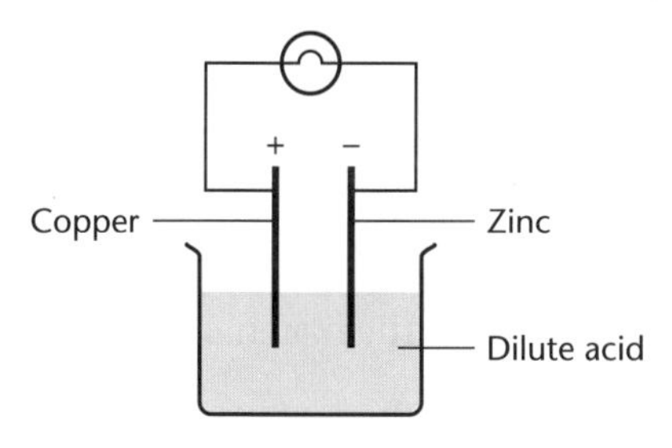

A simple cell

The least reactive metal (in this case copper) will be the + and the most reactive (in this case magnesium) will be the –. The cell only produces current to light the bulb for a short time before the copper plate is coated with small bubbles of hydrogen, which act as an insulator. This is called *polarization*.

Polarization can be stopped by adding an oxidizing agent to turn the hydrogen into water. Another problem is *local action*, where the most reactive metal (the zinc) is rapidly dissolved into the acid by small bits of impurity in the metal forming small cells.

Disadvantages include an acid that is easy to spill and a low voltage produced for a short time.

A *dry cell* is the common sort of cell that you would buy to put into a torch. It will produce about 1.5 V

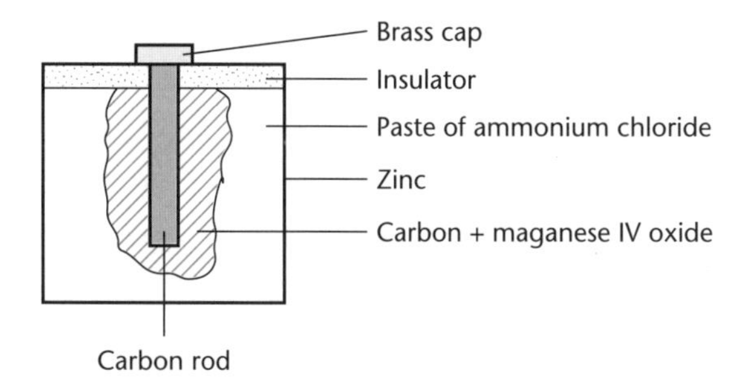

A dry cell (also called a Leclanché cell)

In this case, the carbon rod is the + and the zinc is the –. The cell may leak when zinc is used up and the paste leaks through the holes – this can be prevented by an outer coating of plastic on the sides. There are no liquids to spill and the manganese oxide gets rid of the hydrogen so that the cell works for quite a long time.

Secondary cells

Secondary cells can be recharged. The chemical reaction that produces the current can be reversed by sending a charging current through the cell in the opposite direction, e.g. lead-acid cell (as in a car battery), nicad.

A *lead-acid cell* is first charged by sending a current through it. The + plate becomes coated with a layer of brown lead oxide and the – plate is coated with grey lead. The cell produces about 2 V and has a low resistance so that it can give out a large current (which the dry cell cannot!).

When the cell is discharged it turns the coatings into lead sulphate. The cell gives up hydrogen and oxygen by splitting up water when it is being charged, and this may need to be replaced by adding pure water.

> *CHECKPOINT*
>
> What is the difference between a primary and a secondary cell?
>
> Name an example of each.
>
> Give some advantages of using a secondary cell to power a personal stereo.

Battery, Circuit, emf

Cell membrane

This surrounds the cytoplasm of the ***cell***. Its function is to protect the cell, and to control what enters and leaves. It is made of protein and fat.

Cell wall

This is only found in ***plant*** cells, and in ***bacteria*** and ***yeasts***, *never* in animal cells. In plant cells, the cell wall is made of a type of carbohydrate called *cellulose*. It is strong and tough, so it keeps the cell rigid (keeps it the same shape). It is permeable, so it allows substances to pass through it, going in and out of the cell.

CELLS

All living things are made up of cells: they are sometimes called the units of life or the building blocks of life.

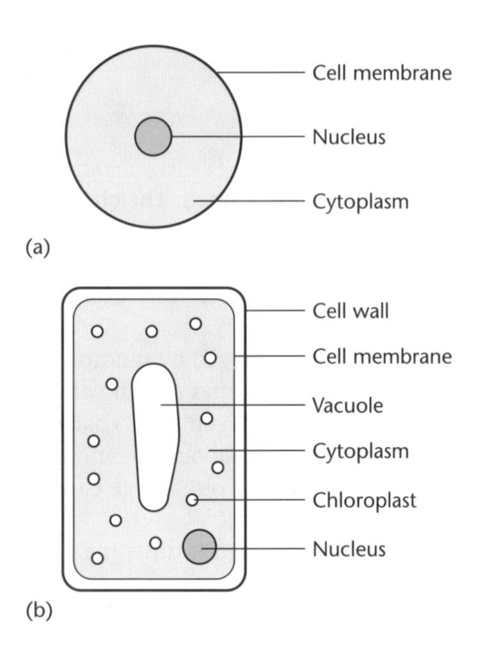

Cells a) and b)
(a) Typical animal cell (cheek cell).
(b) Typical plant cell (palisade cell).

Each cell is made up of a ***nucleus*** and ***cytoplasm***, surrounded by a ***cell membrane***. Plant cells also have a ***cell wall*** made of cellulose, and often have a large ***vacuole***. Some plant cells contain ***chloroplasts***.

Cell components

Part of cell	*Function*
Cell membrane	Protects the cell Controls what enters and leaves the cell
Nucleus	Contains ***chromosomes*** Controls cell division and all the cell's activities
Cytoplasm	Contains dissolved chemicals and stored food Chemical reactions occur here
Cell wall	Gives the cell a fixed shape
Vacuole	Contains cell sap (liquid)
Chloroplasts	Contain ***chlorophyll*** to trap light energy

In multicellular organisms, e.g. humans and plants, different types of cell carry out different functions – this is called ***division of labour***. Cells are specialized (adapted) for the functions they perform.

CELSIUS (°C)

This is the temperature scale that is used in Science. It used to be called Centigrade and was invented by Anders Celsius. There are 100 degrees between 0°C at the freezing point of water and 100°C at the boiling point of water.

✣ ***Temperature scale***

CERAMICS

Ceramics are materials that can stand very high temperatures. Crucibles, used in the laboratory for heating substances, and the protective tiles on the space shuttle are both made from ceramic material. Most ceramics are made from clay, which is composed of layers of aluminium, silicon and oxygen atoms joined together. When heated in a kiln, the water molecules trapped between the clay layers are driven out. The layers then fuse together to form a strong but brittle material.

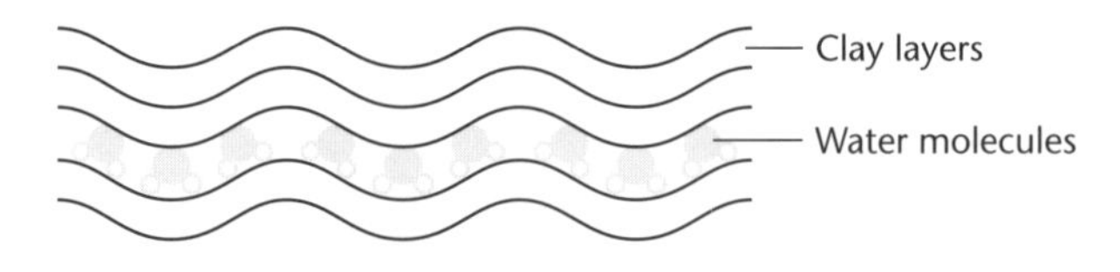

Clay

CHANGES OF STATE

Materials can be either ***solid***, ***liquid*** or ***gas***. These are called ***states of matter***. When a kettle is boiling, the water stays at 100°C and the energy being put in is used to change the liquid water into steam where the particles are a lot further apart. In a similar way ice will melt at 0°C, the heat energy supplied being used to break down the structure of the solid and make the particles free to flow.

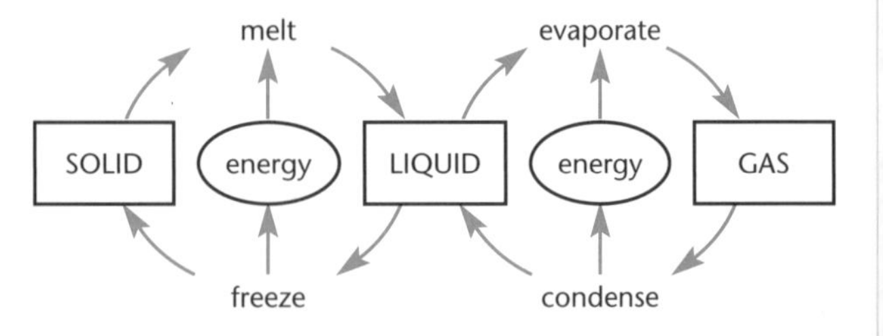

Changing state

Energy is needed to make a material melt and the same energy is released when the material freezes. In

a similar way, energy is needed to vaporize a liquid and the same energy is released when the vapour condenses. This energy is called *latent heat*. The latent heat to vaporize a liquid will be a lot greater than the latent heat that melted the original solid. Different materials will change from one ***state*** to another at different temperatures.

> *Remember: A change of state will happen at a constant temperature that is special for that material. The temperature is the **freezing point** or **boiling point** of the material.*

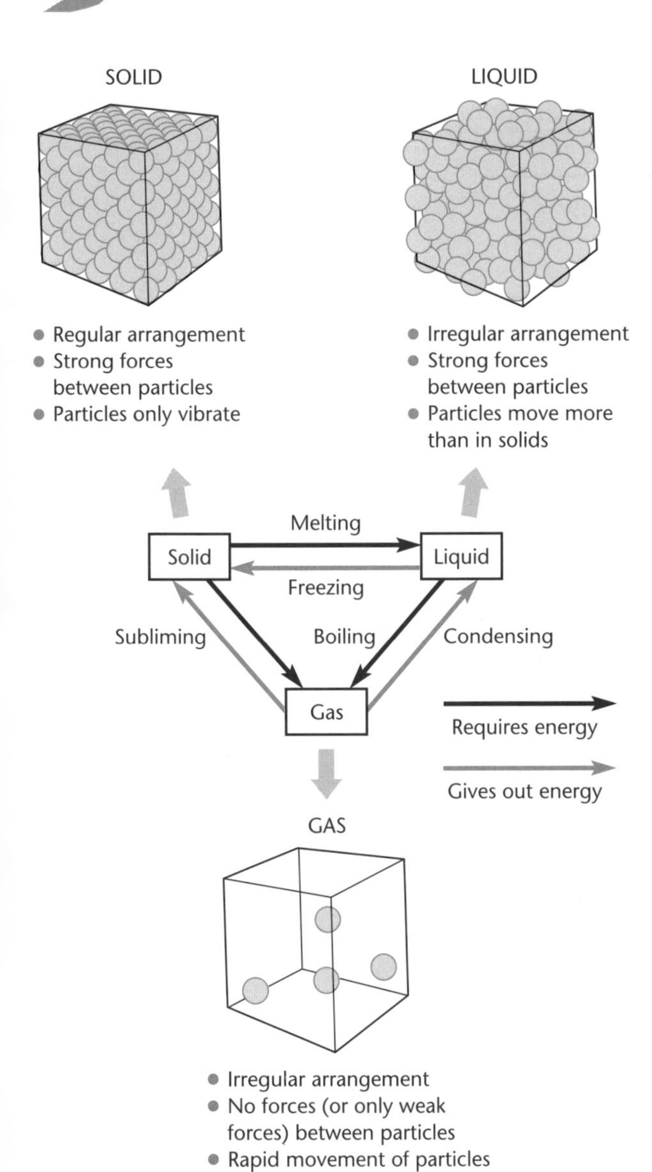

Changing state

A refrigerator is cooled by a liquid that is evaporated in metal pipes in the freezer compartment. The heat energy needed to do this is taken from inside the fridge. The compressor then turns the vapour back into a liquid inside the radiator on the back of the fridge and the heat energy is released into the surrounding air. Liquids that evaporate quickly feel cold if they are spilt on your hand. This is because they get the heat energy needed to evaporate from your hand. A burn caused by steam will often be much worse than a burn from hot water because of the large amount of extra heat that is released as the steam turns back into hot water.

Do not forget that steam is a colourless gas and should not be confused with the clouds of small water droplets that we often call 'steam' in everyday English. Look for steam close to the spout of a boiling kettle, but DO NOT TOUCH!

Water can be used as an example of these different states. As *ice* it is a solid; as ***water*** it is a liquid; as ***steam*** it is a gas. The state of matter can be changed by heating or cooling.

In a solid the particles are close together and are vibrating in 'fixed' positions. In a liquid the particles are moving and are able to move around each other reasonably freely. In a gas these particles are moving very fast and are large distances apart.

Kinetic theory, State

Characteristics of living things

These seven features are sometimes called ***life processes***. They help us to distinguish between living and non-living things. The seven characteristics are: ***movement, respiration, sensitivity, growth, reproduction, excretion*** and ***nutrition***.

Charge

Electric charge is a property of electrons which carry a tiny negative charge and protons which carry a tiny positive charge.

> *Remember: A flow of charge is an electric current.*

Electron, Proton, Static electricity

Chemical energy

Chemical *energy* is contained in the bonds between atoms when they form ***compounds***. If the atoms become bonded together in a different way, by making new compounds, the bonding energy required may be different and the extra energy is released as heat – an ***exothermic*** reaction. The different fuels that we burn may give out different quantities of heat, but they all release some of their chemical energy as heat energy when they burn.

Energy

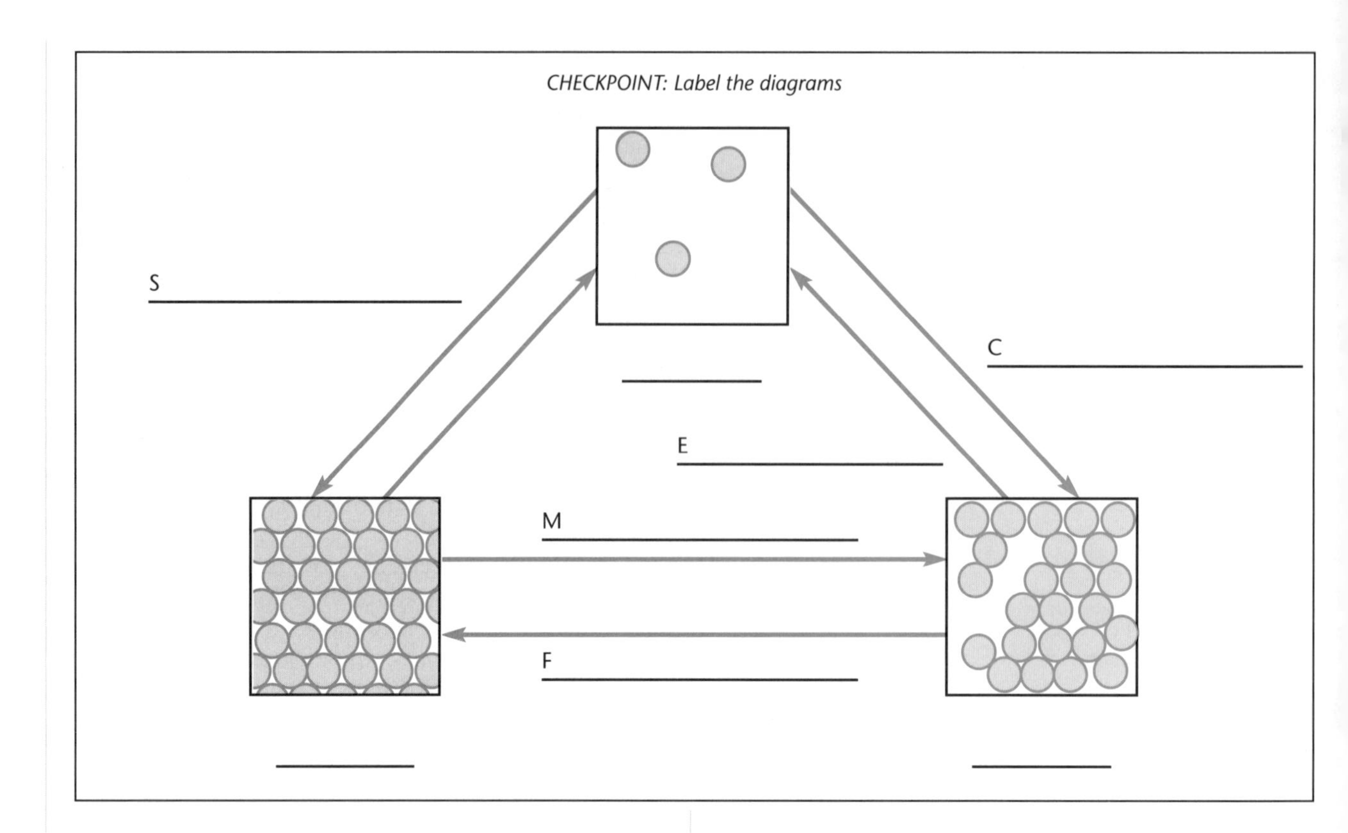

CHEMICAL EQUATIONS

Chemists use ***equations*** to represent the atoms involved in a chemical reaction. The simplest type of equation is a **word equation**.

This is a summary, in words, of a **chemical reaction**:

Hydrogen + Oxygen —Ignite→ Hydrogen oxide (water)

These are the reactants and the special conditions needed and these are the products

The next stage is to use ***symbols*** to represent the ***atoms*** involved in the reaction and to show the amount of reactants and products.

$$2H_2 + O_2 \xrightarrow{\text{Ignite}} 2H_2O$$

CHEMICAL FORMULA

A chemical formula shows the type and number of atoms in a ***molecule***. The numbers are written after the symbol, as subscripts (the numbers below and to the right of the symbol). For example, water is written as H_20. This means there are two hydrogen atoms bonded to one oxygen atom in each molecule. A larger molecule called glucose, made by plants during ***photosynthesis***, has the formula $C_6H_{12}O_6$. This large molecule contains six carbon atoms, twelve hydrogen atoms and six oxygen atoms.

CHEMICAL REACTIONS

When chemical reactions take place, new substances are always produced. The starting materials (the *reactants*) are replaced by entirely new substances

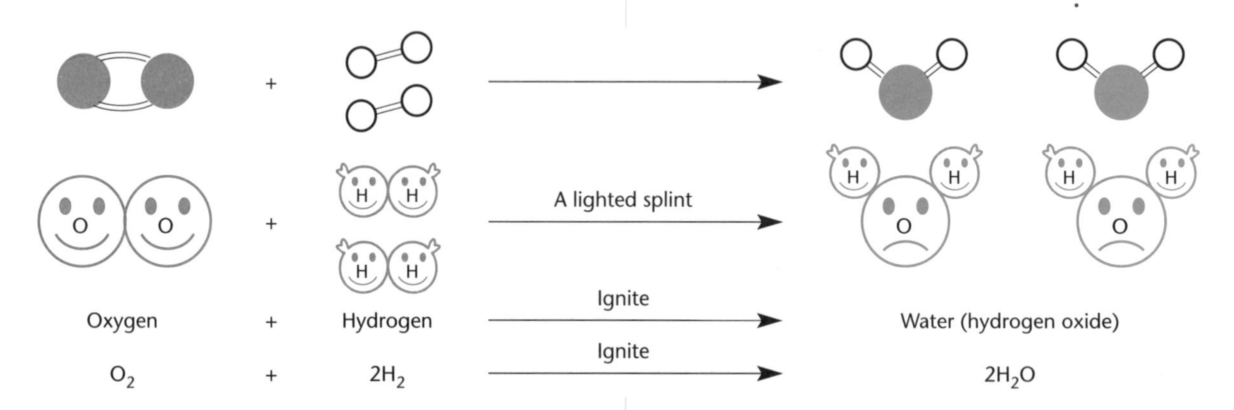

A chemical equation

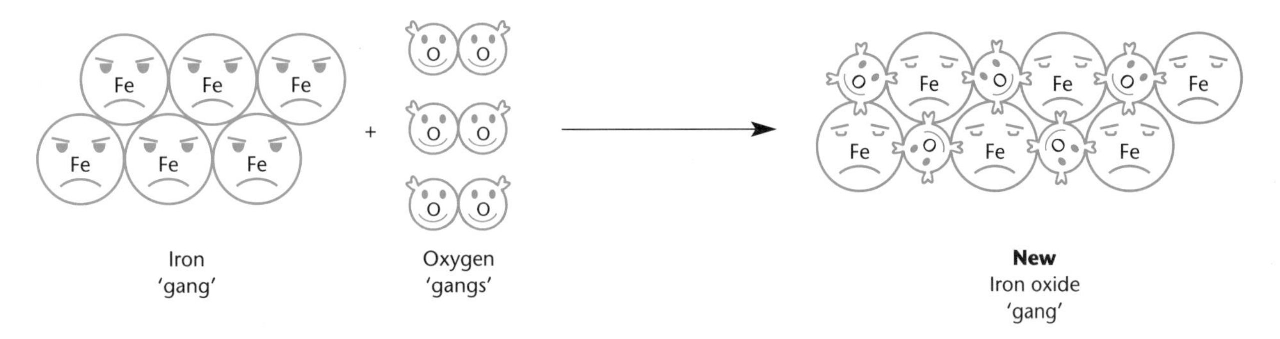

Iron and oxygen reacting

(the *products*). These new substances have their own properties. Unlike *physical changes*, the changes from chemical actions are hard to reverse.

Rusting is an example of a chemical change. Iron reacts with oxygen and water in the air to produce a new substance called rust, which is not as hard as iron metal and crumbles away as the metal is ***corroded***.

You could think of the iron metal as a 'gang' of iron ***particles***. If this gang of iron particles meets other gangs of oxygen and water, then they have a huge fight (the chemical reaction) and end up in different gangs at the end of the fight. Sometimes these meetings get quite heated, and give off heat energy (***exothermic*** reactions) in the process.
The word equation for rusting is:

$$\text{Iron + Oxygen} \xrightarrow{\text{water}} \text{Iron oxide (rust)}$$

There are many types of chemical reaction, some of which are thought to be extremely important. For example, ***photosynthesis*** is a chemical reaction that has allowed life itself to evolve on Earth. Another useful reaction, ***fermentation***, converts sugar into alcohol. This reaction has been known for thousands of years. However, some chemical reactions can be harmful, as with rusting and the spoiling of food.

CHLORINATION

This is one of the stages of ***water treatment*** in which a small amount of chlorine is added to the ***water*** to kill any ***bacteria*** left in it.

Water treatment

CHLORO-ALKALI INDUSTRY

The main *raw material* of this industry is salt or ***brine***. The salt is split up by an ***electrolysis*** reaction into the products of hydrogen, chlorine and sodium hydroxide. These products are then processed to make many useful new substances. Chlorine is used to make plastics and is an important disinfectant. Hydrogen is used in margarine manufacture and sodium hydroxide is used for making soap.

CHLOROPHYLL

This is a green chemical found in plant ***leaves***. It traps light energy, so it is very important in ***photosynthesis***.

CHLOROPLASTS

These are small structures inside some plant cells, particularly in leaves. They contain ***chlorophyll***, which is important in ***photosynthesis***. ***Palisade cells*** contain large numbers of chloroplasts, but they are never found inside root cells.

CHROMATOGRAPHY

This is a method used to separate mixtures ***dissolved*** in a ***solvent***. It is also used to identify substances. The simplest form of chromatography is called paper chromatography.

A drop of solution of the mixture to be separated is placed on a type of blotting paper (called *chromatography paper*) and then dipped into a solvent.

As the solvent soaks up through the paper, it carries the mixture with it, but because different substances dissolve at different rates, the solvent carries some parts of the mixture further than others, so separating them.

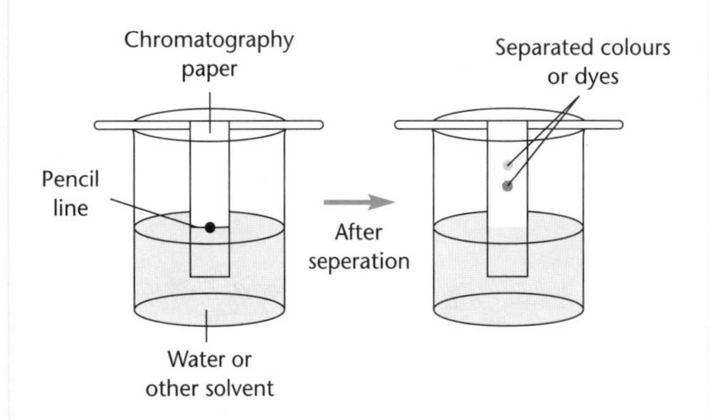

Chromatography

This can be seen if a dot is made with black felt-tip pen on chromatography or filter paper and then dipped into a solvent such as water. The colours that

make up the black (e.g. purple, red, blue, green, etc.) will separate.

This technique can also be used to separate a mixture of amino acids or proteins.

Chromosomes

These are long threads made of ***DNA*** found in the nucleus of all cells. They carry genetic information, so that new copies of the cell can be made, and so that the cell carries out its functions properly.

Each chromosome is divided into small sections called ***genes*** (a chromosome has thousands of genes), and each gene is an instruction about a single feature of the organism, e.g. eye colour.

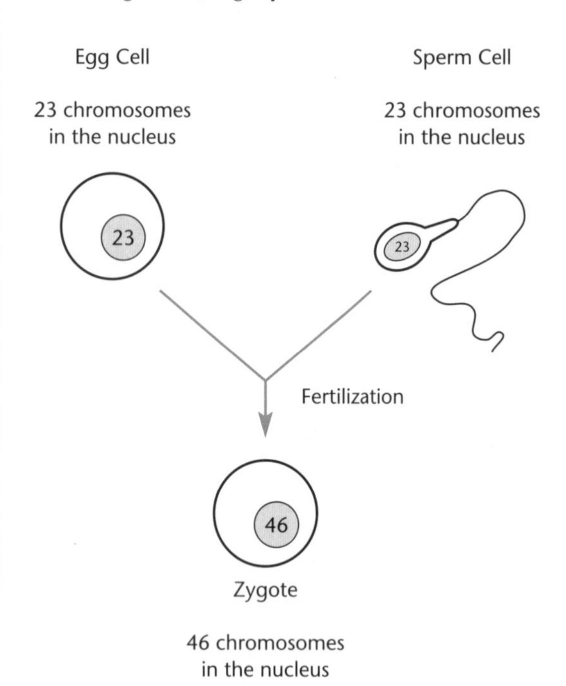

How a zygote is formed

In humans, body cells, e.g. nerve cells, skin cells, muscle cells all have 46 chromosomes, but sperm and eggs (gametes) have only 23. In this way the ***zygote*** (cell formed when ***fertilization*** occurs) will have the right number of chromosomes to develop properly into a baby.

Ciliated cells

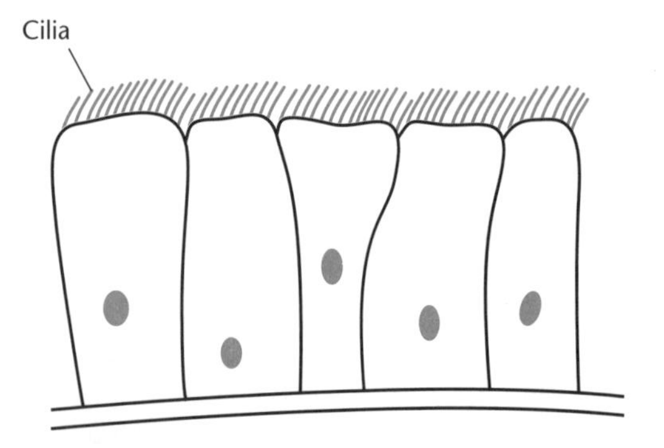

Ciliated cells

These cells are found in the breathing system (nose, and air passages in the lungs). They have tiny hairs called *cilia* to trap dust and dirt, and to remove them from the air passages.

Circuit

Every circuit must have a power supply such as a battery, a generator or 'mains'. No ***current*** will flow unless there is a *complete* circuit from the supply, round the circuit and back to the supply at its other terminal without any gaps. Switches work by making a gap in the circuit to turn off the current – remember that the current is turned off all round the circuit, before the switch as well as after it. Each component (part) in the circuit will have its own *circuit symbol* to make it easy to draw. Remember that current is pushed round the circuit by the voltage – so the current moves, the voltage stays where it is.

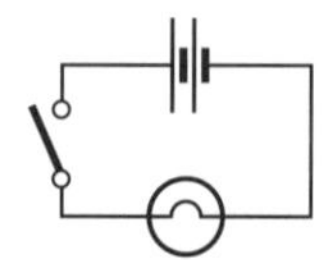

A circuit that will only be complete when the switch is closed

Remember: There must be a complete circuit for current to flow.

Circuit symbols

To make it easier to draw electric circuits there are international symbols for all of the things that are normally used in a circuit. Remember that the wires

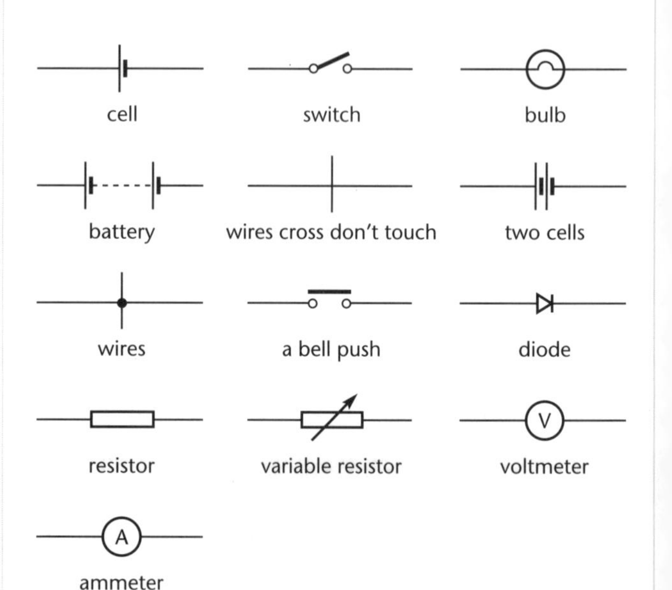

Circuit symbols

in a circuit are always drawn up or down or across and never along diagonals so that the circuits are easier to follow.

The common ones are shown on the previous page.

Current

CIRCULATORY SYSTEM

This system is responsible for moving substances around the body. It is made up of the ***heart***, ***blood vessels*** and ***blood***. The heart acts as a pump to move blood through the blood vessels.

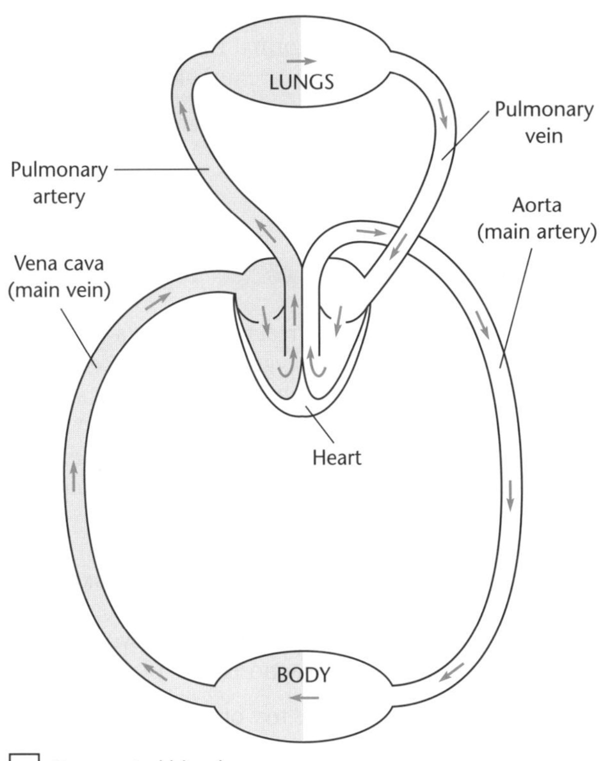

The circulatory system

Most of the substances being carried by the blood are dissolved in the blood ***plasma***, e.g. carbon dioxide, urea, food substances, but oxygen is carried inside the ***red blood cells***.

When blood reaches the tiny blood vessels called ***capillaries***, substances are exchanged between the blood and body cells.

Food substances and oxygen move from blood into body cells. Waste products, e.g. carbon dioxide, move from body cells into the blood.

This happens because:

- capillaries have very thin walls (one cell thick), so substances can pass through them easily,

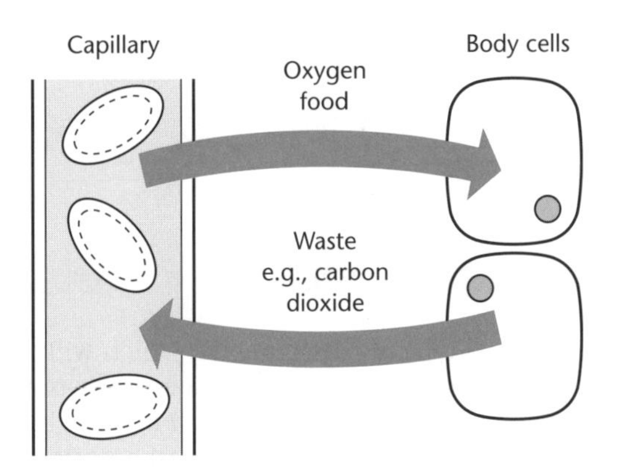

Exchange of substances between blood and body cell

- capillaries are very close to all body cells, so substances do not have very far to travel,
- blood flows quite slowly through capillaries, so there is time for exchange to take place.

Substances move by ***diffusion***.

CLASSIFICATION

This is the way in which scientists sort living things into groups (called taxonomic groups).

They look for similarities and differences between organisms. They have sorted all living things into one of five ***kingdoms:***

Animals
Plants
Fungi
Monera
Protoctists

- Each kingdom is divided into smaller groups called *phyla*.
- Each phylum is divided into smaller groups called *classes*.
- Each class is divided into smaller groups called *orders*.
- Each order is divided into smaller groups called *families*.
- Each family is divided into smaller groups called *genera*.
- Each genus is divided into smaller groups called *species*.

Species is the last group in this classification and each species is given a ***scientific name***. It is important to classify living things precisely, because there are so many of them – there are known to be more than one million types of insect (and probably lots more that have not been discovered yet!).

Invertebrates, Vertebrates

CLAY

Ceramics

CLINICAL THERMOMETER

This is a special type of thermometer, which will record body temperature and keep the reading until it is read. Usually the thermometer can be reset by shaking to get the liquid back down past a narrow part of the tube. If it was like an ordinary thermometer the reading would start to go down as soon as it left the patient. The thermometer usually has a scale that goes between 35°C and 43°C because body temperature is about 37°C.

Thermometer

CLONE

A group of *identical* organisms made by ***asexual reproduction***. For example,

all the bacteria in one colony are a clone,
all the plantlets produced by a spider plant are a clone.

COLLOID

Some substances are composed of ***particles*** so large, that it is not really correct to say that they can be ***dissolved*** in a ***solvent***. For example, orange squash looks cloudy and if you shine a beam of light into the bottle, some of the light reflects off the 'orange' particles, which remain visible in the liquid. This is an example of a colloid. If you do the same to a beaker of brine, the light passes straight through because the sodium chloride particles *have dissolved* to very small particles in the solution.

COLOUR

The different frequencies of light waves that we see have different effects on the retina of an ***eye*** so that we see them as different colours. Lower frequencies are red and higher frequencies are violet.

Spectrum

COLOURED OBJECTS

Only a few objects are hot enough to give out light and be seen by the colours of the light that they emit, e.g. a light bulb, a fire or the ***Sun***.

Most objects are seen by the light that they *reflect*. If an object only reflects red light then it must appear red unless there is no red light to reflect. If an object cannot reflect any light then it will appear to be black. Colours that are not reflected are absorbed by a dye or pigment in the paint or on the surface of the object.

Some objects reflect several colours. If all colours are being reflected, the object appears to be white.

For example:

- A blue object in white light will appear to be blue as it reflects the blue and absorbs all the other colours of the spectrum.
- The same blue object will appear to be black in red light because there is no blue light to reflect and the red is being absorbed.
- The yellow light from sodium street lamps is a pure yellow and gives normal things a strange appearance because they are unable to reflect their normal colours.

Reflection, Spectrum

COMBUSTION

A combustion reaction is a reaction where a substance combines with oxygen and produces energy. When a combustion occurs, *oxides* are formed. Combustion reactions are ***oxidation*** reactions. Burning coal in oxygen is an example. Coal is mainly made of carbon so the word equation for the reaction is:

Carbon + Oxygen ——► Carbon dioxide

- When coal is burned in an open fire, two different combustion reactions take place.
- When the coal is on the top of the pile and there is plenty of oxygen, it burns to produce carbon dioxide.
- When the coal is buried deep in the pile and has only a limited supply of oxygen, it burns to produce carbon monoxide. This burns with a blue flame. You can sometimes see this in the fire.

COMMUNITY

This is all the types of organism found in a single habitat, for example,

- a rock pool community would include seaweeds, limpets, barnacles, sea anemones and fish.
- a woodland community would include oak trees, ash trees, hazel bushes, squirrels, birds, voles, insects, earthworms, etc.

A community is a complex balance of many different types of organism.

Some organisms will depend on others; e.g. animals depend on plants for food and for shelter,

and plants depend on animals for pollination and seed dispersal.

Some organisms will compete with others, e.g. oak and ash trees might compete for light, while mistlethrushes (birds) compete for holly berries.

✦ ***Competition for resources, Environment, Population***

Competition for resources

Many plants and animals produce very large numbers of offspring, and there are often not enough resources to go round. Organisms have to compete with each other for the things they need to stay alive.

Plants compete for:

- light
- water
- space

Animals compete for:

- food
- space
- a mate

Some individuals are better suited to their environment than others; we say they have a ***selective advantage***. These individuals are more likely to get the resources they need to stay alive, so they will survive and breed. Other organisms will not get the resources they need, so they will die.

Organisms have to compete with:

- *other species*, e.g. a limpet and a periwinkle on the shore both feed on algae, so they are competing for food. This is called inter-specific competition.
- *other members of their own species*, e.g. there will be many limpets feeding on algae, so they are competing with each other. This is called intra-specific competition.

Remember: Competition is a natural process. It does not depend on humans.

✦ ***Natural selection, Population***

Composite

Composite materials are those that are ***mixtures*** Concrete is a composite material as it is a mixture of cement, sand and gravel.

Material scientists have developed many new *materials* over the years. They sometimes copy ideas already observed in natural materials. For example, when you look closely at bone it is apparent that it is actually made from two different materials working together. The long *protein fibres* in the bone being surrounded and strengthened by another material called *calcium phosphate*; bone is therefore an example of a natural composite material.

Damon Hill's formula one car contains a wide range of composite materials. The racing car must be able to withstand high forces but must also be as light as possible. The materials used in your family car would not be suitable for this, so special composite materials have been developed for specialist vehicles of this kind.

Compost

This is a type of organic ***fertilizer*** made from waste household materials. Any ***biodegradable*** substance, e.g. potato peelings, tea bags, grass cuttings, dead leaves, etc., is cut up and put into the compost bin, in layers with moist soil or manure. The soil or manure contains ***decomposers***: bacteria or fungi, which feed on dead material and make it ***decay*** The decay process is quicker if the layers are turned and mixed occasionally, or if earthworms are added to the bin to mix the layers.

After a few months, the household waste will have rotted down to a dark, crumbly compost, rich in ***minerals*** This can be dug into the garden, and will improve plant growth.

Making compost is a good idea for two reasons:

- it recycles household waste, so less of it is put into dustbins and dumped or burned. This helps to reduce the problem of waste disposal.
- it is free fertilizer! Many gardens need fertilizer if the plants are to grow properly, and this is an easy, cheap way of getting it.

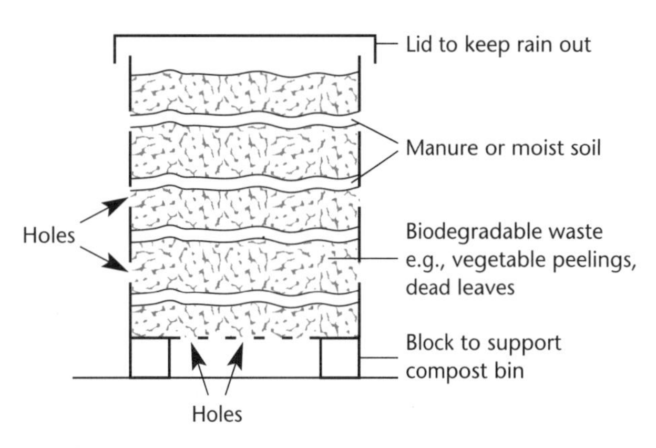

Making compost

CHECKPOINT

Look at the diagram of the compost bin, and look at the conditions needed for ***decay***. Try to decide:

- why there are holes in the bottoms and sides.
- why the soil or manure must be moist.

Some people put earthworms in their compost bin to speed up the rate of decay. How does this work?

It can get very warm inside compost bins (up to 70°C in the middle). Can you explain why?

CLUE: look at the section on ***energy***.

Compounds

A compound is a substance made by chemically combining two or more ***elements***. For example, when the elements aluminium and iodine are combined in a ***mixture***, we get the compound aluminium iodide.

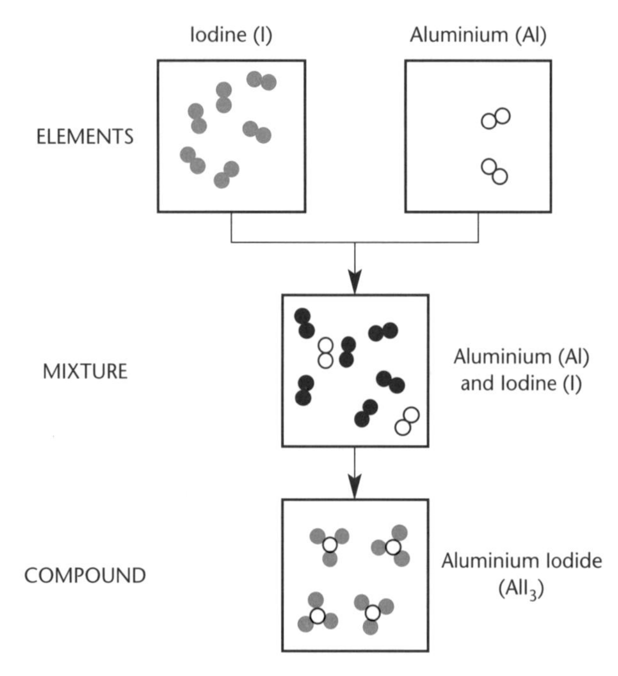

Elements, mixture and compound

When the elements oxygen and hydrogen are mixed together in a small test tube and a lighted splint is added, you hear a squeaky pop as the two elements combine chemically together to make a new compound called water.

An even more spectacular reaction is seen if you put a small piece of sodium metal into a gas jar full of the toxic gas, chlorine. Sodium and chlorine are both elements and the product seen in the gas jar is a white powder, which is the compound sodium chloride. This compound is harmless; in fact it is the salt in salt and vinegar crisps.

Compounds have different properties than those of the elements from which they are made.

CHECKPOINT: Complete the boxes

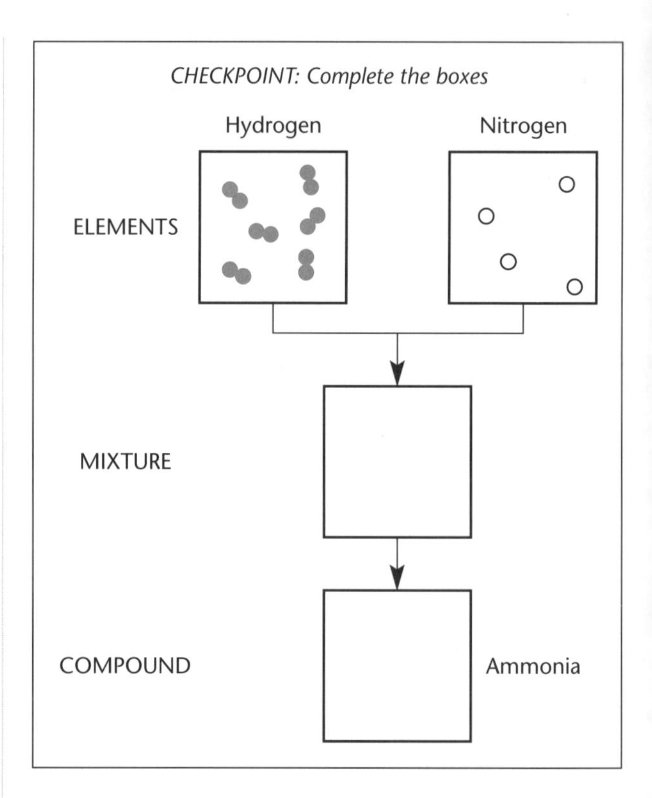

When two or more elements bond together they form a new substance called a compound. In order to show that a new substance has been formed, the non-metal part changes its name. For example, when sodium reacts with chlorine to produce a compound, the new substance will be called sodium chloride.

- If a compound ends in '*–ide*', the compound contains only two elements. Note, however, that sodium hydroxide contains three elements: sodium, hydrogen and oxygen.
- If the compound ends in '*–ate*', the compound contains oxygen. For example, copper sulphate contains copper sulphur and oxygen.

CHECKPOINT:

Which elements do the following compounds contain? Iron oxide, Sodium sulphate, Magnesium hydroxide

Conclusion

Do make sure that you write a conclusion at the end of any practical investigation that you do. Say clearly what you found out and whether your original ideas were correct. Try to give scientific reasons why your results behave as they do. Follow the conclusion with an ***evaluation*** of the experiment.

Investigation

CONDENSATION

When steam is cooled down, it turns back to water. You will have seen the water that forms on a cold window in a steamy kitchen. This change back from steam to liquid water is called condensation. In fact, the term 'condensation' can be used more generally to refer to the liquid formed as a result of cooling a gas.

✦ ***Changes of state***

CONDUCTION OF HEAT

Conduction of heat can occur in two ways: by vibrations and by electrons.

Vibrations

The heat at one end of a piece of material causes the particles there to vibrate rapidly and the temperature rises (***kinetic theory***). This vibration is passed on to the next layer of particles as they bump into each other and the heat energy is passed from one layer to the next until it reaches the colder end. This does happen but it is not a very efficient process and it may take a large ***temperature*** difference from the hot end to the cold end to drive much heat through the material. If the particles are large molecules that are not able to vibrate easily, the result is a poor ***conductor*** or an ***insulator***. This is what usually happens in plastics.

Electrons

The heat is carried through a ***metal*** by electrons in the metal that are free to move around. All metals are good conductors.

Some materials will be better conductors than others – they have a better *conductivity*. The experiment in the figure overleaf shows a simple method of comparing the conduction along rods that are all the same size. The wax will melt first on the best conductor and the drawing pin will fall off.

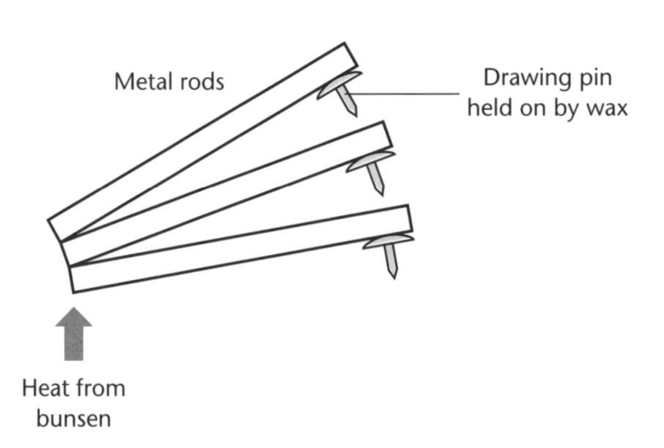

Comparing conduction

Liquids are often poor conductors and heat travels through them by ***convection***. If you heat the liquid at the top then some heat is conducted downwards but not as quickly as in a solid. This is shown in the experiment below. The water at the top is boiling but the ice remains frozen at the bottom.

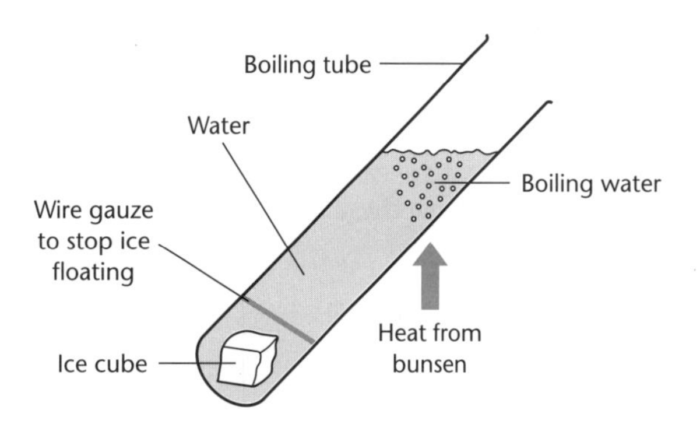

This property is used in hot water tanks, which are filled with hot water from the top downwards so that you do not need to heat as much water.

Gases are very poor conductors because the molecules are too far apart and heat is transferred through them by convection. Trapping pockets or layers of air can make a good insulator. Double glazing works by trapping a layer of poor conducting air between two layers of glass. See other examples under ***insulation***.

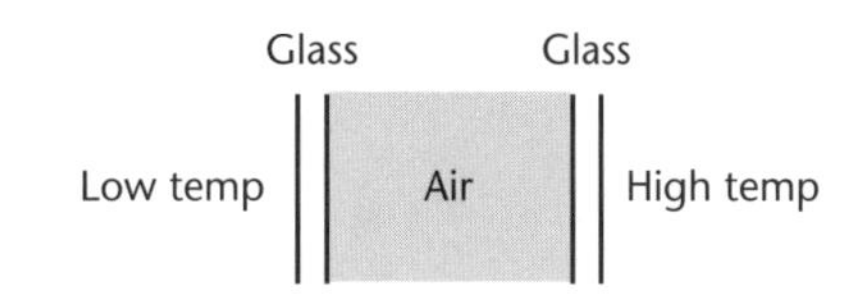

Double glazing

There are many uses for good conductors, such as pans, boiler pipes and the walls of car engines. They are all made from metal.

> *CHECKPOINT*
>
> Which materials are always good conductors?
>
> How is heat transferred in these materials?
>
> Name three uses for good conductors.

✦ ***Conductor, Convection, Infra-red radiation, Insulator, Vacuum flask***

CONDUCTOR

Electrical

A conductor lets ***current*** flow through it easily. Metals are all good conductors. The only non-metal

that conducts well is carbon. (The 'lead' in your pencil is carbon so do not poke it into electricity sockets!) Most other materials are not good conductors and are called ***insulators***. Some materials, such as water, can conduct enough electric current to be dangerous, but they are not good conductors.

You can test for conductors and insulators by putting them into a gap in a simple ***series*** circuit with a battery and a bulb. If the bulb lights then the material is a conductor.

Metals are good conductors because they contain a lot of ***electrons*** that are easily moved around. Insulators do not have these 'free' electrons.

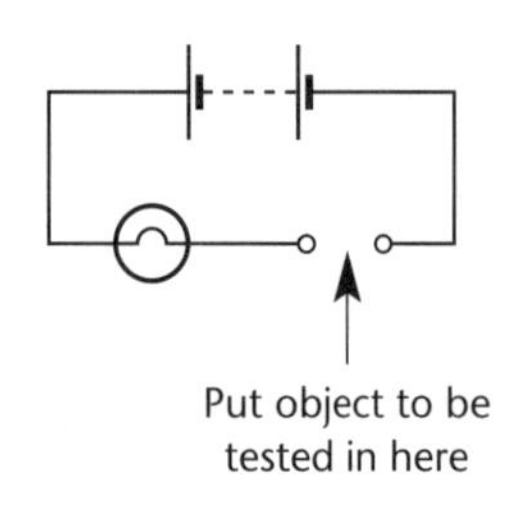

Testing for conductors

> *CHECKPOINT*
>
> Which materials are always good conductors of electricity?
>
> Which non-metal is also a conductor?

Heat

Good conductors of heat will let heat travel quickly and easily through them. Metals are always good conductors.

✦ ***Conduction, Current, Insulator***

CONSERVATION

Whenever humans interfere with a natural environment, they will change the ecological balance, for example:

- land is cleared to build houses and roads, and habitats are destroyed.
- marshy land is drained, or estuaries are dammed so that they flood, and habitats are destroyed.
- animals are hunted for sport or for products that can be used by humans, e.g. fur, ivory, and they may become extinct.
- chemicals such as pesticides and herbicides are used to kill some organisms.
- pollution can damage habitats and kill the organisms that live in them, e.g. oil spills in the sea kill shellfish, seals and seabirds.
- pollution can have serious long term effects, e.g. carbon dioxide gas is linked to the ***greenhouse effect***, CFCs (chlorofluorocarbons) damage the ozone layer.

> *Conservation involves doing things to limit the damage caused by humans, and to maintain the ecological balance.*

Examples of damage limitation are:

- recycle natural resources, e.g. glass, metal, paper, plastics.
- encourage organic farming, without using pesticides and herbicides.
- keep litter and pollution away from natural habitats.
- protect endangered species by law, e.g. in Britain it is illegal to disturb bats.
- protect nature reserves and green-belt land, so that houses and roads cannot be built on them.

Although some of these conservation measures depend on laws, there are many things that all of us can do in our everyday lives to help the environment; for example:

- recycle whenever possible – cans, glass, paper, plastic.
- do not drop litter.
- walk or use a bicycle; do not go in a car for a short journey. If it is too far to walk, catch a bus!
- save energy by switching lights and fires off if they are not needed.
- make sure the houses that we live in and places where we work are well-insulated, so heat is not lost and energy is saved.
- do not buy products made from endangered species, or souvenirs of animals collected from the wild, e.g. rare sea-shells or butterflies.
- do not use pesticides or herbicides in our own gardens.

✦ ***Environment***

CONSTELLATION

This is a pattern of stars that we see in the sky. A lot of the constellations have names and they are useful for finding particular stars. The stars in a constellation are often not really in a group at all and are at huge distances from each other. They just happen to be in a similar direction from our ***solar system***

✦ ***Galaxy, Star***

Consumer

This is an organism that eats other living things (animals or plants). All animals are consumers.

Herbivores are consumers that eat plants.
Carnivores are consumers that eat animals.
Omnivores are consumers that eat plants and animals.

Contraception

There are ways of avoiding becoming pregnant when having sexual intercourse. A couple may choose to use contraception for several reasons:

- they may not want to have children at the moment,
- they may already have a young child, and not want others yet,
- they may have several children, and not want any more.

Some people do not agree with contraception because they feel it is interfering with nature, or it is against their religious beliefs.

There are three main methods of contraception.

Barrier methods – e.g. condom, cap, female condom

These are put in place before sexual intercourse and prevent the sperm from swimming to the egg so ***fertilization*** cannot occur. They are reliable if used properly, and should be used with a spermicide.

The condom also helps to prevent sexually transmitted diseases.

Chemical methods – e.g. the Pill, hormone implants

These are taken regularly (each day) or are left inside the woman's body for several months. They release chemicals that prevent ***ovulation*** occurring, i.e., the woman's ovary does not release eggs, so she cannot become pregnant.

They are very reliable, but are not suitable for all women because they may have side-effects, e.g. making the woman feel ill, increasing the risk of blood clots. They do not protect against sexually transmitted diseases.

The coil (IUD)

This is a piece of plastic or metal, which is fitted inside the woman's uterus and stays there for several years. It prevents a fertilized egg from implanting in the ***uterus*** (sinking into the uterus lining), so the woman cannot become pregnant.

This method is quite reliable but is not suitable for all women because it may cause side-effects, e.g. very bad period pains. It does not protect against sexually transmitted diseases.

Sterilization

If a couple are certain that they do not want to have any more children, either the man or the woman can be *sterilized*. This involves an operation to cut the sperm ducts or the fallopian tubes, so that fertilization cannot occur. The couple can still have sexual intercourse, but the woman will not become pregnant. It is not easy to reverse this operation, i.e., join up the sperm ducts, or the fallopian tubes, so the couple should be certain that they do not want more children before having this operation.

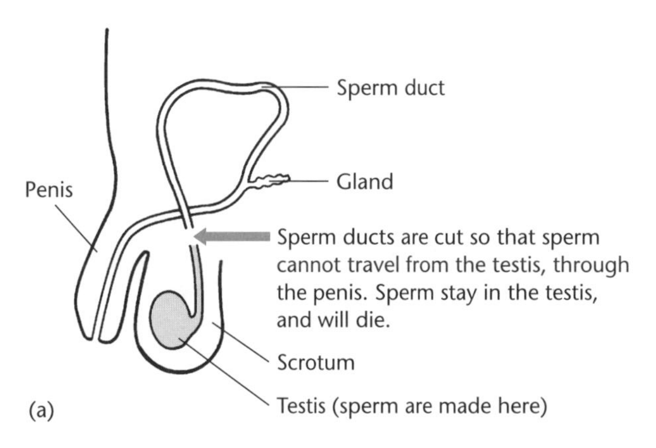

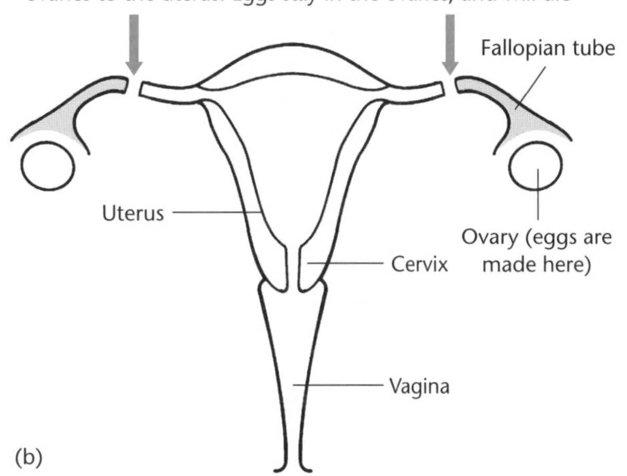

Sterilization
(a) Male – this is called a vasectomy.
(b) Female – this is sometimes called having your 'tubes tied'.

Contraction

Most materials will get smaller when cooled. This is called contraction. It will be a very small effect in solids but can be seen easily with liquids and is quite a large effect in gases. The forces when this happens can be very large, especially in solids.

✦ ***Expansion***

CONVECTION

This is the main way in which heat energy is transferred through liquids and gases. Liquids and gases are called *fluids* because their particles are free to move around. We will use the word fluid because the explanation works with both liquids and gases.

When part of the fluid is heated it expands and becomes less dense. It will therefore float upwards within the rest of the fluid taking heat energy with it. Colder fluid will take its place and the process is repeated. This results in currents of rising warmer fluid and falling colder fluid. This can be seen in the apparatus below. The potassium permanganate crystal dissolves in the water to give a deep purple solution and you can see the convection currents as this colour is carried round.

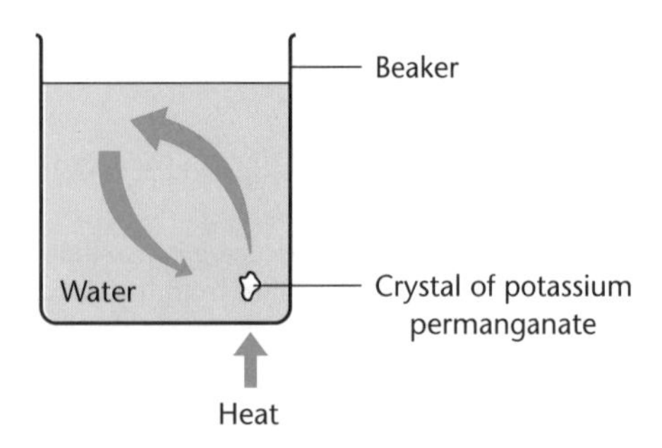

Convection

The reverse process is sometimes noticed near windows where the air cools and becomes more dense so that it sinks. You may feel the cold air falling over the window sill on a cold day.

Room and caravan heaters are often convectors as it is a good way to spread the heat round the room without an exposed flame. A very large room will have the process speeded up by fans that blow some of the warm air round the room and this is then called 'forced convection'. The hot water system in your house may work by hot water from the boiler rising to the storage tank and being ıeplaced by cooler water from the bottom of the tank.

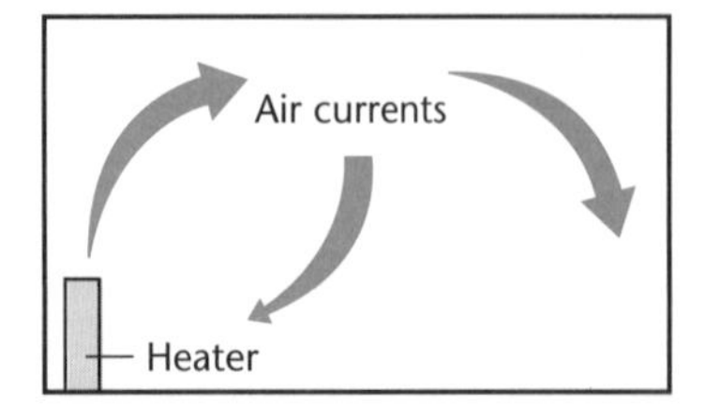

Convection

Remember: Gases are poor conductors but they can transfer heat by convection. If you use a gas to make an insulator, make sure that it cannot move around by trapping it in layers or small pockets in a solid insulator, e.g., plastic foam to insulate pipes against frost damage.

✦ ***Conduction, Infra-red radiation, Vacuum flask***

CORROSION

One of the problems associated with using ***metals*** is that they corrode. Corrosion is a kind of reaction that makes metals useless. Iron corrodes, or rusts, very easily and this causes serious problems for motorists. Nearly two million cars are scrapped each year because of rust.

Corrosion takes place when a metal reacts with air, usually in the presence of water. In the case of iron, the word equation for the reaction is:

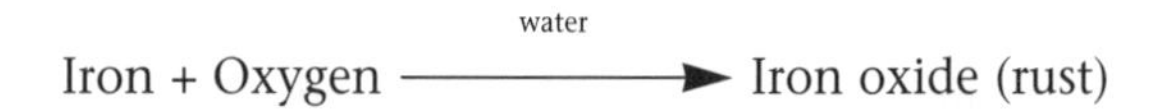

$$\text{Iron} + \text{Oxygen} \xrightarrow{\text{water}} \text{Iron oxide (rust)}$$

CORROSIVE

This is one of the hazards associated with acids. They burn your skin and clothes if they come into contact with them. The hazard warning symbol for corrosive substances is shown below.

Corrosive symbol

COUNTER FORCES

These are the forces that act in the opposite direction to something that is moving so that it is being slowed down.

The forces are often different sorts of ***friction***. When you ride a bike, the force used to push it forwards (you pedalling) is the *driving force*. Acting against this will be air resistance, friction in the axles and pedals, and rolling friction. The air resistance will be bigger if you ride against the wind. Friction could be less if you grease your bike properly. Rolling friction is caused by soft tyres or by riding on soft ground. If you are riding uphill, your weight will also be a counter force.

When the driving force and the counter forces are equal in size, the object will travel at a constant speed. This is often called *terminal velocity*.

For example: a parachute is made to make the air resistance larger so that there is a bigger counter force at a low speed. This can balance the weight (which is the driving force) and the parachute can fall at a constant speed. A free-fall parachutist would fall at a much bigger terminal velocity before the parachute is opened because he has to fall faster for the air resistance to balance the weight.

Another example: you will reach your terminal velocity on your bike when your pedalling force is balanced by the counter forces. When you go uphill, the counter forces would be greater so you are slowed down until the forces balance again at a slower speed.

CHECKPOINT

Make a list of the counter forces that might act if you were riding a motor cycle.

 ***Force***

CRICK, FRANCIS (1916–)

Francis Crick is a British scientist who worked in the team which discovered the structure of ***DNA*** in 1953. He was awarded the Nobel Prize for this work, and later investigated the genetic code (how ***genes*** carry instructions for the characteristics of an individual).

CRUDE OIL

Oil is a very important ***fossil fuel*** and an even more important raw material. It is made from the remains of living things that have been chemically changed over millions of years. Crude oil contains a wide range of different substances. These are separated by ***fractional distillation*** at a refinery. Many useful substances are produced. In fact, most plastics and medicines are made from oil products. At the present rate of use, it is predicted that the world reserves of crude oil will run out in 2050.

CURRENT

An electric current is a flow of electric ***charge*** going round a ***circuit***. The electric current is measured in ***amps*** by using an ***ammeter***.

The charge is actually carried by *electrons* which move round the circuit. Each electron carries a *very* tiny amount of electric charge.

The electric current is NOT 'used up' by any of the parts of a circuit that it flows through, no matter what they do. This is because the electrons cannot suddenly vanish or be created and they have to keep on going round the circuit whenever they are pushed by the ***voltage***.

If current is not used up then it must be true that the *total* current will be the same all the way round the circuit. Sometimes this is a written as a rule that says 'the total current entering any point on a circuit is the same as the total current that leaves it'.

Current through a part of a circuit, such as a bulb, will get bigger if you use a bigger voltage across it (perhaps from a battery with a bigger voltage), or if you put less ***resistance*** in the circuit (so that it is easier for the current to go round).

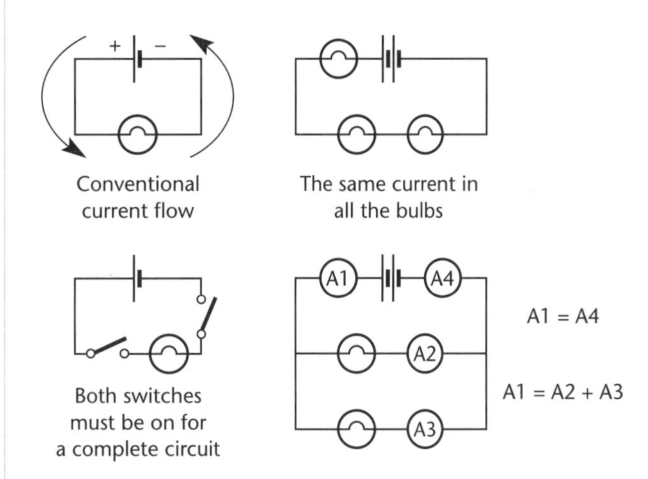

Current in battery circuits

As the electrons are negatively charged, an electric current consists of electrons drifting slowly along the wire in very large numbers from the negative side of the supply round to the positive. (They will be repelled by the negative and attracted by the positive – see ***static electricity***.) This was not known when most of the rules were discovered about how electric currents behave and the rules often refer to the *conventional current*, which is imagined to flow from positive round to negative. The conventional current is the direction of current that is always used in this book.

CHECKPOINT

A circuit has a battery, bulb and a switch in series.

What will you see if you place an ammeter before and after the bulb?

Alternating current, Ammeter, Ampere, Circuit, Direct current

CYCLING IN NATURE

This is a natural form of recycling that does not rely on humans. It means that chemical substances are transferred between living things and the environment, and can be used over and over again.

The water cycle, nitrogen cycle and carbon cycle are all examples of cycling in nature.

CYTOPLASM

This is a jelly-like substance that fills most of the ***cell***. Important chemical reactions take place here, e.g. making new proteins. Food is sometimes stored in the cytoplasm inside small granules, e.g. starch granules, oil droplets.

DALTON, JOHN (1766–1844)

John Dalton was a teacher in Cumbria who taught maths and physics. He was also interested in meteorology and kept a life-time record of the weather in his area. As a result of this, he also studied mixtures of gases and developed a system for naming chemical elements based on a series of circles.

ELEMENTS

Element	W^t	Element	W^t
Hydrogen	1	Strontian	46
Azote	5	Barytes	68
Carbon	54	Iron	50
Oxygen	7	Zinc	56
Phosphorus	9	Copper	56
Sulphur	13	Lead	90
Magnesia	20	Silver	190
Lime	24	Gold	190
Soda	28	Plantina	190
Potash	42	Mercury	167

Dalton's symbols

CHECKPOINT

Which of Dalton's 'elements' were later found to be compounds?

DARWIN, CHARLES (1809–1882)

Charles Darwin was a British scientist, famous for the theory of *evolution* by ***natural selection***. He published this theory in 1859 after studying plants and animals on a voyage to South America. It suggests that in order to survive and be successful, living things must be ***adapted*** to (suitable for) the place where they live – this is sometimes described as 'survival of the fittest'. Darwin used this to explain why there is such a huge variety of living things on Earth, and how they could continue to evolve.

DAVY, SIR HUMPHREY (1778–1829)

Sir Humphrey Davy investigated gases and almost killed himself during one of his experiments when he inhaled laughing gas. He developed this gas as an anaesthetic. He made science very popular in his time by giving lectures to the general public in the Royal Institution, where the Christmas lectures are now filmed each year. He made one member of the public, ***Michael Faraday***, his apprentice. Faraday later went on to make many discoveries of his own.

Davy managed to separate sodium, potassium, strontium and magnesium using his newly developed ***electrolysis*** equipment. However, he is best known for the Davy lamp, used by miners to detect explosive gases.

DECAY

This happens when ***decomposers*** (***bacteria*** and ***fungi***) break down dead organisms or their waste products, so that they rot. The decomposers feed on these remains, and release valuable nutrients back into the environment. Decay is an important process for two reasons:

- it gets rid of dead organisms and waste products, e.g. faeces, so they do not build up.
- when the material decays, ***minerals*** are released, and these can be used by other organisms. This is an example of ***cycling in nature***.

Decay happens most rapidly in the following conditions:

- warm,
- moist,
- plenty of air.

If we want to avoid decay, e.g. to keep food fresh, it is important to store it properly. We could:

- keep it cool, e.g. in a fridge or freezer.
- keep it dry – lots of foods are sold dehydrated, e.g. custard powder, instant potato, milk powder.
- exclude air – food may be sold vacuum packed, e.g. bacon, or tinned.

Compost, Decomposer

DECOMPOSER

This is the type of microbe that causes ***decay***. Some ***bacteria*** and ***fungi*** feed on dead material and cause decay, so they are called decomposers. They are very important for two main reasons:

- they get rid of dead organisms and their waste products, so these do not build up.
- when the material decays valuable ***minerals*** are released, and these can be used by other organisms. This is an example of ***cycling in nature***

Decomposers can be a nuisance when they start the decay process in things we want to keep; for example:

- when mould grows on jam or cheese,
- when bacteria make milk go sour,
- when mould grows on damp towels or shoes.

Decomposers need three things to make substances decay:

- water,
- air,
- warmth.

So, if we want to stop decay happening, we must store ***biodegradable*** materials in the right conditions, e.g. somewhere cool and dry.

✦ ***Compost***

Decomposition

A substance is said to decompose when it splits up into two or more new substances. Some substances do this slowly, as when hydrogen peroxide gradually breaks down to give off oxygen and water. ***Enzymes*** in your body often act to decompose toxic molecules into harmless products.

When the decomposition occurs on heating, it is called a ***thermal decomposition*** reaction. An example is heating green copper carbonate to give black copper oxide and carbon dioxide (see figure below).

Some substances cannot be broken down by heating because they are strongly combined chemically. These substances need electricity in ***electrolysis*** reactions if they are to be broken up.

Defence against disease

These are the ways in which the body protects us from ***infectious diseases*** (caused by ***bacteria***, ***viruses*** and ***fungi***).

They include:

- a tough waterproof barrier all over the body (the ***skin***).
- chemicals to kill microbes where they might enter the body, e.g. acid in the stomach, mild disinfectant in tears and ear wax.
- some ***white blood cells*** can change shape to surround and destroy microbes.
- some white blood cells make ***antibodies*** to destroy microbes.

✦ ***Immune system, Vaccination***

Deficiency diseases

These occur if we do not have enough of a particular substance in our diet. This table shows some of the most important deficiency diseases.

Table to show important deficiency diseases

Disease	*What is missing from the diet*	*Symptoms*
Anaemia	Iron	Not enough red blood cells, so the person is pale, weak and tired
Scurvy	Vitamin C	Skin and gums are weak and bleed easily. Wounds take a long time to heal
Rickets	Vitamin D	Children's bones do not grow properly, and they bend under pressure
Kwashiorkor	Protein	Children do not grow properly, and they feel very weak and tired

✦ ***Balanced diet***

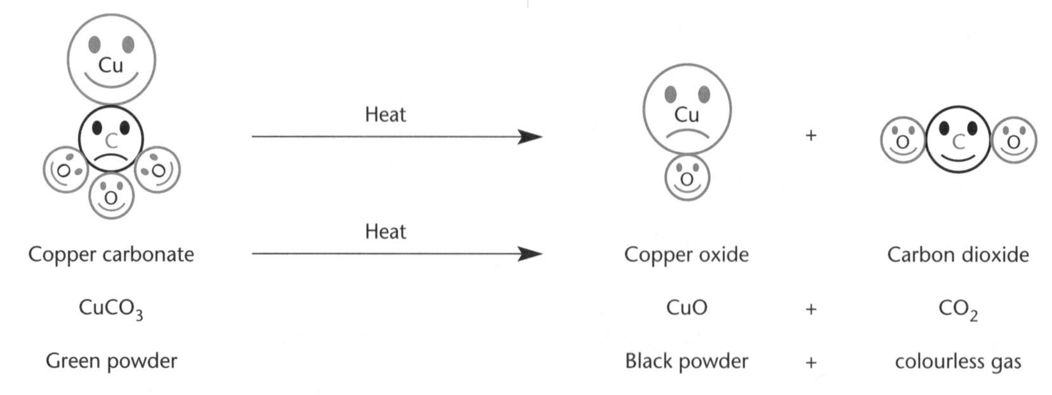

Thermal decomposition of copper carbonate

DEFORESTATION

This is one of the ways by which humans change their ***environment***. Forests are cleared (i.e. trees are cut down) for one of the following reasons:

- to plant other crops,
- to clear the land so that it can be used for animal grazing,
- to clear the land so that houses, roads or factories can be built.

It is a problem for three reasons:

1. forests are very rich ***habitats***, which may contain thousands of types of plants and animals. When their habitat is destroyed, these organisms may die out.
2. tree roots help to hold the soil in place. When trees are cut down, the soil is more likely to be blown away by strong winds, or washed away by rain. This is *erosion*.
3. trees use up a lot of carbon dioxide gas when they ***photosynthesise***. If trees are cut down, less carbon dioxide is used and this can contribute to the ***greenhouse effect***

DENSITY

We often think of some materials as being heavy (e.g. lead) or light (e.g. polystyrene) and density is a way of being more exact about this. The weight or mass really depends on how much of the material you measure. If you measure the ***mass*** of the *same* ***volume*** of each material then you can get a useful way to compare different materials.

> Density is the mass of one unit of volume of a material.

The mass is usually given in kg and the volume in m^3 so that the density will be in kg/m^3. Sometimes we use g/cm^3 for small objects because it is more convenient. When you measure a density it is not likely that you will find exactly one m^3 to measure, so you will divide the whole mass by the number of m^3 to find the mass of each one.

$$\text{Density} = \frac{\text{mass}}{\text{volume}}$$

$$D = \frac{m}{v}$$

For example:

- A block of concrete has a volume of 3 m^3 and a mass of 7200 kg. What is its density?

$$\text{Density} = \frac{\text{mass}}{\text{volume}}$$

$$= \frac{7200}{3}$$

$$= 2400 \text{ kg/m}^3$$

- A wooden beam has a volume of 0.1 m^3 and the wood has a density of 600 kg/m^3. What is the mass of the wood?

$$\text{Density} = \frac{\text{mass}}{\text{volume}}$$

$$600 = \frac{\text{mass}}{0.1}$$

$$\text{mass} = 600 \times 0.1$$

$$= 60 \text{ kg}$$

(This also means that its ***weight*** would be 600 N.)

You might find it useful to remember that the density of water is 1000 kg/m^3 or 1 g/cm^3. Materials that are less dense than this will float on water and those that are more dense will sink in water. This might help you to avoid giving answers that are obviously wrong.

Here is a table of some common materials and their densities.

Material	*Density in kg/m³*	*Material*	*Density in m³*
water	1000	brick	2300
concrete	2400	wood (oak)	600
iron	7870	mild steel	7860
aluminium	2710	lead	11 340
gold	19 300	ice	920
nylon	1150	polythene	950
olive oil	920	air	1.29
carbon dioxide	1.98	hydrogen	0.09
oxygen	1.43	methane	0.72

Measuring density is fairly easy. You need to find the mass and the volume and then divide using the equation.

To find the mass put the object on a balance, making sure that the balance will give a reading that is accurate enough. If the material is a powder or a liquid then you should first find the mass of the empty, dry container so that you can subtract it from the total.

To find the volume you will need to use a method that depends on the type of material. Look at ***volume*** to see how to do this.

CHECKPOINT

Write down the equation for density.

If an iceberg has a volume of 2000m³ and a mass of 1 840 000 kg, what is the density of the water in it?

Mass, Volume

DIAPHRAGM

This is a sheet of ***muscle*** running right across the body, dividing the ***thorax*** (containing the lungs and heart) from the ***abdomen*** (containing the liver, intestines and kidneys).

When the diaphragm is relaxed it is curved, or dome shaped. When it contracts it becomes flatter. The diaphragm is very important in the process of ***breathing*** (getting air in and out of the lungs). If your diaphragm contracts in an unco-ordinated way, you get hiccups!

DIFFUSION

If you walk past a coffee shop you can smell the coffee well before you get to the door of the shop. It is possible to account for this if we use the ***particle*** theory. This theory suggests that the 'coffee smell' particles are carried away from the beans by moving air particles. This is diffusion in action. Diffusion is the movement of a gas to fill any space which is available.

Diffusion also takes place in liquids but it is then much slower. This is because the particles in the liquid are moving more slowly than in the gas, as they have less energy.

Diffusion can even take place in solids. In this case it takes place more slowly than in gases or liquids, as the particles move still more slowly.

The only way to explain all these results is to assume that substances are made of particles and that these particles have kinetic energy (i.e. are moving). The particles move from a region where there is a high concentration of the substance to a region where there is a low concentration.

This is a very important process in living things, e.g. oxygen diffuses from the alveoli into the blood, and digested foods diffuse from the ileum into the blood.

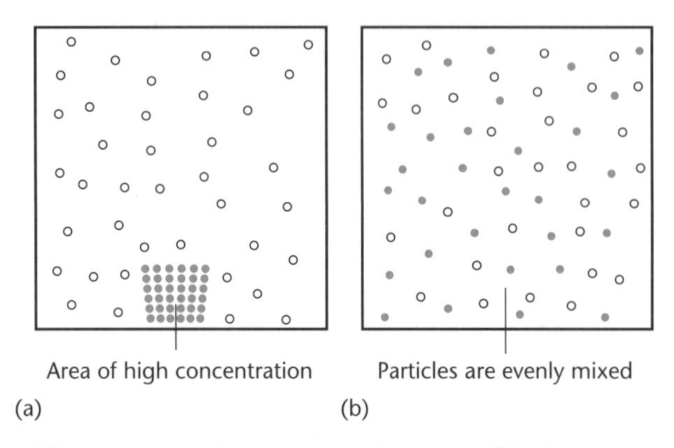

Diffusion: (a) at the start, and (b) when diffusion is complete

DIGESTION

This means that large food molecules are broken down into smaller food molecules that can dissolve, e.g. starch is broken down into sugars.

It happens inside the gut when food is mixed with ***enzymes***.

Proteins, ***fats*** and ***carbohydrates*** all have to be digested before the body can use them, because they are made up of large complicated molecules. Once they have been digested, they are small enough to pass through the gut wall and into the blood – this process is called ***absorption***.

Vitamins and ***minerals*** do not have to be digested because they are made up of molecules small enough to pass through the gut wall into the blood.

Fibre cannot be digested, because humans do not make the right enzymes to do this. The molecules are too big to pass through the gut wall, so fibre stays inside the gut and forms most of the ***faeces***.

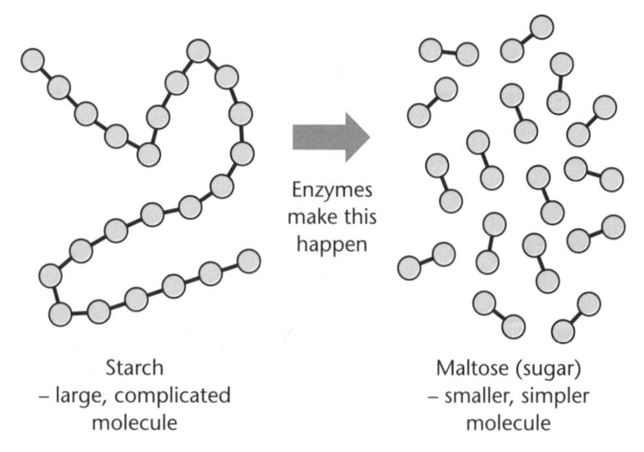

Enzymes digest food molecules

Digestive system

DIGESTIVE SYSTEM (ALIMENTARY CANAL, GUT)

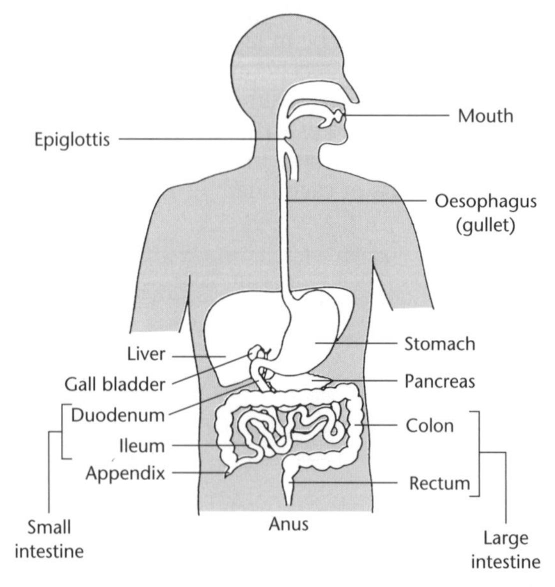

Digestive system

This is a tube about 8m long running through the body from the mouth to the anus.

Food is ***digested*** here, then ***absorbed*** into the blood. Food that cannot be digested forms ***faeces*** and is ***egested*** from the anus.

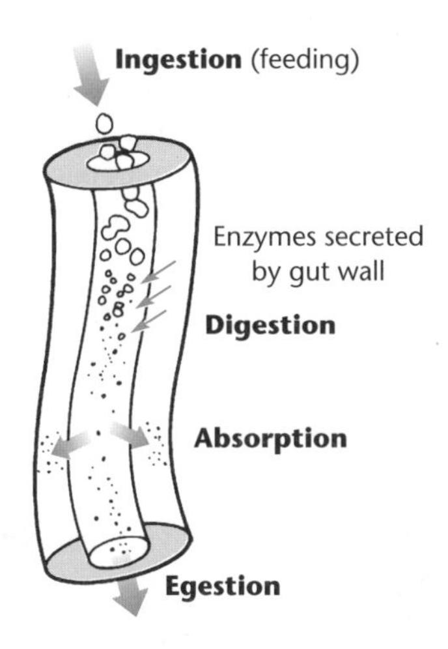

Processes occurring in the digestive system

DIRECT CURRENT

Direct ***current*** always flows in the same direction round an electric ***circuit***. It can be supplied by ***batteries*** or by a power supply which makes a ***voltage*** that is always the same. In simple circuits direct current will also stay the same size when it has been switched on.

Alternating current, Current

DISEASE

This means that some part of the body is not working properly, so the person is unwell. There are three main causes of disease:

Bacteria and viruses

These cause ***infectious diseases***, e.g. colds, measles, mumps. We catch them by taking in infected food or water, or by being in contact with infected people. These diseases can often be cured by ***antibiotics*** or anti-viral drugs.

Faulty genes

These diseases are passed on from our parents through ***genes***, e.g. haemophilia, cystic fibrosis, sickle cell anaemia. They cannot be caught from other people and they cannot be cured, although doctors might prescribe drugs to reduce the symptoms.

Lifestyle factors

These diseases are caused by harmful things in our environment, or by a lack of necessary things.

smoking causes lung ***cancer***
excess ***alcohol*** causes liver damage
lack of ***vitamin C*** causes ***scurvy***.

They cannot be caught from other people, and they can be avoided by having a healthy lifestyle. Stress can cause many health problems.

Of course, other animals and plants can also suffer from diseases, e.g. distemper in dogs, potato blight, soft rot in carrots.

Balanced diet, Deficiency diseases, Health

DISPERSAL OF SEEDS

This means that ***seeds*** are spread away from the parent plant. It is important for two main reasons:

1. The seeds are more likely to grow successfully if they are not overcrowded, i.e. there is less competition for resources.
2. The seeds are able to colonize new areas. Plants are very good at this – think about all the weeds that start to grown in your garden!

Plants have several ways of dispersing their seeds.

Table to show methods of seed dispersal

Method	*How it works*	*Examples*
Wind	The seeds are small and light so they can easily be blown to new areas. Often they have 'wings' or a parachute of hairs.	sycamore, ash, dandelion, rose bay willow herb
Animals	Seeds or fruits are covered in hooks so that they stick to an animal's fur. They will eventually be brushed off.	burdock, cleavers, agrimony
	Seeds are inside brightly-coloured sweet fruits. The fruits will be eaten, and the seeds will pass through the animal's gut without being damaged.	raspberry, bramble, rose-hip, tomato
Self-dispersal	The seeds are inside a fruit called a pod. When the pod dries out it splits open, so the seeds are released.	pea, bean, lupin, geranium
Water	The seeds are inside buoyant fruits that can float. They will be carried by waves or water currents, and when they are washed up on to land, they can start to germinate.	coconut

CHECKPOINT

Look at these drawings of fruits and seeds, and decide how each is dispersed.

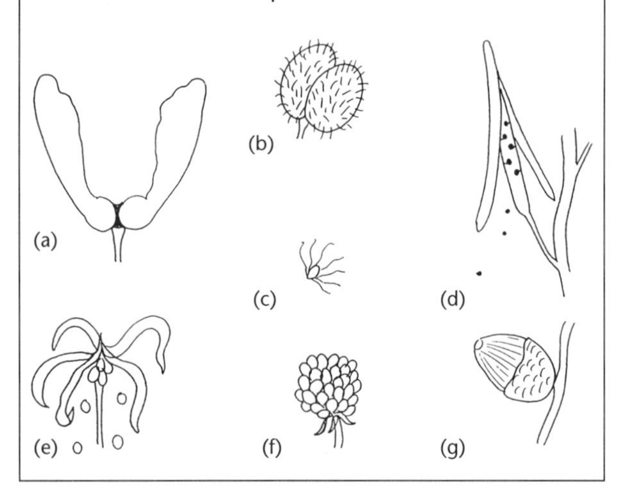

✦ *Germination, Reproduction*

DISPERSION

This is the name for the splitting up of the colours in white light into a ***spectrum***

✦ *Spectrum*

DISPLACEMENT

Displacement is a type of chemical reaction in which an element displaces a less reactive element from one of its compounds. For example, zinc will displace copper from copper sulphate solution. Displacement reactions can be explained by the idea of a ***reactive series*** of metals or non-metals.

DISSOLVING

If a test tube is filled to the brim with water and salt is added very carefully, the salt dissolves. The salt granules break down into smaller and smaller pieces, until eventually you cannot see them. However, you know they are still there because the water tastes salty. The water does not overflow from the test tube since the small pieces of salt fill the spaces between the water molecules.

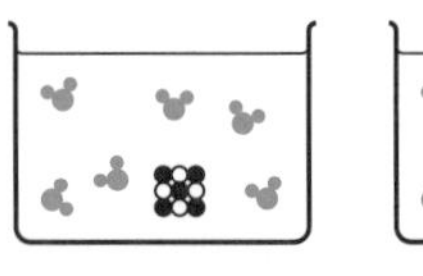

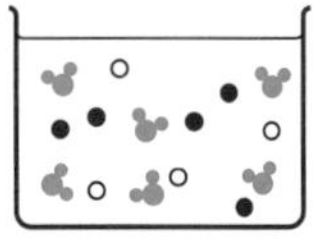

= water molecules
= salt crystals
= dissolved salt particles

Salt dissolving

DISTILLATION

This is the method used to separate two ***liquids*** which have different ***boiling points***. Distillation is in effect the ***evaporation*** of the liquid followed by its ***condensation***. It is the method used in distilleries to separate alcohol from water. Alcohol boils at about 78°C and water boils at 100°C. If the alcohol vapour travels through the condenser, it comes into contact with a cold condenser and changes back into a liquid (the distillate). Here the liquid collected would be the alcohol.

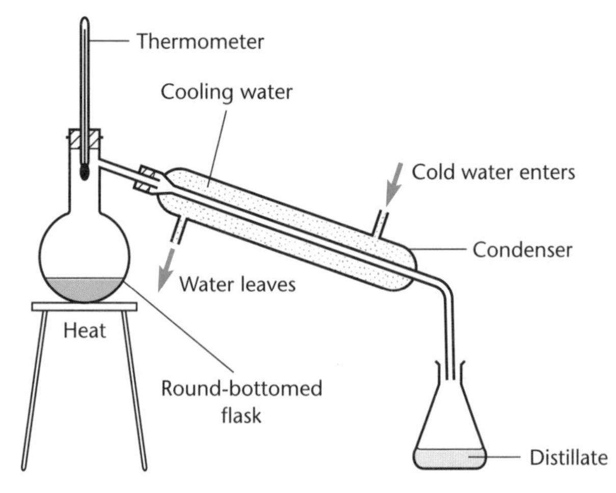

Distillation apparatus

Chay Blyth, on his round-the-world trip, used chemistry to make a supply of drinking water. He attached a length of tubing to the top valve of his pressure cooker and then heated sea water in the pressure cooker. The steam coming out of the top was cooled down as it passed through the tube immersed in a bowl of cold water. Pure drinking water was produced.

DISTRIBUTION

This means where plants and animals are found within their ***habitat***; e.g. if we are told that there are 20 buttercup plants in a field, they could be:

1. evenly distributed,
2. unevenly distributed.

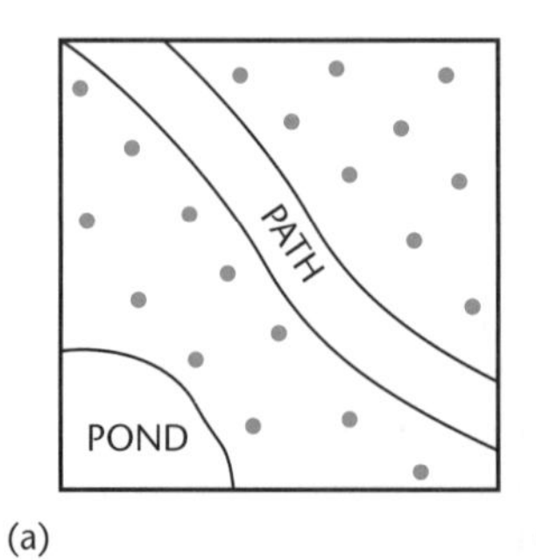

(a)

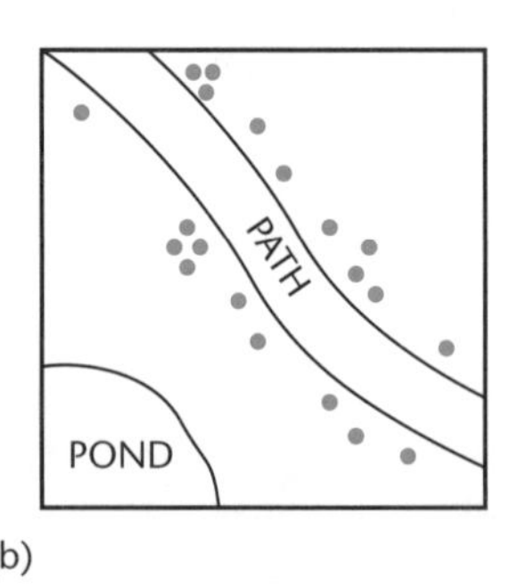

(b)

(a) Even distribution of buttercups in a field.
(b) Uneven distribution of buttercups in a field.

The best way to find out about distribution is to sample using a ***quadrat*** or a transect.

✣ ***Ecology***

Division of Labour

This means that an organism contains different types of ***cells***, which have different functions. Cells are adapted (specialized) for the functions they carry out.

e.g. *in plants:* ***palisade cells*** are specialized for photosynthesis, ***root hair cells*** are specialized to absorb water and minerals.

e.g. *in animals:* ***red blood cells*** are specialized to carry oxygen, ***muscle*** cells are specialised for contraction.

> *CHECKPOINT*
>
> The diagrams show four different plant and animal cells. The jobs they do are listed below:
>
> 1. send impulses from one part of the body to another,
> 2. carry water in the stem of a plant,
> 3. swim towards an egg cell and fertilize it,
> 4. move dust and dirt out of the respiratory tract.
>
> In the box next to each cell, write the number of the job it does.
>
> 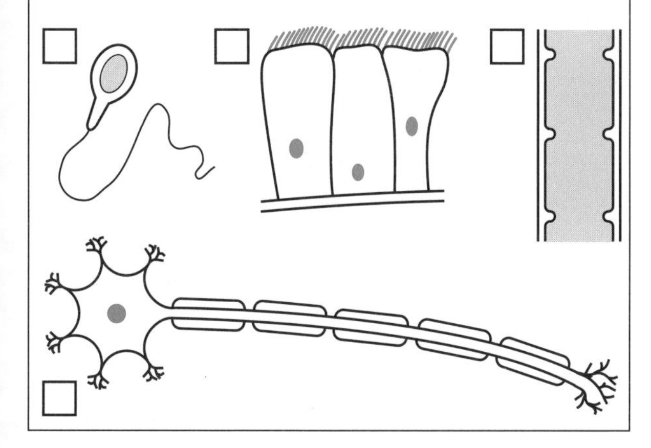

DNA

This is the abbreviation for *d*eoxyribo-*n*ucleic *a*cid, a chemical found in the ***nucleus*** of all cells.

Chromosomes are made of DNA. They carry the genetic information (inherited information) for the cell, so that new copies of the cell can be made.

Drugs

These are chemicals that change the way the body works. For example:

alcohol
aspirin
caffeine (in tea, coffee, coke)
penicillin
nicotine (in cigarettes)
LSD
solvents
} all are drugs

All drugs carry a *risk* for the person who uses them; for example:

- the person might be allergic to them.
- the body might be harmed by them, so that it does not function properly.
- the person may take more than is safe, i.e., an overdose.
- the drug may affect concentration or co-ordination, so the person is more likely to have an accident.
- the drug may affect moods or behaviour, so the person may do something they later regret.
- if two or more drugs are mixed, the effects on the body can be unpredictable.
- the person may become addicted (dependent on the drug).

Legal and illegal drugs

In Britain, some drugs are *legal* – they can be bought at a chemist or prescribed by a doctor, or they can be bought by adults.

Examples of legal drugs are: alcohol, antibiotics, aspirin, caffeine, nicotine (cigarettes), paracetamol, tranquilizers. These drugs are manufactured carefully and labelled properly. People who use them know which substances are in them, and what the concentration (dose) is.

Many drugs can only be obtained after advice from a doctor.

In Britain, other drugs are *illegal* – it is against the law to possess them or to sell them. Some of these are legal drugs being used by the wrong people, i.e., not the people they were prescribed for.

Examples of illegal drugs are: amphetamines (speed), cannabis, cocaine, ecstasy, LSD, steroids*, solvents, tranquilizers*.

(* = can be prescribed legally, but it is illegal to sell them to other people.)

There are more health risks with illegal drugs than with legal drugs because:

- there is no guarantee that the drug is pure. Many drugs are cut (mixed) with cheaper substances, e.g. sugar, talc or with other drugs.

- there is no way of knowing what the dose is. The amount of Ecstasy in one tablet may be completely different from the amount in another tablet from another batch, or even the same batch. This means that it is easy to overdose.
- some illegal drugs are injected. This is particularly dangerous for three reasons:
  1. dirty or shared needles can cause blood poisoning and infections. Some of these can be very serious, e.g. hepatitis, AIDS.
  2. the blood vessels and muscles can be damaged by the injections, causing abscesses and gangrene.
  3. the drug is injected straight into the bloodstream and reaches the brain within seconds, so the effects are very sudden.

Remember: All drugs carry a risk to the person using them. Illegal drugs are more risky, because they might be mixed with other substances, and because you have no idea of the amount you are taking. Many drugs are addictive.

Addiction, Alcohol, Ecstacy, LSD, Smoking, Solvents

EAR

The human ear is able to detect sounds that vary in ***frequency*** from about 20 Hz up to 18 kHz, but different people have different audible ranges. It can also detect a very wide range of ***loudness***, but can be damaged by ***sound*** that is very loud for a short time or less loud for a long time. It is usual to protect it by 'ear defenders' when working in a noisy situation.

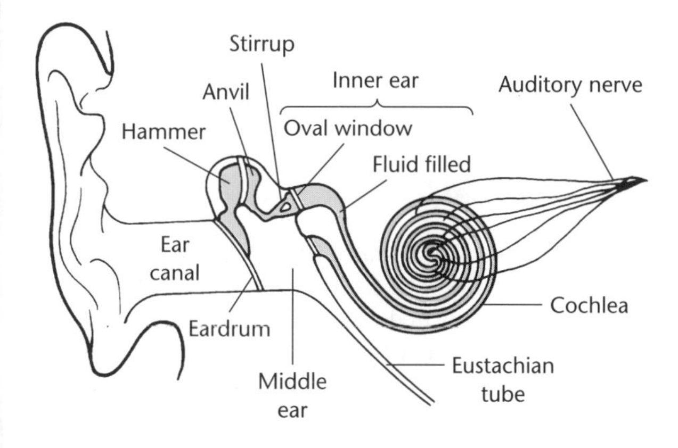

The ear

Sound is a series of compressions in the air that enter the ear down the ear canal. This causes the eardrum to vibrate and pass on the vibration to three small bones called the ossicles. The ossicles (called hammer, anvil and stirrup) act as small ***levers*** and make very small vibrations a little bigger – they amplify the quiet sounds. The vibration is then passed though the oval window into the fluid inside the cochlea. The fluid will cause tiny hairs in receptor cells to vibrate and pass a signal as electrical impulses along the auditory nerve to the brain.

Hearing defects

The defects may be *temporary*: wax or other blockage in the ear canal, infection of the middle ear, minor damage to the eardrum.

The defects can also be *permanent*: damage to the eardrum or ossicles by loud sounds or explosions, growths that stop the ossicles moving, damage to the hair cells or the auditory nerve.

Frequency, Loudness, Sound

EARTH

The Earth has a layered structure, rather similar in some ways to that of an apple. An apple has a thin skin, so has the Earth. The fleshy part of the apple can be compared with the magma layer of the Earth (called the mantle), and both apple and earth have a core. The Earth's core is mainly made of nickel and iron. These metals are both magnetic, which is why the Earth has a ***magnetic field*** around it. The inner core is solid, and the outer core is molten.

The 'skin' of the Earth is the part with which we have direct contact. Information about the mantle has been collected indirectly; for example, through *seismic* data when earthquakes occur and from the *lava* that is forced onto the surface of the Earth by volcanic activity.

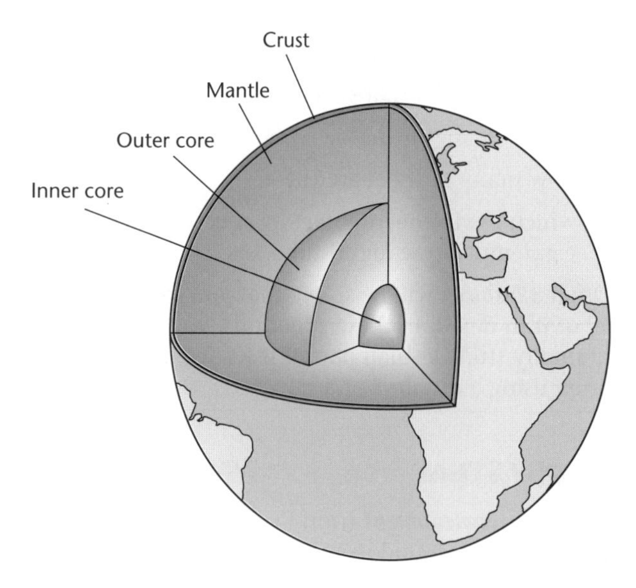

The Earth

	Phase	Composition	Density (g/cm^3)
Inner core	Solid	Iron and nickel	17
Outer core	Molten	Iron and nickel Convection currents cause the Earth's magnetic field	12
Mantle	Plastic	Magnesium- and iron-rich silicates	3.3
Crust	Solid	Rock	2.9

The Earth orbits around the ***Sun*** once every year and is the third planet in the ***solar system***. It is an average distance of 150 million km from the sun and is about 12,700 km in diameter. We think that the Earth was formed about 4.5 billion years ago.

Planet, Solar system, Sun

ECHO

An echo is caused by ***sound*** being reflected back to the listener by a large flat surface. Sound travels at 330 m/s in air so the reflecting surface must be quite a long way away from the listener so that the original sound and the echo are heard separately. If you do any calculations about the speed of sound and echoes, remember that the sound goes out to the reflector *and back!*

Sound, Speed

ECOLOGY

This is the study of ***ecosystems***, i.e., of living things in their natural ***environment***.

In order to study ecology, you have to go out and look at things – you cannot do it in the classroom! Fieldwork often involves four questions:

1. which organisms are there?
2. where are they living? i.e., what is their ***distribution***?
3. how many of them are there?
4. which environmental factors affect them? e.g. temperature, light, tides, etc.

Often a ***habitat*** will be so big that you cannot study all of it in detail. In these situations, you will normally study a small part of it (called a sample), often using a ***quadrat*** or a transect.

ECOSYSTEM

This is an ***environment*** (non-living) and all the living things that are found in it; for example,

- a rocky shore ecosystem includes the rocks, the sand, the water, seaweeds, limpets, mussels, fish.
- a woodland ecosystem includes the trees, the soil, rocks, birds, insects, mammals.

An ecosystem is usually divided up into different ***habitats***.

The living and non-living parts of an ecosystem will affect each other, so scientists normally try to study them together; for example,

- tides (non-living) will affect seaweeds and animals living in rock pools.
- animals and plants will affect the soil (non-living) – in a woodland: e.g. plants will absorb minerals and water from it, and will anchor it with their roots, animals will burrow through it, and add urine and faeces containing minerals to it.

An ecosystem is a complicated balance of plants, animals and non-living factors, e.g. soil, climate, landscape, water. It can be easily damaged by human interference, e.g. pollution, woodland clearance.

Adaptation to the environment, Ecology, Environment

ECSTASY ('E')

This is an illegal stimulant drug.

It is sold as tablets and is often associated with raves. The effects start about 20 minutes after taking it, and last for several hours. They include feelings of friendliness and extra energy, but when this wears off the person feels very down. Large amounts can cause anxiety and confusion. Ecstasy has been linked to several deaths in Britain, because

- it has caused heatstroke when taken by people dancing at raves.
- if the person drinks *too much* water (to avoid heatstroke), this may make the brain swell and cause death.

Ecstasy should be avoided by anyone who has epilepsy or heart problems, because it can make these conditions worse.

Drugs

EGESTION

This is the removal of waste food substances (***faeces***) from the ***digestive system***. Faeces collect in the rectum and are pushed out through the anus when muscles in the gut contract.

EHRLICH, PAUL (1845–1915)

Paul Ehrlich was a German doctor who was the first to use chemicals to kill bacteria inside the human body. He developed a drug called Salversan which was used to treat syphilis.

ELECTRIC BELL

When the switch is pressed on ***current*** flows round the complete ***circuit*** through the coil, the spring and the contacts. The current in the coil magnetizes the core, which attracts the iron armature. The iron then moves, towards the core and the hammer hits the

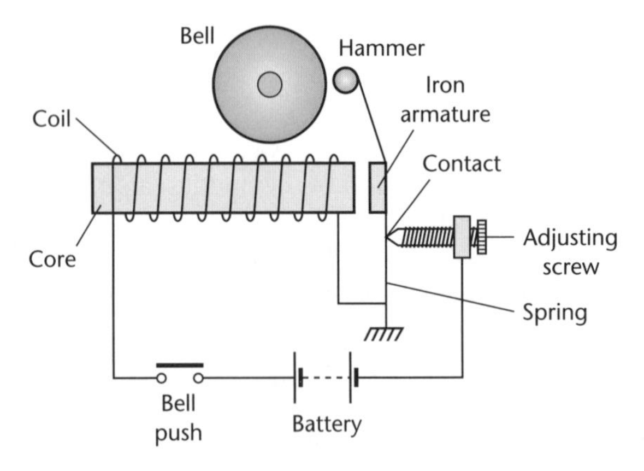

Electric bell

bell. As the iron moves, the circuit is broken as the contacts are separated and the current is turned off. The core stops being a magnet and the spring pulls the iron back to its original position. As soon as the contacts touch again, the current flows and the whole process starts again. The hammer will keep on hitting the bell until the switch is released.

Note that the switch is the 'bell push' type, which is only on while it is being pressed, and that both the core and the armature must be soft magnetic materials.

There are other types of bell that also work by using an electromagnet.

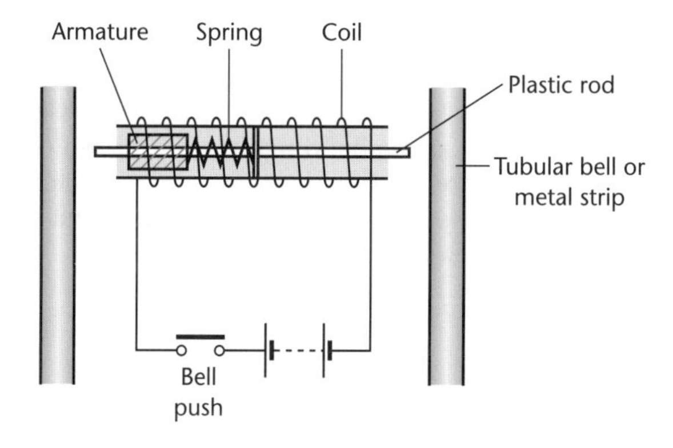

Electric bell

When the switch is pressed, current in the coil creates a magnetic field and the iron armature is pulled into the centre of the coil. This makes the central plastic rod hit the metal bell and compresses the spring. When the switch is released, the coil stops being a magnet and the spring pushes the iron armature and the rod back so that it hits the other bell. Again, the armature must be made from a soft magnetic material. The bell tubes or strips are usually different thicknesses and lengths to make a pleasing combination of sounds.

Electromagnet, Magnetic materials

ELECTRICAL ENERGY

When an electrical current flows round a circuit it has electrical ***energy***. This can be changed into other forms of energy such as heat and light.

Energy

ELECTROLYSIS

The term electrolysis was devised by ***Humphrey Davy*** who used Latin names for his discoveries. *Electro* comes from electric and *lysis* from the Latin 'to split up'. So, electrolysis simply means splitting something up using electricity.

In order for the substance to be split up, it must be able to conduct an electric current. Metals are good ***conductors***, solid salt is not. However, if salt is melted or dissolved in water, then it does conduct. This is because ***ions*** are released and so current can flow.

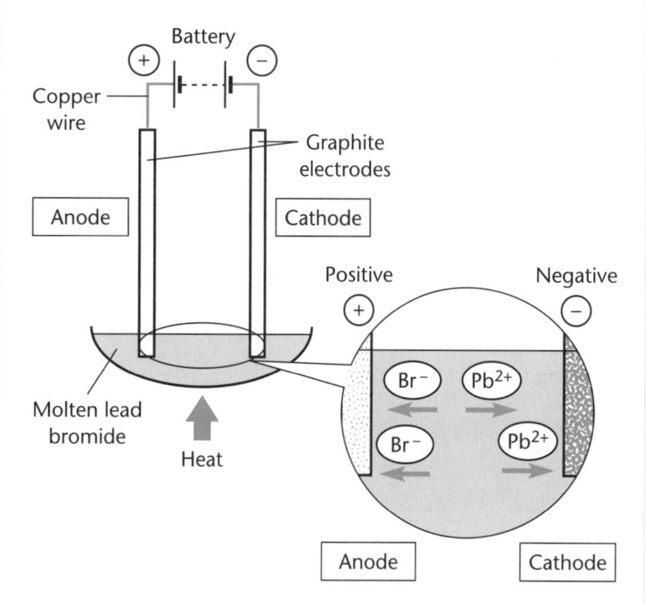

Electrolysis of molten lead bromide

The two carbon (graphite) rods or electrodes are connected to a ***battery*** and placed in a solution of molten lead bromide. This liquid, which conducts electricity, is called an *electrolyte*. When the circuit is completed, the ***electrons*** start to flow from the battery. The copper wires are very good conductors and the electrons can travel easily.

When they reach the carbon rod at the negative end of the battery there is an electron 'traffic jam'. This means the carbon rod has a build up of negative electrons. It is now called a ***cathode***. The battery continues to pump electrons so the easiest place to keep up the supply is the other carbon rod. It will then have less electrons. It becomes positively charged and is now an ***anode***.

As the electricity is passed into the electrolyte, the positive ions will be attracted to the negative electrode (cathode) and the negative ions will be attracted to the positive electrode (anode). The end result is that this process of electrolysis will break down the electrolyte solution into its elements or products.

In the case of the electrolysis of lead bromide, the electrolysis will produce bromine gas at the anode and molten lead at the cathode.

ELECTROMAGNET

You make an electromagnet by winding a coil of wire round an iron core. It will become a ***magnet*** when an electric ***current*** is sent through the wire. It will stop being a magnet when the current is turned off.

You can try this by winding a length of insulated wire round a large nail and connecting the ends to a battery.

You will probably find that it takes more turns of wire than shown in the diagram. You can experiment by using the electromagnet to pick up paper clips to see how strong it is. You will find that it will get stronger if you put more turns of wire in the coil or send more current through the coil (use more batteries in series.)

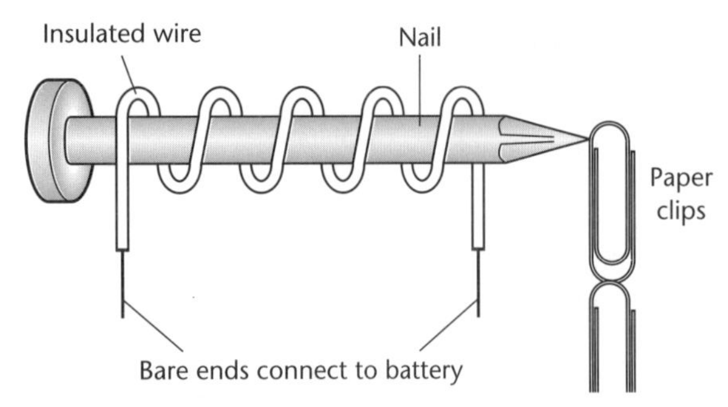

Making an electromagnet

Remember: More current or more turns on the coil will make a stronger electromagnet.

The iron used for nails is not really a very *soft* ***magnetic material*** and you will probably find that it will keep some of its magnetism after you turn off the current. You will also find that connecting a bulb in series with the coil will make your battery last a lot longer and you can see when the current is bigger because the bulb is brighter. Look up ***magnetic materials*** and ***magnetic field*** for more information.

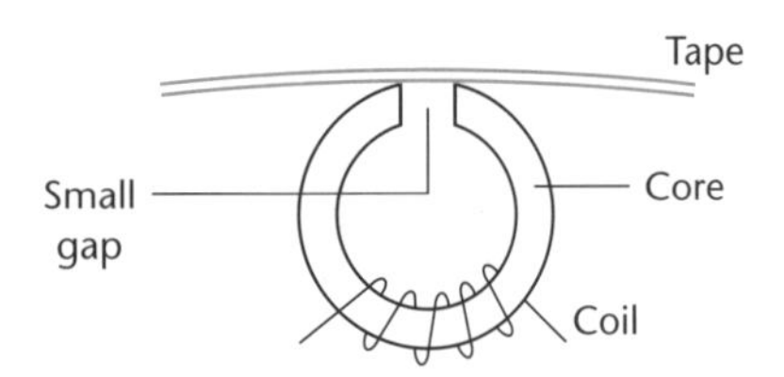

A tape recorder head

Tape recorder heads are a good illustration of electromagnets in action. The recording head is an electromagnet that carries a current whose ***frequency*** and strength follows the sound to be recorded. The tape is a thin plastic backing tape with a magnetic material on one side. As the tape passes the head a magnetic pattern is recorded in this magnetic layer. It can be erased by sending it past the erase head, which is another electromagnet. The erase head carries a high frequency current so that its rapidly changing field demagnetizes the tape. The playback head can reproduce the sound when the tape goes past it. Information is recorded on magnetic disks for use in computers and the process is similar to tape recording except that the information is stored in circles on the disk called tracks.

Electric bell, Magnetic field, Magnetic materials, Magnets, Relay

Electromotive force

emf

Electrons

An indivisible unit of negative electricity which rotates about the positive nucleus of each ***atom***.

Element

Everything is made up of elements. Elements are pure substances that cannot be split up into anything simpler by ***chemical reactions***. It is possible to think of them as the building blocks from which other materials are made. An element contains only one type of ***atom***. For example, oxygen (an element) contains only oxygen atoms, whereas water (a compound) contains oxygen atoms bonded to hydrogen atoms.

Water molecules

There are one hundred and ten elements in the ***periodic table***. On the surface of the ***Earth*** most elements are ***solids***. There are a few non-metal elements which are gases, and two liquid elements, mercury and bromine.

Each element has its own symbol.

EMBRYO

This is the name for the developing baby for the first eight weeks of ***pregnancy***. During this time its organs and limbs are developing, and it can easily by harmed by drugs or illnesses caught by the mother.

Reproduction

emf (ELECTROMOTIVE FORCE)

Electromotive force is the driving force that makes the ***current*** go round an electric ***circuit*** (including through the supply). It is made by the supply, which can be a ***battery***, power supply, 'mains', generator, or a solar cell.

emf is usually given the symbol E and is measured in ***volts***.

The emf in a circuit will be divided up so that each part of the circuit gets a share of the voltage to drive the current through it. This share of the emf across each part of the circuit is called a ***potential difference*** (pd). If you add together all the voltages round the circuit you will find that they add up to the voltage of the supply, so you can also say that the emf is the total of all the potential differences in a complete circuit.

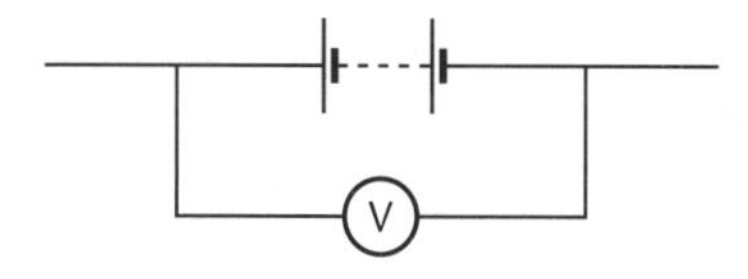

Measuring the emf of a battery

Circuit, Current, Potential difference

EMULSION

If you have ever made a 'French dressing' for a salad, you will know that the oil and vinegar do not mix. The liquids are said to be ***immiscible***. If you shake the bottle vigorously, the oil disperses into the vinegar and forms what is known as an emulsion. It is not very stable and, after a few minutes, it will separate back into a vinegar layer with an oil layer on top.

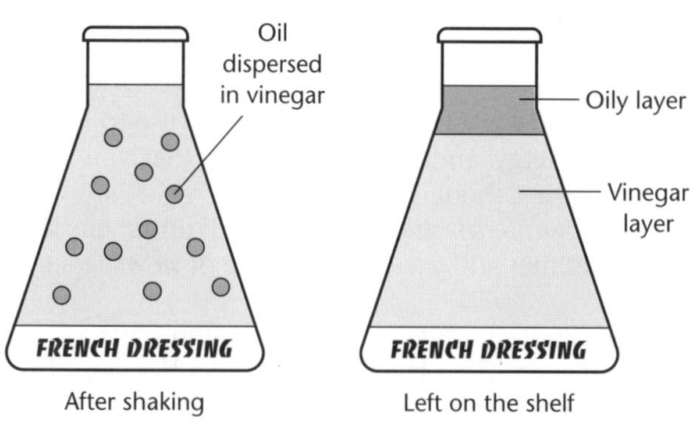

An emulsion

Mayonnaise and salad cream are also made from oil and vinegar but these do not separate into layers. They are re-*stabilised emulsions*. During their preparation, the oil droplets are coated with egg yolk which prevents them from joining together to form an oily layer. The egg yolk is an *emulsifier*; it stops the immiscible liquids from separating.

ENDOTHERMIC

A chemical reaction that takes in heat to make it work is an endothermic reaction. For example, dissolving ammonium sulphate in water.

Exothermic

ENERGY

This section, and the others that it refers to, should help you to understand how energy:

- is in moving things,
- is in some things because of their position,
- transfers from one place to another by ***light***, ***sound***,
- spreads out and becomes less useful,
- does not get created or destroyed,
- enables ***work*** to be done.

There are many forms of energy and they can be converted from one to another. When this happens, energy is neither created nor destroyed so that the total energy after the conversion is the same as the total energy before. This is called *conservation of energy*.

As we can do work by transferring the same amount of energy, we use the same unit for energy, the ***joule***, as we do for work done. The symbol for a joule is J. Some of the places where energy is found are described in their own sections: try ***electrical energy***, ***chemical energy***, ***potential energy***, ***kinetic energy***, ***heat energy***.

Machines transfer energy from one form to another and we can often trace the energy through a series of different forms within a complete process. For example, in a hydroelectric power station the water has ***gravitational potential energy***. As it falls the energy becomes kinetic energy, which is used to drive the turbines. The rotating shaft from the turbine now carries the kinetic energy, into the generators where it is becomes electrical energy.

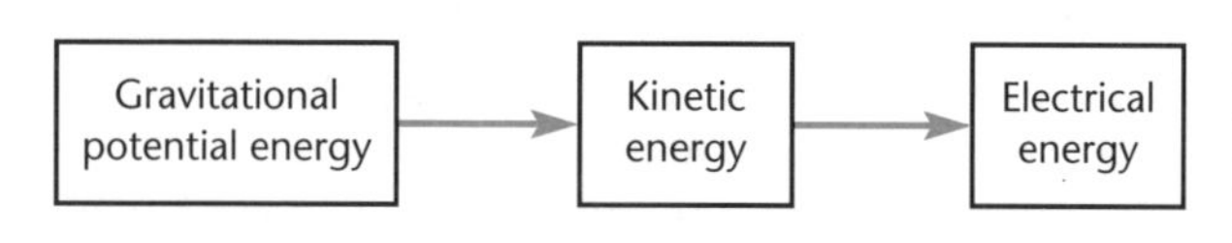

An energy conversion

None of these machines will be perfect and the final quantity of electrical energy will be less than the original potential energy. The 'missing' energy has not been destroyed, it is simply not where we would like it to be! In this case, most of it will have been 'lost' as heat to the surroundings because of friction. We measure how good machines are at converting energy by measuring their *efficiency*.

Our bodies take in chemical energy as ***energy in food*** (and store some of it as fat!). When the cells need energy, they can burn some of this fuel by combining it with the oxygen that is transported by the blood stream. The waste products from the reaction are taken away by the blood stream and we breathe them out as carbon dioxide and water vapour, i.e., we use an ***exothermic*** reaction called ***respiration***.

Glucose + Oxygen ⟶ Carbon dioxide + Water + Energy

Energy is often transferred from one place to another by a ***wave*** and we often use the waves of the electromagnetic spectrum to do so. For example, the walls of a room are warmed by the heat produced when the infra-red waves from an electric fire are absorbed. We also send radio waves from one place to another, carrying our messages.

CHECKPOINT

Name five different sources of energy.

Explain what is meant by conservation of energy.

Sources of energy

ENERGY CHAINS AND ARROWS

When energy is transferred from one form to another it is often easier to show the changes on a diagram. When there is only one stage, you can use an energy arrow that splits into the new forms.

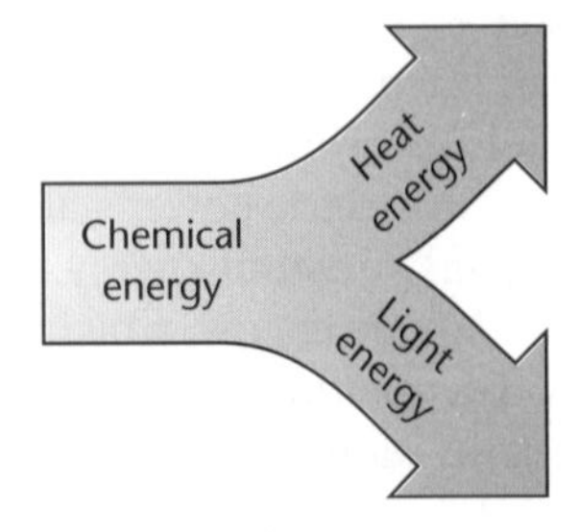

An energy arrow for a candle

You do not have to try to make the width of the arrows show the amounts of energy.

When there is more than one stage, you can use a flow diagram to show the changes. You can use this instead of an arrow for simple changes if you prefer.

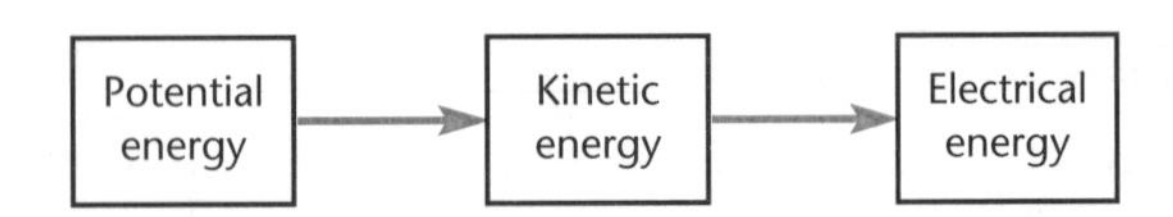

An energy chain for a hydroelectric power station

You will often leave out some of the energy to show the most important changes. In the diagram, I have not drawn boxes to show where heat is being 'lost' into the air.

CHECKPOINT

In a torch bulb the energy transformation is:

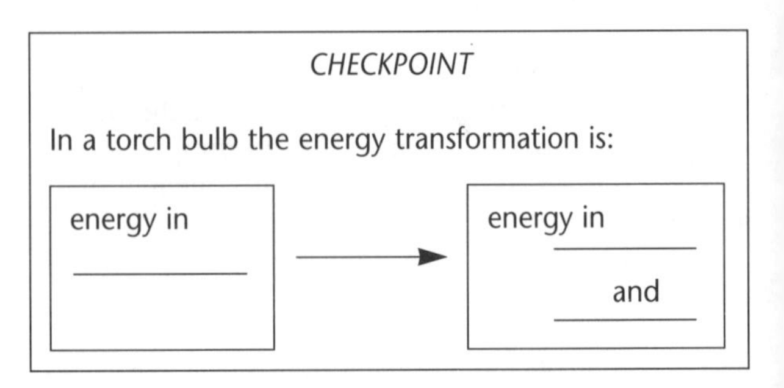

Energy

ENERGY DISSIPATION

Whenever we use ***energy*** and change it from one form to another it will always end up being less concentrated, more spread out, even though the total remains the same. This is *always* true when you look at *all* of the energy involved. Because the less concentrated energy is of less or no value to us we have to keep on finding new resources.

For example, when we use petrol in our cars most of the energy eventually ends up being thinly spread out in the surroundings as heat in the air where we cannot use it again.

Sources of energy

ENERGY IN FOOD

All food contains energy – this is one of the main reasons that we eat it. If you look at the nutrition information panel on the label of processed foods, you will be able to find out the amount of energy in 100 g of the food. This is often given in two forms

e.g. Baked beans : 100 g gives you 312 kJ
75 kCal

kJ (kilojoules) are the units that scientists use to measure energy, and they are the units that you would use in school.

kCal (kilocalories) are 'old-fashioned' units, but they are sometimes still used in magazine or newspaper articles.

Foods containing a lot of energy often have a lot of ***fat*** in them. This is because 1g of fat has over twice as much energy as 1g of carbohydrate or protein.

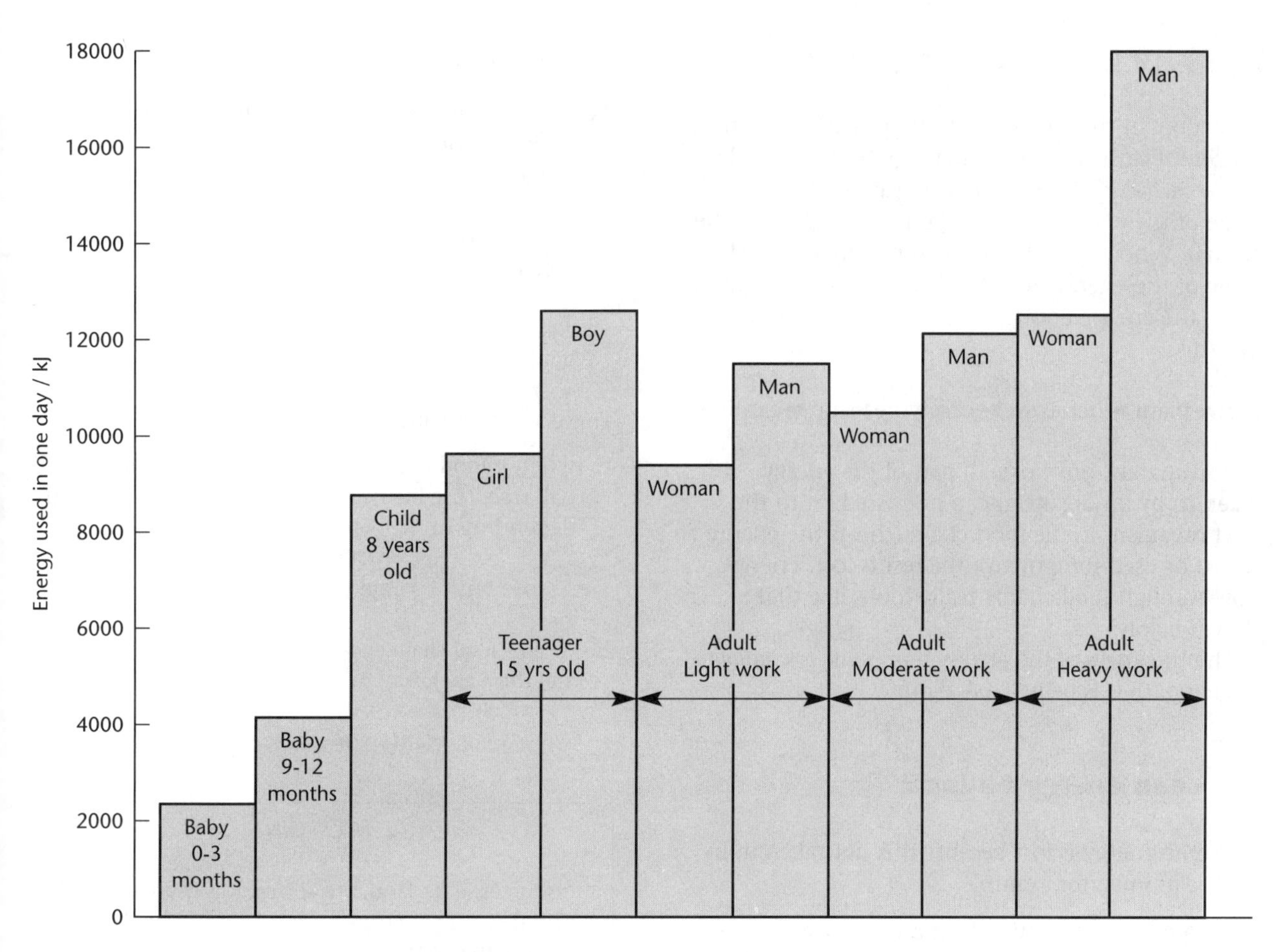

Energy requirements of various groups of people

It is important that the energy we take in from our food balances the energy we use up in our daily activities, e.g. growing, moving around, keeping warm. Different groups of people have different energy requirements.

You can find the approximate energy value of a food by using it as a fuel, and burning it to heat up some water. This experiment is often done in schools to find the energy value of a peanut by holding a test tube of water which contains a thermometer, over a peanut, which is burning.

Before you start you must know:

1. the mass of food being burned,
2. the volume of water in the tube,
3. the temperature of the water.

You then set fire to the food (by holding it in a Bunsen burner flame) and use it to heat the water. As soon as the food stops burning, you record the new temperature of the water.

You can calculate the amount of energy in the food using the following equation:

$$\text{Amount of energy (kJ)} = \text{volume of water (ml)} \times \text{rise in temperature (°C)} \times \frac{4.2}{1000}$$

This experiment will give you an *approximate* energy value for the food. It is not completely accurate because not all the energy in the food is used to heat the water, i.e.,

some heat energy escapes into the air,
some energy is used to heat the glass tube.

> *CHECKPOINT*
>
> A peanut with a mass of 2g is used to heat up 20ml of water. The temperature rises from 15°C to 57°C.
>
> How much energy was in the peanut?
>
> How much energy would there be in 100g of peanut?

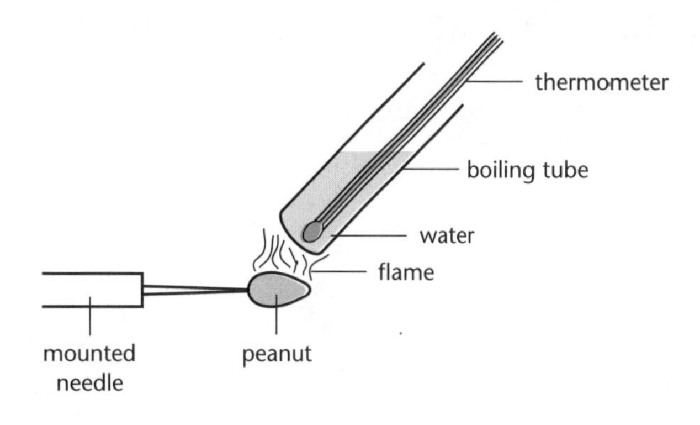

Finding the energy in a peanut

ENERGY IN THE ENVIRONMENT

All energy in the environment originally comes from the Sun. Plants use sunlight energy to make food by ***photosynthesis***. When plants are eaten by animals, some of the energy from the Sun is passed on to the animal. When animals are eaten by other animals, some of the energy from the Sun is passed on again.

So, the energy flow through food chains looks like this:

Sun ➤ plant ➤ herbivore ➤ carnivore ➤ top ➤ carnivore

Unfortunately, only a small part of the energy taken in by an organism can be passed on to the next organism in the food chain (this is the energy stored or used for growth); the rest is lost. Energy flow through food chains really looks like that shown below.

The thickness of the arrows represents the *amount* of energy that is being passed on.

How can energy be lost?

- Some energy is lost because it is not taken in by the animal; for example,

  a caterpillar may not eat a whole leaf,
  a cow may feed on the leaves of a plant, but not on the root.
- Some energy is lost because the food is not digested, i.e., it passes out of the gut in the faeces. Many plants are hard to digest because they contain lots of cellulose, and so a lot of energy is lost this way.
- Some energy is used for vital body processes to keep the animal alive, e.g. moving, breathing, heart beat, etc.
- Some energy is lost as heat to the environment.

> *Remember: Only the energy that is used to make the animal grow, or is stored inside it, e.g., as fat, can be passed on to the next stage in the food chain.*

Energy and food chains

As a lot of energy is lost at each stage of a food chain, it cannot be very long. Most food chains involve only three or four stages.

As you go along a food chain, you normally find *fewer* organisms at each stage, but the organisms get *bigger*,

e.g. algae ➤ tadpoles ➤ water scorpion ➤ perch

There are two main *exceptions* to this:

1. when a food chain starts with a large plant, e.g. oak tree, rose bush, that has lots of small animals depending on it,

   e.g. rose bush ➤ aphid ➤ ladybird ➤ blue tit.
2. when a food chain ends with parasites, e.g. fleas, ticks, and there are lots of them feeding on one animal,

   e.g. plants ➤ rabbits ➤ ticks.

> *CHECKPOINT*
>
> If resources, e.g., land, are *scarce*, it is more efficient for humans to eat crops, e.g., wheat, maize, beans, potatoes, than animals.
>
> Can you use the information in this section to explain why?

✣ ***Food chains, Pyramid of biomass, Pyramid of numbers***

ENVIRONMENT

This is rather a vague word, which means an organism's surroundings.

When people talk about 'saving the environment' or 'environmental issues' they are often referring to worldwide problems, for example:

marine pollution,
destruction of the rainforests,
killing whales,
damaging the ozone layer,
recycling waste materials, e.g. metal, paper, glass.

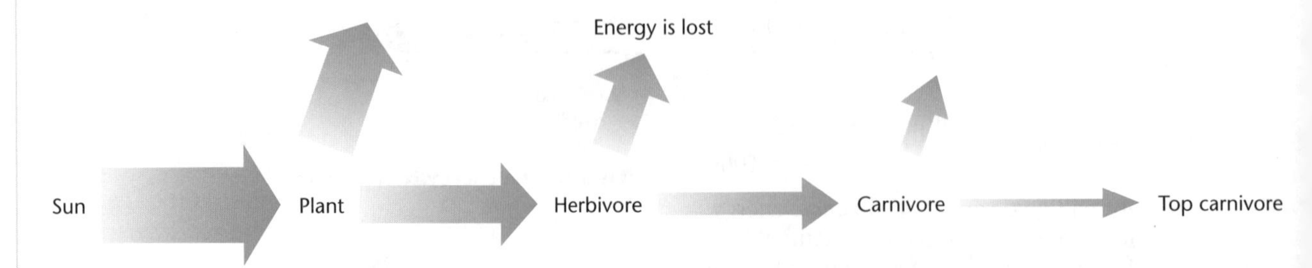

Energy flow through food chains

When scientists talk about 'the environment' they usually mean an organism's immediate surroundings, for example:

a limpet's environment is a rock pool on the shore,
a squirrel's environment is a wood.

There are several factors that are important in an organism's environment.

Non-living factors

- climate, e.g. temperature, rainfall, wind,
- amount of light,
- amount of water,
- wind or water currents,
- soil type, e.g. particle size, pH,
- aspect, e.g. shape of landscape, slope of hills, etc.,
- pollution.

Living factors

- which plants are present – this affects animals because they may depend on plants for food or for shelter,
- which animals are present – this affects plants, because they may depend on animals for pollination or for seed dispersal, or they may be harmed by animals, e.g. by being eaten! It also affects animals because they may depend on other animals as food, or they may be in danger of being eaten.
- how much ***competition for resources*** exists between individuals.

Changes in the environment

An organism's environment does not remain exactly the same all the time. There are three main types of changes: daily changes, seasonal changes and long-term changes.

Daily changes (changes over 24 hours)

- *amount of light* will vary between day and night
- *temperature will vary* (it is warmer during the day)
- *tides* will change the amount of water in rock pools, and whether a rocky shore is covered by water or exposed.

Seasonal changes (changes over one year)

- *amount of light* will vary: sunlight is stronger and lasts longer in summer
- *temperature* will vary: it is warm in the summer, and cold in winter
- *amount of water* will vary: it is wetter in autumn and winter than in summer. In summer, ponds and streams may even dry up.
- *leaves* fall from trees in autumn and do not grow again until spring, so this affects the amount of light reaching other organisms in a wood, e.g. small plants.

Long-term changes

If a particular habitat is left completely undisturbed, it will not stay the same. The size of the plants will increase, and different plants will start to grow there. As this happens, many different animals will move into the habitat. This process is called *succession*.

You can see the process of succession happening in a derelict garden or on a piece of waste land. Small weeds are gradually replaced by bigger plants and long grass. Eventually, shrubs and even trees will grow there.

Humans often deliberately change environments, and so may make them unsuitable for the animals or plants that used to live there,

e.g. building roads and houses,
clearing land for animal grazing or to plant crops,
dumping waste material in landfill sites, rivers or the sea.

Why do animals live in a particular habitat?

Each habitat has its own set of environmental conditions (both living and non-living). In order to survive, an organism must be adapted for its environment, i.e., have characteristics that help it to survive there, e.g. a polar bear has thick, white fur so that it can survive the cold temperatures of the arctic.

In order to understand this properly, you have to know about the conditions in a particular habitat, and then think what an organism needs to survive there. You can ask yourself the same question in two different ways:

- what does a fish need to live in a lake?
- why does a fish not live in a wood?

✦ ***Adaptations to the environment, Ecology, Ecosystem***

ENZYMES

These are chemicals made by glands in the gut wall. They help to ***digest*** (break down) the food we eat, to turn it into smaller, soluble molecules.

Enzymes act as ***catalysts*** – this means that they speed up the rate of digestion. There are different types of enzymes to digest different types of food,

e.g. *protease* enzymes digest proteins,
carbohydrase enzymes digest carbohydrates,
lipase enzymes digest fats (fats are sometimes called lipids).

EQUATIONS

Chemical equations

ETHANOIC ACID

This is commonly called vinegar. It is a weak acid with a pH of 4–5.

EVALUATION

Always write an evaluation at the end of your investigations.

Try to include answers to the following questions:

- Were your results good enough and clear enough to get good conclusions?
- Did all of your results fit the pattern that you expected?
- What did you do about any 'odd' ones?
- Could your experiment have been improved if you did it again?
- What would you change?

Conclusion, Fair test, Graphs, Hypothesis, Investigation, Results, Variable

EVAPORATION

Have you ever wondered what happens to the puddle of water that results from a downpour? The water disappears but it does not boil; instead evaporation takes place. Evaporation is like boiling but it occurs at any temperature *below* the ***boiling point*** of water. In this example, the tiny water particles escape into the air as evaporation takes places. Evaporation can, of course, occur for liquids other than water.

EXCRETION

This is the removal of waste products made inside an organism,

e.g. carbon dioxide is excreted by the lungs,
urea is excreted by the kidneys.

Excretion is an important ***life process***.

Remember: Egestion (removal of faeces) is not the same as excretion, because faeces were not made inside the body.

EXERCISE

This is an important part of being healthy. Exercise is important because:

- it strengthens the ***muscles***,
- it strengthens ***joints***, and keeps us flexible,
- it keeps the ***heart*** muscle healthy,
- it keeps ***blood vessels*** healthy,
- it increases the ***breathing*** rate and ***gas exchange***,
- it increases stamina (the ability to keep going),
- it makes us feel more positive and motivated,
- it often involves being outside and meeting other people, so it is an important social activity.

There is strong evidence that people who exercise regularly are generally healthier than those who do not. This exercise may be organized, e.g. tennis, football, or something you do alone, e.g. swimming. It is easy to build exercise into our everyday lives, e.g. walking instead of catching a bus or using the car.

It is better to exercise for a short time, regularly, than to exercise for a longer time less often. To be effective, you should exercise for at least 20 minutes, three times a week.

Fitness

EXOTHERMIC

A ***chemical reaction*** that gives out heat is exothermic. Many chemical reactions do this including burning a fuel. ***Respiration*** is exothermic.

Endothermic

EXPANSION

Materials will get larger when their ***temperature*** increases. This effect is called expansion.

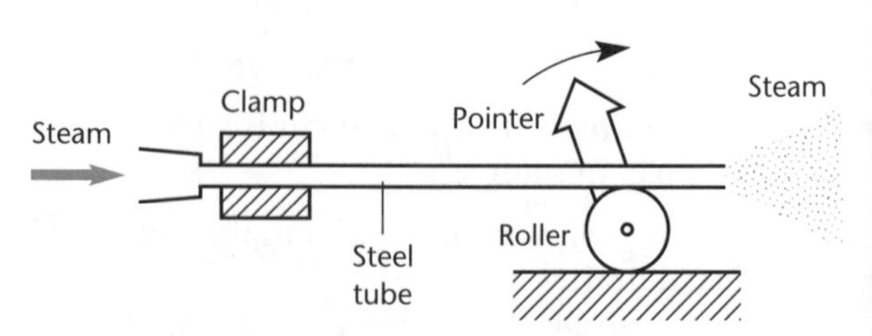

Showing expansion of a solid

The *expansion* of ***solids*** is usually very small but the forces when it happens can be *very* large. You can make the expansion of a steel tube large enough to see by blowing steam through it and making it turn a roller with a pointer on it at one end. As one end of the tube is fixed, all the movement is at the end with the roller and the small expansion is magnified enough for us to see it.

The large forces involved are often demonstrated in school by an apparatus called a bar breaker. The large bar is heated by a Bunsen burner and the nut is tightened as it expands. When it is allowed to cool it contracts and the smaller metal bar is pulled tight against the thick metal base and is broken.

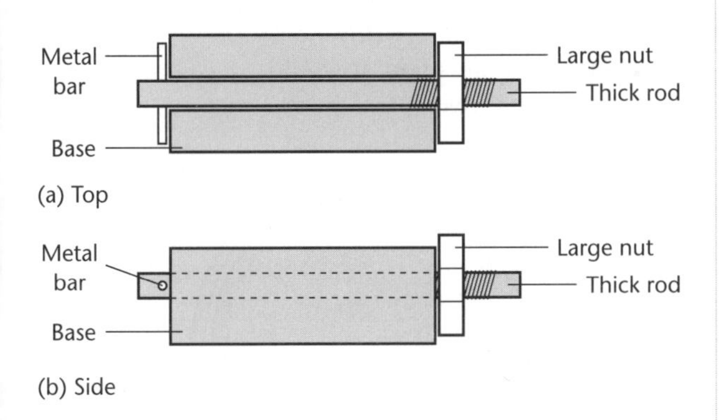

The bar breaker

- *Bridges* must have an expansion gap to allow for the expansion and contraction in very hot or cold weather or they may collapse. The gap is often covered by a metal plate. Some large bridges, such as those over motorways, may also move slightly on large rollers. The gaps are often filled with foam rubber so that they are not filled with stones.
- *Railway lines* are made in long lengths and taper at the ends so that the rails can slide past one another when they expand. If the gaps are not large enough the lines will be buckled by the expansion forces.
- *Steel tyres* are fitted to railway wheels by making them very slightly too small. The tyre is then heated so that it expands and can be fitted over the wheel. When the metal cools, it will be so tightly fitted that it would have to be cut off it to replace it. An alternative would be to cool the wheel in liquid nitrogen so that it became smaller, fit the tyre, and wait for the wheel to warm up. Gear wheels can be tightly fitted to their shafts in the same way.
- *Bimetallic strips* are made from two strips of different metals fastened together. When the bimetallic strip is warmed, one metal expands more than the other and the strip curves so that the longer metal is on the outer side on the bend. This has uses in heat detectors and in thermostats.

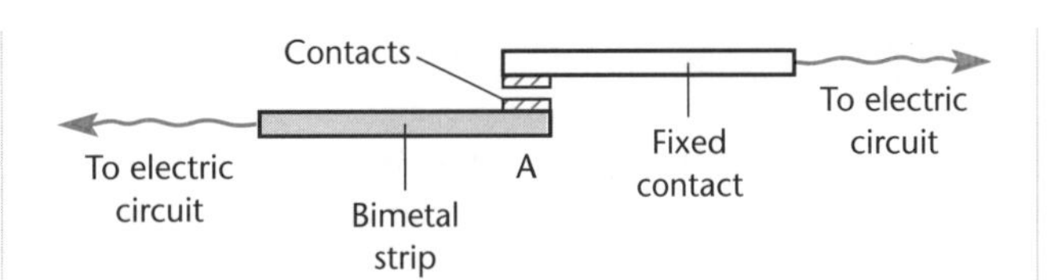

A simple thermostat

In the simple thermostat, the end of the bimetallic strip labelled A will rise and make contact as it cools and then bends away again breaking contact as it is warmed. The thermostat can be made adjustable to different temperatures by using a plastic screw to move the fixed contact. This changes how far the strip has to bend to make or break contact, which then happens at a different temperature. This sort of thermostat is used to switch central heating on and off by controlling the pump. A spiral of bimetallic strip will curl or uncurl a little more depending on its temperature. If it is fixed at one end and has a pointer at the other it can be used as a fairly reliable and strong thermometer.

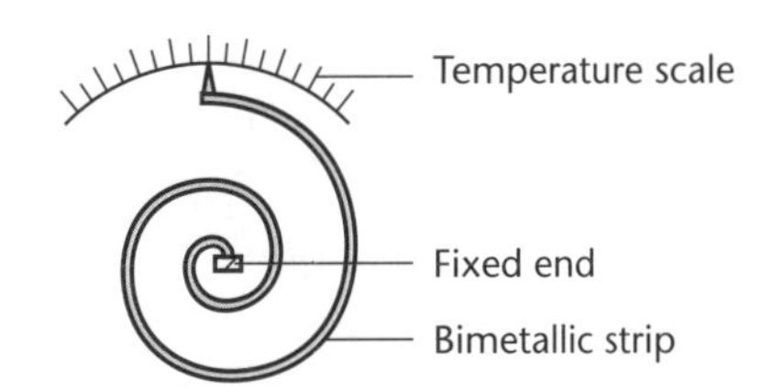

A bimetallic thermometer

> *Remember: When a solid is heated, holes in it get larger. (Think of the strip of metal round the inside of the hole which must be expanding.)*

Liquids will expand a lot more than solids and also expand with large forces. You will have seen and used this expansion each time that you use a mercury or alcohol ***thermometer***. The liquid expands along the bore of the glass tube so that it reaches different points along the scale as it expands.

Gases will expand most but they have large spaces between their particles and they can be kept at the same volume so that the ***pressure*** increases instead.

> *CHECKPOINT*
>
> Write down two problems caused by expansion and briefly explain how they are overcome.
>
> Name two uses for expansion and briefly explain how they work.

Heat energy, Kinetic theory

EYE

This is an important ***sense organ*** in many animals, including humans. It has cells that are sensitive to *light*.

Light enters the eye through a hole at the front called the pupil. Surrounding the pupil is a coloured part (the iris): this can change size to change the size of the pupil, and alter the amount of light entering the eye.

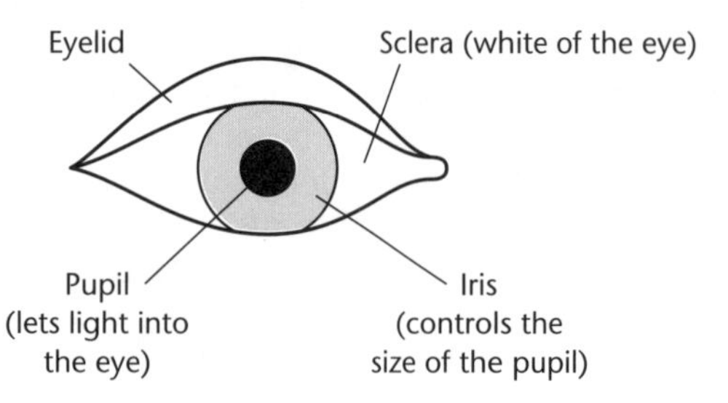

Front view of the eye

The eye is a complex organ, with lots of different parts. The main parts you need to know about are:

- the cornea — this is a transparent layer at the front of the eye. It lets light in, but protects the eye from dust and germs. It also bends (refracts) the light rays.
- the lens — this focuses the light rays on the retina at the back of the eye. It can change shape to focus the light rays precisely.
- the retina — this is a screen at the back of the eye containing light sensitive cells (rods and cones). When light is focused here an image is formed.
- the optic nerve — this carries information about the image to the brain, where it can be processed. The brain can then decide what action you need to take, e.g. if the image is of a hungry lion running towards you, it would be sensible to move!

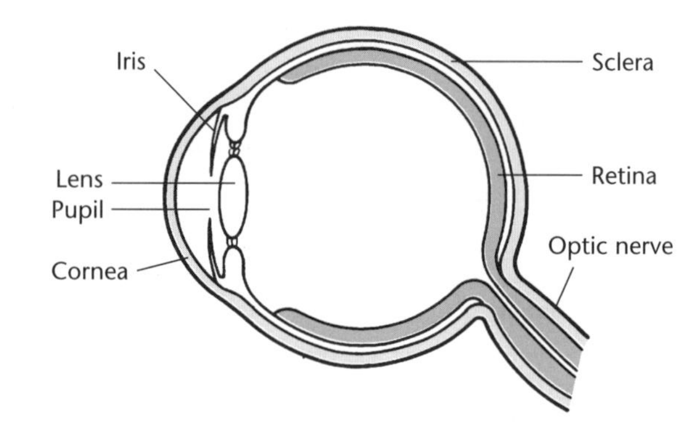

Inside the eye

FAECES

Most of the food we eat is digested by ***enzymes*** and absorbed into the blood. ***Fibre*** cannot be digested, so it stays inside the gut and forms the faeces.

Faeces are made up of undigested food (mainly fibre), dead bacteria and water. The faeces are moved along the gut when muscles contract, and are eventually pushed out of the gut through the anus. This is called ***egestion***.

FAIR TEST

If you are doing an investigation you must make sure that you carry out a *fair test*. This means that you only change *one* ***variable*** at a time and see what difference it makes. If you changed more than one ***variable*** you would not know which one was having an effect – it might even be both!

All the other possible variables must be kept the same and it is important that you tell the person who is marking your work what you are going to *keep the same* to make sure of a fair test. Include it in your method or even as a separate section, but you *must* make sure that you write it down. For example, if you are testing the effect of insulation on the temperature of water in a metal beaker, you would always use the same beaker with the same mass of water in it and start your measurements at the same temperature each time with the apparatus in the same place in the room.

✣ ***Conclusion, Evaluation, Graph, Hypothesis, Investigation, Results***

FARADAY, MICHAEL (1791–1867)

Michael Faraday started his working life as a bookbinder. His main interest, however, was science. He attended all of ***Sir Humphrey Davy's*** lectures at the Royal Institution. He wrote notes during the lectures and presented a hand bound copy to Davy, who was so impressed that he recruited Faraday as his assistant.

Faraday went on to develop the dynamo that you may use on your bicycle, as well as many other ideas involving electricity.

FAT

This is one of the main food groups making up a ***balanced diet***. It is important because it is a very good source of ***energy*** (1g of fat contains more than twice as much energy as 1g of carbohydrate or protein). It is found in red meat, butter, margarine, nuts, cheese and all fried foods, e.g. chips, crisps.

It is essential to eat some fat to stay healthy, but eating too much can cause serious health problems; for example,

obesity: excess fat is stored under the skin and around the body organs.

heart disease: a type of fat called *cholesterol* builds up inside the ***arteries*** and can cause blockages. This can lead to heart attacks.

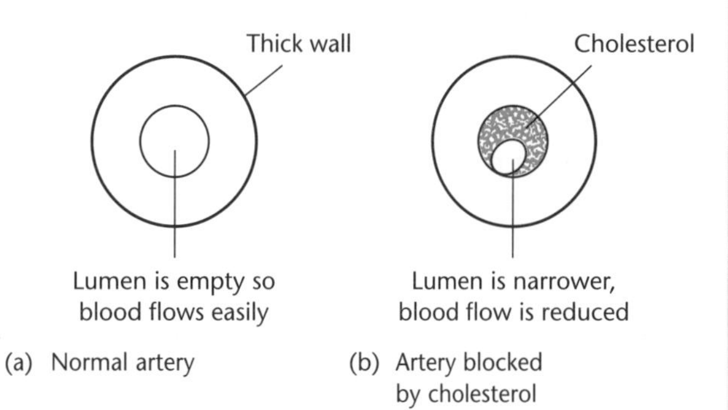

Blockage of an artery

✣ ***Energy in food***

FERMENTATION

This important ***chemical reaction*** involves micro-organisms to produce useful products. For example, ***yeast*** (a micro-organism) can be used to convert sugar in ***solution*** into ethanol (alcohol) and carbon dioxide gas. ***Enzymes*** in yeast cells act on the sugars in grape solutions to produce wine and on the sugars in hop solutions to produce beer.

Conditions need to be warm to ensure good yeast growth. The fermentation reaction stops when the yeast cells are poisoned by the ethanol produced.

Beer, bread and winemaking are all a result of fermentation (or anaerobic ***respiration***) by yeasts. Lactic acid bacteria convert milk into yoghurt and micro-organisms are needed to convert milk into cheese. Fermentation of some ***moulds*** and ***bacteria*** produce ***antibiotics***, whilst others can produce industrial chemicals.

FERTILIZATION

This means that a male ***gamete*** has joined to a female gamete. It is an important part of ***sexual reproduction***.

In humans: a ***sperm*** joins to an ***ovum*** to form a ***zygote*** inside the fallopian tube. The zygote will develop into a baby.

In plants: a ***pollen*** grain nucleus joins to an egg cell nucleus inside a ***carpel***. A ***seed*** will then develop.

Reproduction

FERTILIZER

A fertilizer is a substance containing ***minerals***, which is added to soil to improve plant growth.

Soil naturally contains minerals, but plants absorb them and use them for growth. Over a period of time, the soil can become deficient (lacking) in minerals, so that plants cannot grow properly. This is a serious problem if the soil is used year after year to grow the same crop, or if the amount of soil is small, e.g. in a plant pot.

Fertilizers put back the minerals that plants take out of the soil. There are two main types of fertilizer.

Organic fertilizer

This is a natural substance made from waste animal or plant matter,

e.g. manure – animal urine and faeces mixed with straw, compost – biodegradable household waste, e.g. vegetable peelings, teabags, grass cuttings.

These materials are allowed to rot, and are then dug into the soil. They release minerals slowly as they ***decay***

Inorganic fertilizer

This is made in chemical laboratories and factories. It contains high concentrations of minerals, especially nitrate, phosphate and potassium, so it is sometimes called NPK fertilizer. It is dug into the soil, or dissolved in water and used to water the plants. This provides the plants with minerals much more quickly, but it is important not to add too much or the plants may be damaged.

Both types of fertilizer will cause damage if they are washed off the land and into rivers. This type of ***pollution*** is a big problem where rivers run through farmland.

Compost

FIBRE

Although we cannot digest fibre, it is still an important part of a ***balanced diet***. It is needed to keep the ***digestive system*** healthy, to encourage ***peristalsis*** (the muscle contractions that move food through the gut), and to prevent constipation.

It is found in most foods that come from plants, e.g. brown rice, potatoes, fruits, vegetables, wholemeal bread and pasta.

If we do not have enough fibre in our diet, ***faeces*** are not moved through the digestive system properly, and too much water is absorbed from them. This leads to constipation, and may be linked to other diseases of the digestive system.

FILTER

A colour filter is made from a transparent material with a dye (pigment) added to it. The dye will absorb some colours and let others pass through. We can only see the ones that are not absorbed. A red filter will absorb all the other colours but lets red light pass through.

Remember: White is a mixture of all the colours and black is when you see no light at all.

Filter	*colours let through*
red	red
blue	blue
green	green
magenta	red and blue
yellow	red and green
cyan	blue and green

When two filters follow each other, they will both subtract some colours. If there are none left you will see black!

If a green filter is followed by a red filter, the result is that no colour can get through both filters and the combination appears to be black.

Filters are often used in stage lighting and in photography. To make clouds stand out against a blue sky in a black and white picture you would use a yellow filter. This makes the blue sky darker because the blue light cannot pass through the yellow filter.

CHECKPOINT

A blue filter allows only ____ light to pass through.

A blue and a red filter together will appear ______.

Explain the last answer.

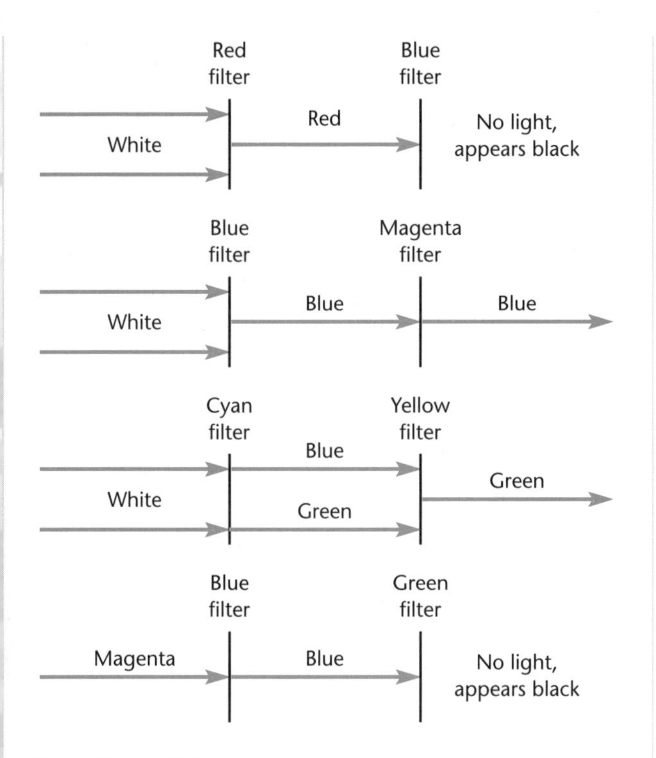

The effect of filters

Colour, Coloured objects, Spectrum

FILTRATION

This is a very useful method for separating ***insoluble*** particles from a liquid. The filter paper used has many tiny holes in it. Liquid particles are small enough to pass through the holes. Insoluble particles are quite large and cannot pass through the holes. They are trapped in the filter paper.

Filtering is quite a straightforward method providing you remember a few basic things:

- The filter paper should be folded in half and then in half again.

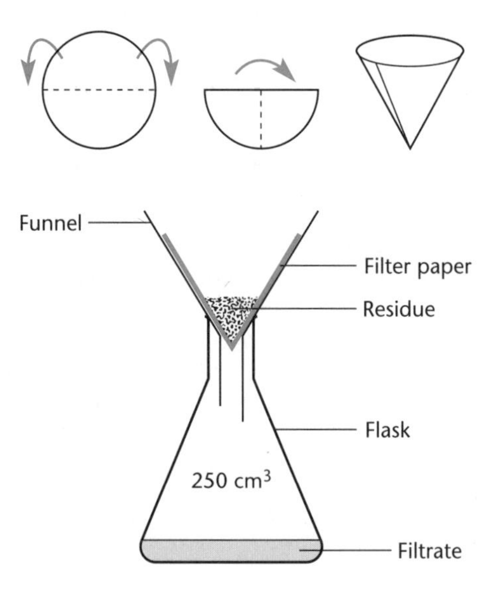

Filtration

- The filter paper is then opened out into a cone shape and placed in a funnel.
- You must be careful not to overfill the funnel with liquid.
- Avoid disturbing the wet filter paper while it is filtering.

The solution that passes through the paper is called the *filtrate* and the solid left behind in the paper is called the *residue.*

FIRE TRIANGLE

There are three necessary ingredients for fire to take place. Heat, oxygen and a fuel. They are often represented as the sides of a triangle. The fire will stop burning if any one of the sides of the triangle is removed. Firefighters mainly try to prevent oxygen from getting to the fire to help put it out.

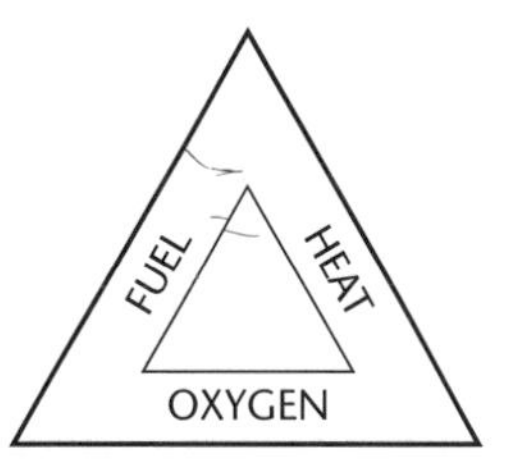

Fire triangle

FITNESS

This means that your body is used to ***exercise***, and is operating efficiently. You can improve your level of fitness by exercising regularly.

A person who is fit will:

- be supple, i.e., have flexible, mobile joints and not be stiff,
- have stamina, i.e., be able to keep going for long periods of time,

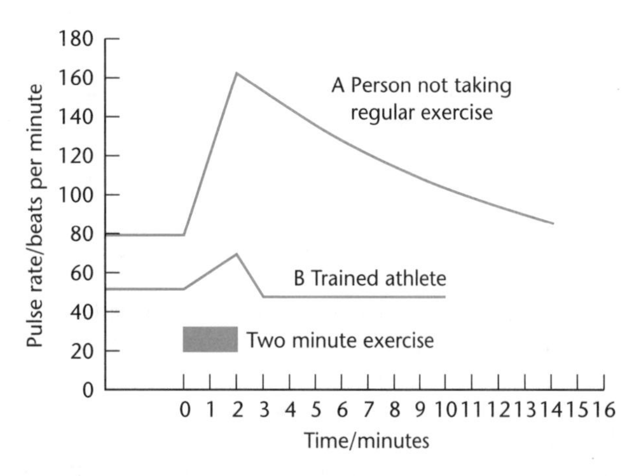

Comparison of the pulse rate of a fit and an unfit person

- have a low pulse rate and a short recovery time, i.e., get over exercise quickly,
- be strong, i.e., have powerful muscles that work well.

Fleming, Alexander (1881–1955)

Alexander Fleming was a British scientist who discovered that a ***fungus*** (*Penicillium*) makes a substance which kills bacteria. This was the first ***antibiotic*** to be discovered (in 1928), although it was not developed for use with patients for several years.

Florey, Howard (1898–1968)

Howard Florey was an American scientist who purified the substance which killed bacteria, discovered by ***Fleming***. He named it Penicillin (the fungus which made it was called *Penicillium*), and it was quickly developed to treat patients with infections. It was the first ***antibiotic***.

Flower

The flower contains the reproductive organs of the plant. The structure of the flower will vary depending on the type of ***pollination*** that occurs, but the same basic parts are always present.

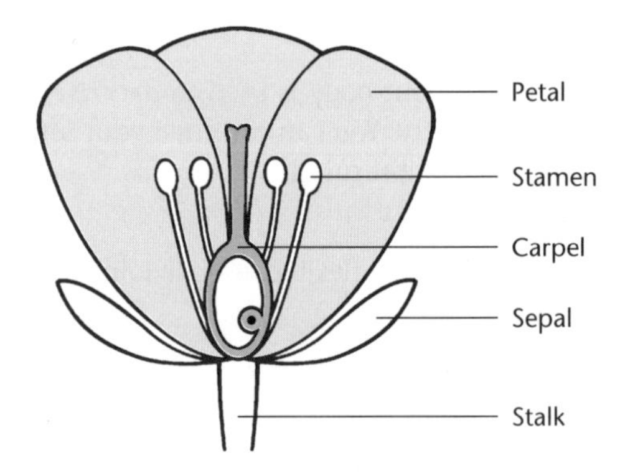

Parts of a flower

In *insect pollinated plants*, the petals are often large and brightly coloured, and may have a pleasant scent. At the base of the petal there may be a nectary that produces sugary liquid. All of these things will attract insects, which will pollinate the plant. The stamens are short, and the stigma is protected by the petals.

In *wind pollinated plants*, the petals are usually small and difficult to see, and may be missing altogether. The flowers will not be scented or have nectar. The stamens are long, and hang outside the flower and the stigma is like a net. Wind pollinated plants do not need to attract insects, but the stamens and stigma must be exposed so that pollen can be blown in the wind.

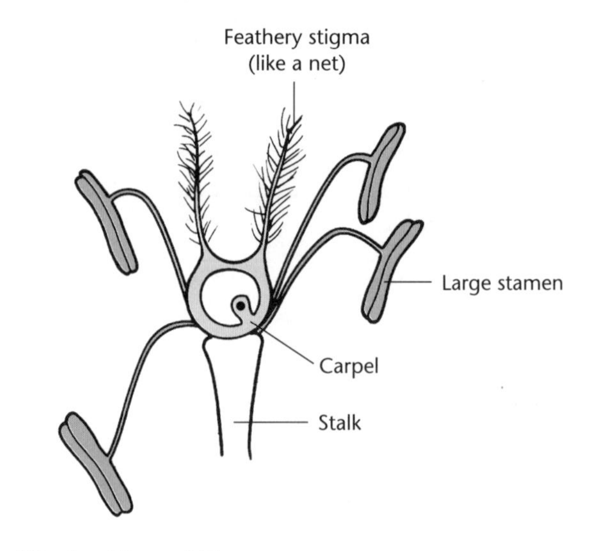

Wind pollinated flower

✦ *Reproduction*

Foetus

This is the name for the developing baby from eight weeks of pregnancy up to the birth. Although it is very small at first (about 2.5cm long), most of its organs are already formed and it quickly grows bigger. By the time it is born, it will weigh around 3.5kg and be able to survive outside its mother's body.

✦ *Reproduction*

Food

Food is important to living things for two main reasons:

1. it is used as a fuel to provide ***energy*** in the process of ***respiration***.
2. it is used as a raw material for ***growth*** and replacement of cells.

Animals get the food they need by eating other living things (plants or animals), so they are called ***consumers***.

Plants get the food they need by making it in their leaves, from carbon dioxide and water. This process is called ***photosynthesis***, and plants are called ***producers***.

✦ *Balanced diet, Nutrition*

Food chains

These are a simple way of showing what animals eat,

e.g. oak tree ➤ caterpillars ➤ shrews ➤ owl

oak tree	caterpillars	shrews	owl
producer	primary (1st) consumer	secondary (2nd) consumer	tertiary (2nd) consumer

The oak tree is a ***producer*** – it makes its own food by ***photosynthesis***. The caterpillars are primary ***consumers*** – the first animals in the food chain. They eat plants, so they are ***herbivores***. The shrews and owls are secondary and tertiary ***consumers***. They eat animals, so they are ***carnivores***. The owl is at the end of the food chain, so it is called a top carnivore. ***Decomposers*** are never shown in food chains.

e.g. algae ➤ tadpole ➤ water scorpion ➤ perch
seaweed ➤ limpet ➤ oystercatcher (bird)

CHECKPOINT

The first organism in a food chain is always a ______ , which can make its own food by ____________ . This organism is known as a ________ . A caterpillar that eats an oak leaf is a ______________ . A shrew that eats the caterpillar is a ____________ .
All the animals in a food chain are ______ . The owl is a ______________ because nothing eats it. ________________ are never shown in food chains.

Pollution in food chains

If a habitat becomes polluted, the substance can pass along a food chain and cause damage to many different organisms.

In the 1940s, a pesticide called DDT was used in Britain to kill insects. This pesticide was sprayed onto plants where the insects fed. The DDT then entered the food chain and was passed to other animals:

plants ➤ insects ➤ blue tits ➤ peregrine falcons

Because each blue tit eats large amounts of insects, a lot of DDT will build up in blue tits (it *accumulates*). Because each peregrine falcon eats lots of blue tits, very large amounts of DDT will build up in peregrine falcons, i.e., *the DDT passes along the food chain, and it accumulates in the top carnivore.*

By the 1950s and 1960s, the numbers of peregrine falcons in Britain had decreased because:

- some peregrine falcons died due to the effects of DDT,
- some peregrine falcons could not breed; they became infertile due to the effects of DDT.

DDT is no longer used in Britain, but it is still found in the environment because it cannot easily be broken down: we say it is *persistent*.

Many other toxic (poisonous) substances can be passed along food chains in this way, e.g. oil, heavy metals, and so lots of other top carnivores could be affected.

✣ ***Energy in the environment, Food webs***

Food webs

A food web is a set of interlinked ***food chains***. Most organisms do not eat only a single type of food, so complex food webs exist in all habitats, e.g.

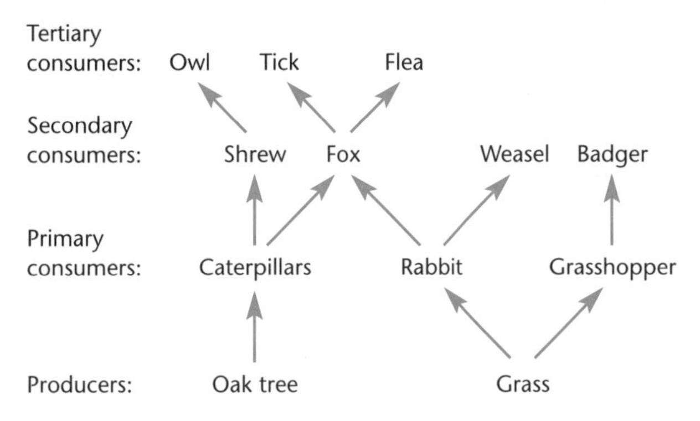

Food web

Each species in the food web will affect the balance of the food web, and the other organisms in it. For example, if the number of rabbits increased:

- there would be less grass, so this would affect grasshoppers and badgers,
- there would be more food available for foxes and weasels, so numbers would increase,
- if the number of foxes increase, they will feed on more caterpillars, so shrews will be short of food, and some may die,
- a decrease in the number of shrews means that owls have less to feed on, and some will die.

CHECKPOINT

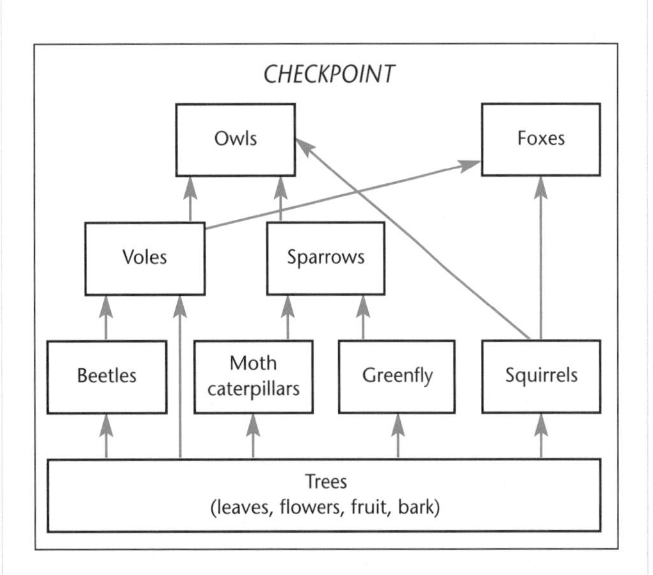

CHECKPOINT CONTINUED

a) If the number of foxes in the wood *increased*, how would this affect the owls?

Effect ______________________________
Reason ______________________________

b) If the number of caterpillars *increased* how would this affect sparrows?

Effect ______________________________
Reason ______________________________

c) If the number of caterpillars increased, would you expect the number of voles to increase or decrease?

Effect ______________________________
Reason ______________________________

d) If all the squirrels died of a disease, how would this affect numbers of voles?

Effect ______________________________
Reason ______________________________

FORCE

Forces can pull, push, bend and twist things.

Forces produce a number of effects and these can be used to find the size of the force in ***newtons*** (N).

Forces can bend, stretch, or 'deform' a material and the amount that the material is deformed may help us to find the size of the force. Stretching a spring or bending a ruler are good examples of this. The bigger the stretch or bend, the bigger the force. A newton meter works in this way – as the spring is stretched the pointer moves along the scale.

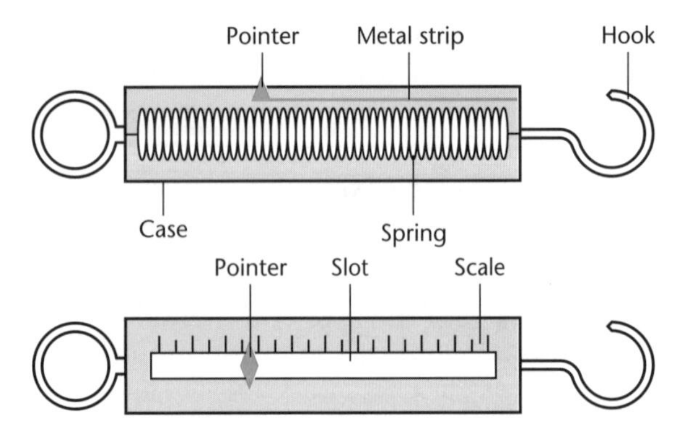

The newton meter

When no force is acting on an object it will remain stationary or, if it was moving, it will carry on in the same direction at the same speed. The same will be true if the forces on an object are equal in size and opposite in direction so that they are balanced. This idea is called *Newton's first law*. Sometimes it is difficult to see that this is correct because there are always forces acting on objects that are on the Earth (weight or air resistance for example).

Examples:

- In the case of a weight hanging on a spring, the force stretching the spring is balanced by the elastic force of the spring. This means that the spring puts a force on the weight that is the same size as the force that the weight puts on the spring.
- In the case of a book standing on a table, the weight is balanced by an upwards force from the table called a *reaction*. A reaction will always be at 90° to the surface that produces it.

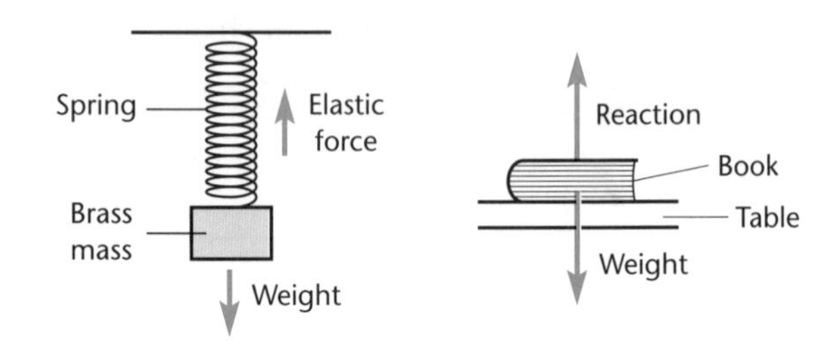

Balanced forces

If there is an overall force acting on an object then either its speed or its direction of movement will change. We say that it is accelerated. Bigger forces make bigger accelerations. Larger masses will need larger forces to produce the same acceleration. This is part of *Newton's second law*.

A large car with a big mass will need a bigger force to make it accelerate at the same rate as a small car, so it usually has a bigger engine. A racing car will have a small mass and a big force from its engine to make it accelerate quickly.

A force will act in a particular direction. The force is changed if either its size or its direction is changed. To make a car change direction, there must be a sideways force. This is usually caused by turning the front wheels so that the ***friction*** force pushes them sideways.

Forces can also make things turn on a pivot or axle. The size of a turning force is called its ***moment***.

✣ ***Counter forces, Moment, Pressure, Terminal velocity***

FORMULA

✣ ***Chemical formula***

FOSSIL FUELS

The fossil fuels are coal, ***gas*** and ***oil***. They all contain ***carbon*** and were made millions of years ago by the

action of heat and pressure on decaying plants and animals. The ***chemical energy*** in the ***cells*** of the plants and animals was trapped in the fossil fuel and is released when the fuel is burned.

Remember: The energy in the plants (and therefore the animals), which is trapped in the fuel, originally came from the Sun and was used in photosynthesis.

Sources of energy

FRACTIONAL DISTILLATION

This is a particular type of ***distillation*** process. Fractional distillation is a process used in industry and in laboratories to separate liquids of different boiling points. A 'fraction' is a mixture of liquids with similar boiling points.

A mixture of ethanol (alcohol) and water can be separated in this way. Ethanol boils at 78°C and water boils at 100°C. If you heat the mixture slowly, the ethanol starts to boil at around 78°C and passes through the fractionating column into the receiver, where it is cooled and condenses as a *distillate*. This is the first 'fraction'.

Fractional distillation is used to separate the gases in air and the many substances found in crude oil. It is also how whisky is separated from an alcohol and water mixture.

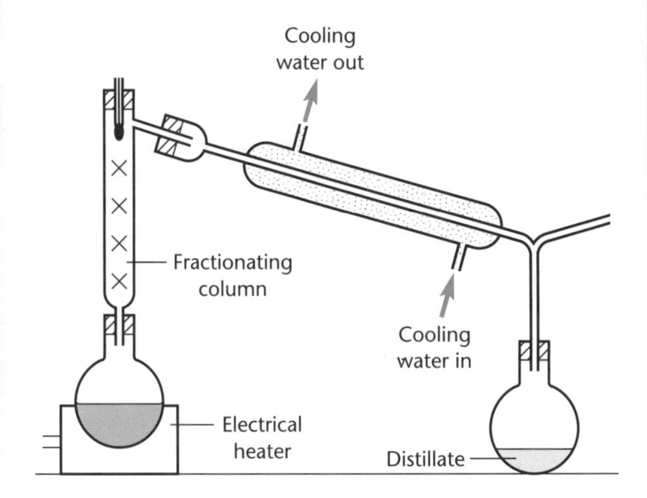

Fractional distillation

Air, Distillation

FREEZING

When water is cooled down, it turns back into ice at 0°C. This is called freezing, and 0°C is known as the freezing point of water.

Changes of state

FREQUENCY

This is the number of times that something happens each second. It is measured in *hertz*, where 1 hertz (1 Hz) means one per second.

The frequency of a wave is the number of waves that pass a point each second. We can hear sound waves from about 50 Hz up to about 17 kHz (17,000 Hz). We hear sounds with a higher frequency as a higher *pitch*.

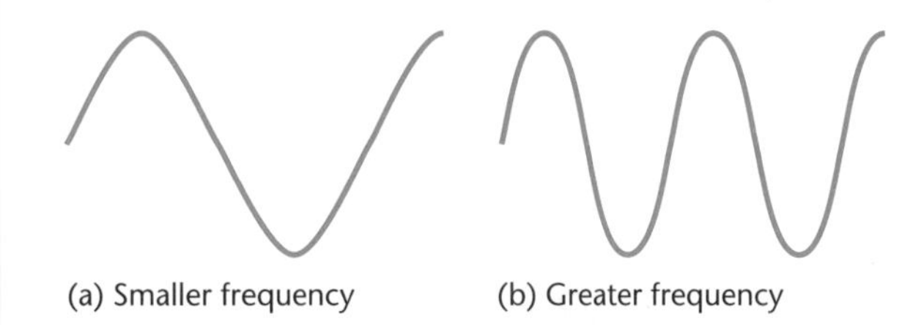

Frequency

Wavelength

FRICTION

When two surfaces slide over each other there will be a ***force*** acting against the movement called friction. The size of the force will depend upon the material of both surfaces and on how 'rough' each one is.

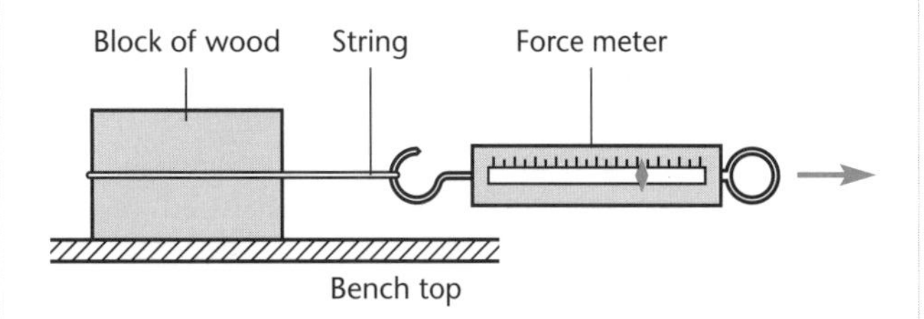

Testing friction

Fasten a force meter to a wooden block and use it to pull the block across the bench. At first, the force increases but the friction force is always equal and opposite to it and the block does not move. The largest value of the force when the block just begins to move is called 'static friction' for the two surfaces. Once the block is moving, the force needed to maintain a constant speed is smaller than the force of static friction and is called 'dynamic friction'.

You can investigate the frictional force between lots of surfaces using this apparatus. You should be able to show that the size of the force depends on the weight of the block but does not vary much with surface area. The size of frictional forces can be made smaller by various lubricants (scope for another investigation!). Friction is often a nuisance in machines where heat is produced at sliding surfaces and is made smaller by using oil or ball bearings. It is also necessary – we could not walk if there was no frictional force between the soles of our feet and the ground, and tyres work because of the frictional force between the tyre and the road. We also use friction in most braking systems.

Air resistance is also a friction force caused by the rubbing of the air on the surface going through it. Air resistance gets bigger at bigger speeds.

Counter forces, Force

FRUIT

After ***fertilization*** of a plant, the ***ovary*** will develop into a fruit containing the ***seeds***. A fruit may contain one or more seeds, depending on the arrangement of ovules in the ovary.

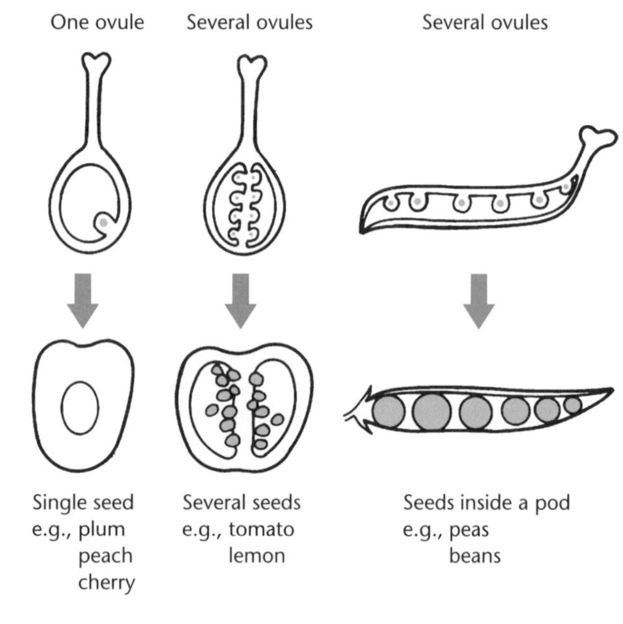

Different types of fruits

The fruit often protects the seed, and helps with its ***dispersal***.

FUEL

A fuel is a concentrated ***source of energy***.

Many fuels, such as fossil fuels, are burned to get some of their ***chemical energy*** produced as heat.

Energy, Fossil fuels, Sources of energy

FUNGI

There are many different types of fungi – they make up one ***kingdom*** in ***classification***.

Some of them are single celled, e.g. ***yeasts***, and others are multi-cellular, made up of threads called hyphae. Multicellular fungi are usually called ***moulds***.

All fungi feed on dead, or waste material (they are ***decomposers***), or they live inside a host (they are ***parasites***).

Some fungi are useful to humans, and others are harmful.

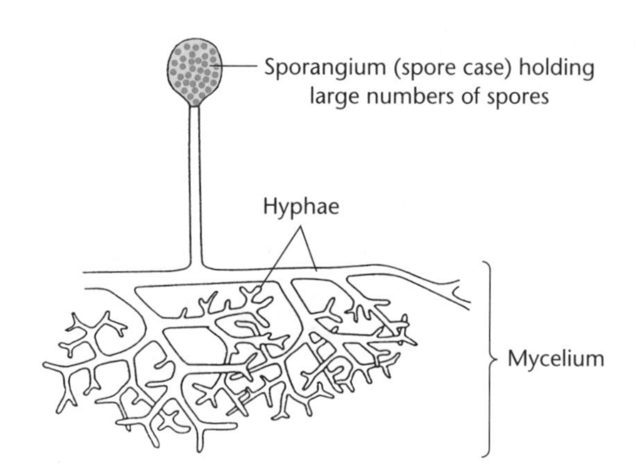

Multicellular fungus (mould), showing hyphae and spores

Useful fungi

- Some are ***decomposers***, which make dead material rot. They help to get rid of dead material, and to release useful substances so they can be re-used.
- Fungi may be used in sewage treatment (these are decomposers).
- Some fungi are used as a food, e.g. mushrooms, mycoprotein (Quorn).
- Fungi may be used in food manufacturing, e.g. yeast in breadmaking.
- Fungi may be used in alcohol production, e.g. yeast in wine-making, brewing.
- Fungi make ***antibiotics***, e.g. Penicillin, which kill bacteria.

Harmful fungi

- Those fungi that cause disease in humans, e.g. athlete's foot, thrush, ringworm.
- Some fungi cause disease in other animals or plants, e.g. Dutch elm disease, potato blight.
- Some fungi make food go off, so people will be ill if they eat it.

Antibiotics will not kill fungi – they can only be killed by anti-fungal drugs.

Yeasts can reproduce asexually to form a ***clone*** (this is called budding). In ideal conditions they can double their numbers every two hours.

Moulds reproduce by making spores. These will float through the air and if they land on a suitable material, e.g. jam, old wood, soil, they will germinate.

*Remember: Fungi are **not** plants. They do not contain chlorophyll, and they cannot photosynthesise.*

GALAXY

A galaxy is a collection of a huge number of ***stars*** Our nearest star, the ***Sun***, belongs to a galaxy called the ***Milky Way***. There are millions of galaxies in the *universe*.

Milky Way, Star

GALVANIZING

Zinc is a more reactive ***metal*** than iron. When the two metals are next to each other, the zinc prevents the iron from rusting. Zinc reacts with oxygen before the iron. This is a very effective way of preventing ***corrosion***. When iron objects are coated with zinc this is called galvanizing.

GAMETE

This is the name for the sex cells involved in ***sexual reproduction***

In humans: the gametes are ***ova*** and ***sperm***
In plants: the gametes are ***ovules*** and ***pollen*** grains.

Fertilization occurs when male and female gametes join.

Reproduction

GAS

Gas is one of the three ***states of matter***. In gas, the ***particles*** are moving very fast and are large distances apart. Gases are made up of either single ***atoms*** or small ***molecules***.

Gases have no fixed shape or volume. They spread out or *diffuse* to fill all the available space. Gases exert ***pressure***.

Changing state, Diffusion

GAS EXCHANGE

This means that gases are being transferred between the air and the cells of an organism.

Some gases move *into* an organism where they will be used, e.g. oxygen is *used* for respiration.

Some gases are made inside organisms and move *out* into the air, e.g. carbon dioxide is *made* in respiration.

Gas exchange in humans

This occurs deep inside the ***lungs***, in little air sacs called ***alveoli***. When we breathe in, air is drawn down into the lungs through tiny tubes until it reaches the alveoli. Here oxygen ***diffuses*** into the ***blood***, and carbon dioxide diffuses in the opposite direction.

You can find out about gas exchange using apparatus like that shown alongside. ***Limewater*** or bicarbonate indicator will change colour when carbon dioxide is present.

When you breathe in, air bubbles through tube A. When you breathe out, air bubbles through tube B.

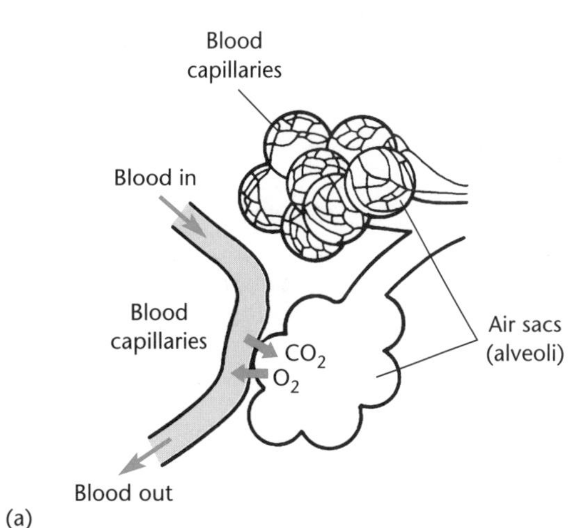

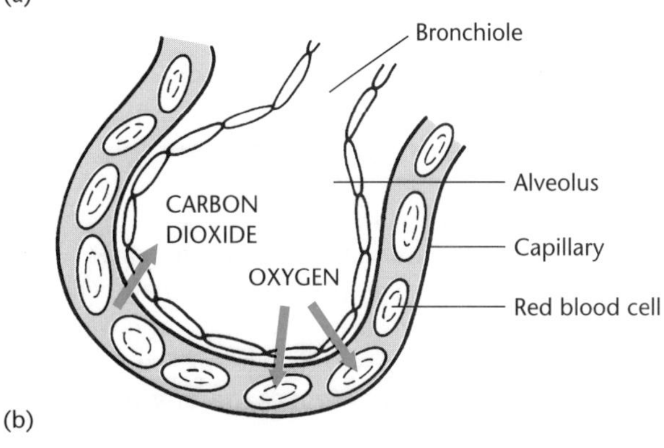

Gas exchange in humans
(a) Each alveolus is surrounded by capillaries
(b) One alveolus enlarged to show gas exchange

Scientists have used more precise apparatus to find out about the quantities of each gas in the air we breathe in and out. This proves that gas exchange is occurring.

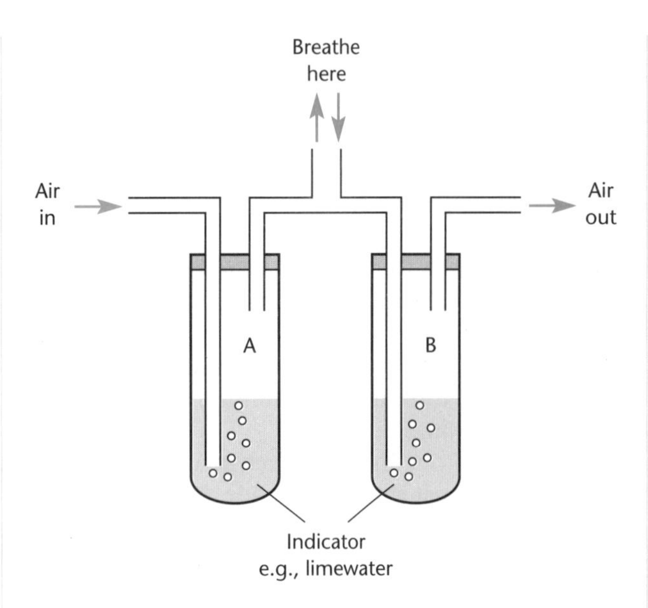

Apparatus used to compare inhaled and exhaled air

> CHECKPOINT
>
> Which indicator would you expect to change colour first, A or B? Why?

Table to compare inhaled and exhaled air

Gas	*Amount in air breathed in*	*Amount in air breathed out*
Oxygen	21.00%	17%
Carbon Dioxide	0.04%	4%
Nitrogen	78.00%	78%
Other gases, including water vapour	0.06%	1%

Gas exchange in other animals

Not all animals have lungs!

Fish have gills so that they can transfer gases between the water where they live and their cells.

Frogs and *earthworms* use the damp skin covering their whole body as a gas exchange surface.

Insects have a network of tubes running through their abdomen leading to a row of holes (spiracles) on the abdomen wall.

Gas exchange in plants

On the underside of each leaf are thousands of tiny holes called ***stomata***. Gases diffuse in and out through these holes, directly to the cells that use or make them.

Plants ***respire*** all the time (day and night), so they use up oxygen and make carbon dioxide. However, during the day they also ***photosynthesise***, so they have to take in extra carbon dioxide, and they release oxygen to the air.

✦ ***Breathing***

GENES

These are instructions about the features of an individual organism. They are important for two reasons:

1. *so that cells carry out their functions properly*
   e.g. red blood cells contain ***haemoglobin*** so that they can carry oxygen efficiently.
   e.g. cells lining the gut make ***enzymes*** to digest food properly.
   e.g. root hair cells in plants have long, thin, ***root hairs*** to absorb water and minerals efficiently.

2. *so that parents will produce offspring like themselves*
   When two gametes join at ***fertilization***, they are both carrying genes passed on from the parents inside their nuclei.
   The sperm cell contains 23 ***chromosomes*** carrying thousands of genes and the egg cell contains 23 chromosomes carrying thousands of genes. Together, these genes will provide a 'blue-print' for the new individual.
   The baby will not be exactly like either parent, but will inherit features from both.

Genes are carried on the chromosomes as part of the genetic code in the ***DNA***. In this way it is possible for huge amounts of genetic information (enough to make a human being) to be carried in a very small space (smaller than a full stop).

How do genes work?

Genes always work in pairs: you have inherited 23 chromosomes from your mum, and 23 chromosomes from your dad, so you have 23 pairs of chromosomes (46 altogether).

The genes making up a pair may be the same or different. For example, think about the gene for freckles – you will have inherited one of the following sets of genes from your parents:

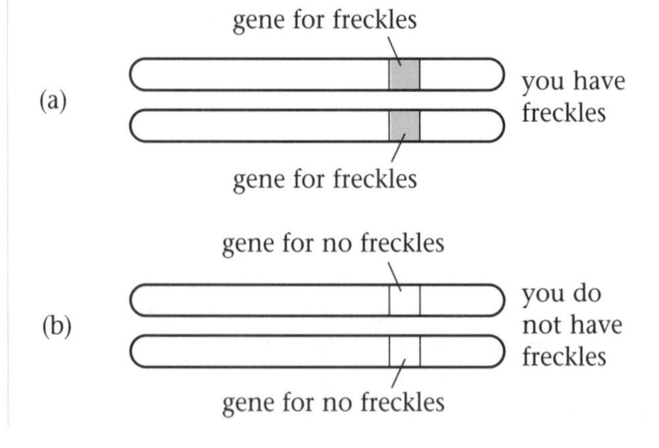

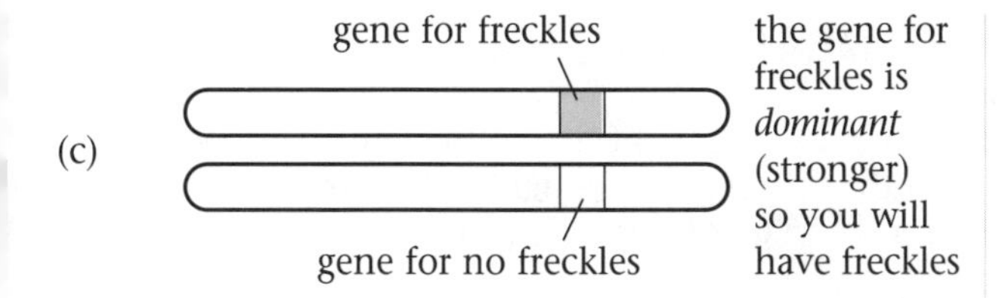

Biologists usually find it easier to use symbols instead of drawing pictures:

e.g. F is the symbol for gene for freckles
f is the symbol for gene for no freckles

A person could be FF – freckles
ff – no freckles
Ff – freckles (because the gene for freckles is dominant)

Variation

GENETIC DISEASES

These are diseases caused by faulty ***genes*** inherited from our parents. They cannot be caught from other people, and they cannot be passed on (except to our children).

Genetic diseases cannot be cured, but doctors may prescribe drugs to reduce the symptoms. Scientists are working on a process called *gene therapy* to replace a person's faulty genes with genes that work properly, but this is still at an early stage of research.

Examples of genetic diseases include:

cystic fibrosis
haemophilia
Huntington's disease
muscular dystrophy
sickle cell anaemia

Diseases

GEOTHERMAL ENERGY

Geothermal ***energy*** is the energy that is contained in the hot rocks below the surface of the ***Earth***. It is used by pumping water under pressure down to the hot rocks below the Earth's surface. The water returns heated, sometimes as steam, and the heat energy can be used as the alternative resource. Sometimes, drilling releases steam from underground water that has been heated. The original source of the energy is radioactive decay within the Earth's core. The process has been trialed in a number of areas, including Cornwall, in this country but it is only successful where the hot rocks are close to the surface. Countries such as New Zealand and Iceland have geothermal power stations already working.

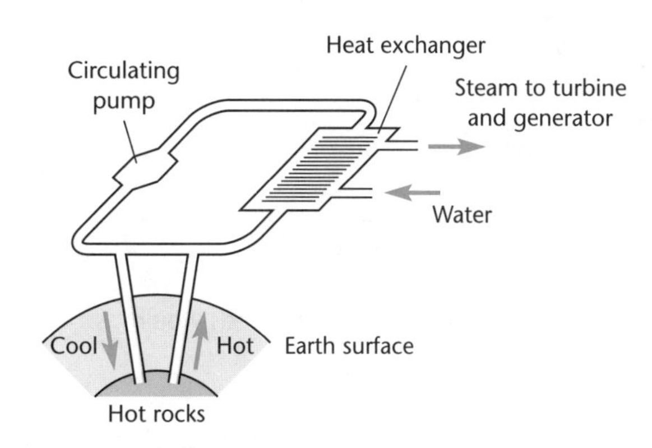

Geothermal power station

Sources of energy

GERMINATION

When a ***seed*** is released from the parent plant it is dormant (inactive), but as soon as conditions are right the seed will start to grow. This process is called germination, and there are four main stages:

1. the seed absorbs water, so the testa (seed coat) breaks,
2. the food stores inside the seed are broken down to provide energy (this is ***respiration***),
3. the energy is used to make the embryo plant grow,
4. the shoot and root start to develop. After a few days leaves will grow, so the new plant can start to ***photosynthesise*** and make its own food.

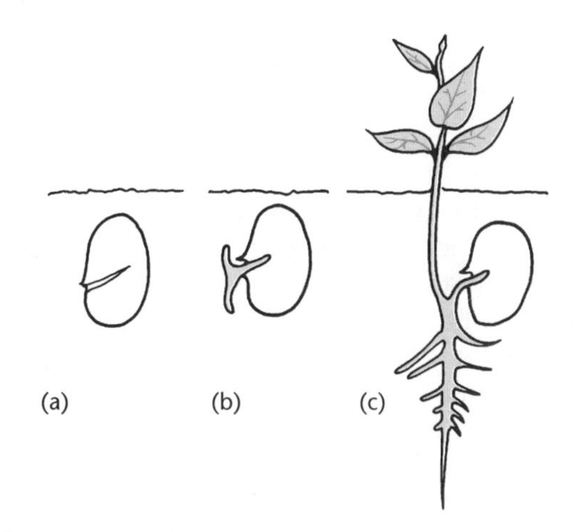

Stages in germination of a seed
(a) Seed coat breaks and food stores are broken down to provide energy
(b) Embryo plant starts to grow
(c) Root and shoot develop

Conditions needed for germination

All seeds must have three things before they start to germinate:

1. water,
2. air,
3. a suitable temperature.

CHECKPOINT

Can you predict which of these seeds would germinate?

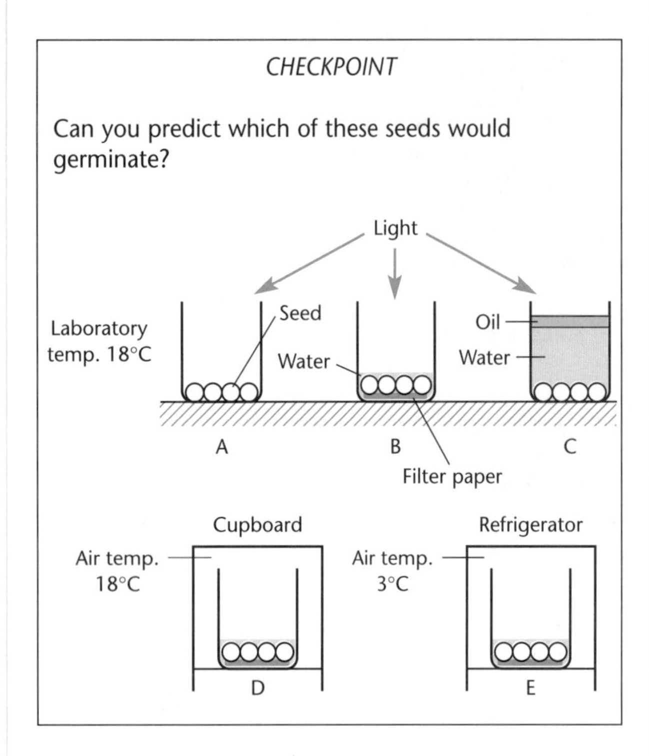

Germs

This is a general name for microbes that cause disease.

Bacteria, Fungi, Viruses

Glass

Glass-making is a very old process. The first glass was probably made in Ancient Egypt. It is a material used in the manufacture of a wide variety of materials. It is hard (but can also be brittle), it does not react with acids, and it is transparent.

Glass is made mainly from sand, which is heated to very high temperatures along with a few other ingredients. The *molten* mixture is then cooled down quite quickly in a mould or is blown into shape. The particles in the molten mixture do not have time to arrange themselves into a regular arrangement.

Glass is a very versatile material; for example by adding light-sensitive chemicals to the mixture the resulting glass can be used in light-reactive sunglasses. Glass has a range of optical properties (e.g. different focal lengths), and special lenses can be made from glass. Glass can also be coloured by adding other substances, for example gold is added to produce a deep red colour.

Global warming

Some scientists believe that the temperature of the Earth is rising. It is thought to be due to a build-up of ***carbon dioxide*** gas. This stops heat from the Sun escaping back into space, so it is sometimes called the ***greenhouse effect***. Although the rise in temperature is likely to be small (scientists cannot agree, but most think it will be less than 3°C on average), it could have serious effects, e.g. allowing polar ice to melt causing flooding, and causing tropical pests and diseases to spread.

Glucose

This is a type of sugar that is very important in living things.

- ***Plants*** make glucose when they ***photosynthesise***

$$\text{Carbon dioxide + Water} \xrightarrow{\text{light}} \text{Glucose + Oxygen.}$$

- ***Plants*** and ***animals*** use glucose as a fuel in ***respiration***

$$\text{Glucose + Oxygen} \longrightarrow \text{Energy + Carbon dioxide + water.}$$

Granite

Granite is an ***igneous rock***, which forms deep down in the ***Earth's*** crust. The magma takes a long time to cool down and the rock formed has large interlocking crystals.

Graphs

Whenever you get a set of results from an investigation or an experiment you should try to show them as a graph. This will usually make it easier to see what happened and you will be able to get clearer conclusions. Clear tables of results and a graph are usually needed to get good National Curriculum levels for an investigation.

The two things that you are plotting on the graph will be called ***variables***. You will have chosen one of these and then measured the second one at regular intervals. The first one is called the *independent variable* and it will be plotted across the bottom of your graph – on what is often called the x-axis. The second one is called the *dependent variable* and will be plotted on the y-axis.

For example, if you are measuring how a beaker of hot water cools, you might measure the temperature after every half minute. You have fixed the time intervals and this is the independent variable, which goes on the x-axis. You have found out how the temperature depended on time, so the temperature is the dependent variable and goes on the y-axis.

Try to do the following to get the best marks:

- Always use the largest possible scale. You will lose a lot of marks if your graph is always in one corner of the graph paper and is too small to be used accurately.
- Do make sure that your scales are uniform. The numbers should increase by the same amount across each square. You do *not* have to use the same scale on each axis.
- Make sure that the axes are labelled. You should write in what you have measured and what the units were, e.g. in a cooling curve the x-axis might be 'time in seconds' and the y-axis might be 'temperature in °C'.
- Make sure that you have plotted all the points as accurately as you can.
- If all the points are on a straight line, or very close to one, then fit the best straight line that you can as close as possible to all the points. This is called a *line of best fit*. The small distances from your points to the line are caused by errors in your measurements – the smaller the distances to the line, the better your results are – but all experiments have some error, so do not cheat!
- If all the points are on, or very close to, a curve then fit in the nearest *smooth* curve that you can. DO NOT join up the dots.
- If one point is a long way from your line then check that you have plotted it correctly. If you have plotted it correctly then ignore it when you put in your line of best fit. A point like this is called a *rogue result*. You should always try to correct a result like this if you can. Repeat it and see if you can get a better result that fits. The commonest cause of rogue results is writing down results carelessly or untidily – so take care, it saves you time and work.
- If a test question gives you axes and scales then you must use the ones that you are given.

✣ ***Investigation, Results***

Gravitational potential energy

This is the ***energy*** that is gained by an object which is lifted up against gravity. If you climb a ladder you will gain gravitational potential energy. If a car is driven up a hill, it will gain gravitational potential energy. The energy must have come from somewhere – the energy in your food or the ***chemical energy*** in the petrol of the car. The energy is released when the object falls – the car goes faster as it goes down the hill and the gravitational potential energy is turned into ***kinetic energy***

Remember: Lifting a bigger weight or lifting by a bigger distance will increase the energy stored.

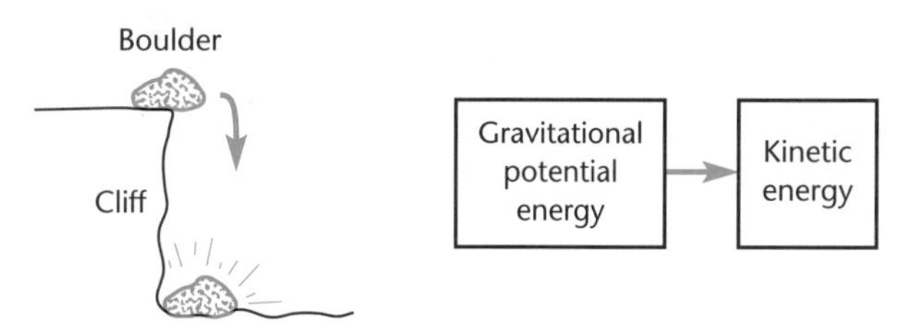

(a) Boulder starts with gravitational potential energy (b) The energy change as the boulder falls

Transforming the energy

✣ ***Energy***

Gravity

This is a ***force*** that acts between any two masses, pulling them together. The force gets bigger when the masses get bigger and rapidly gets smaller when the masses move apart. The force is only big enough to matter when at least one of the masses is very big – but it can then be very important.

It is this force between you and the Earth that is called ***weight***. Things fall downwards because they are attracted by the Earth.

It is the attraction between planets and the Sun that keeps the planets in orbit. It is the attraction between a satellite and the Earth that keeps it in orbit.

✣ ***Weight***

Greenhouse effect

This occurs if too much ***carbon dioxide*** builds up in the atmosphere. Heat from the Sun is trapped close to Earth, because it cannot escape back into space. The Earth then warms up – this is ***global warming***. The extra carbon dioxide is made by burning fossil fuels, e.g. coal, oil, gas, petrol. The situation is made worse by ***deforestation***, i.e., cutting down trees, because trees use up large amounts of carbon dioxide when they ***photosynthesise***

✣ ***Pollution***

Group

In the ***periodic table***, the vertical columns are called groups. Each group of ***elements*** has similar chemical properties. For example:

- Group one elements are also called the ***alkali*** metals.

- Group two elements are called the alkaline earth metals.
- Group seven elements are known as the ***halogens***
- Group zero, or eight, elements are called the ***noble gases***

✦ ***Periodic table***

GROWTH

This is an important ***life process***. Living things increase in size either by making new cells, or because the cells they have get bigger.

Some organisms, e.g. most plants, grow throughout their lives.

Other organisms, e.g. most animals, grow quickly in the early part of their lives, then stop growing.

To find the rate of growth, you could measure mass, length, height or girth (distance around an organism) over a period of time.

Habitat

This is the precise place where an organism lives,
e.g. on a rocky shore (***ecosystem***) there are many different habitats:

- rock pool habitat
- cliff face habitat
- sandy habitat

in a woodland (ecosystem) there are many different habitats:

- inside a rotted log
- in the tree canopy
- in the leaf litter

Organisms tend to stay in a particular part of their ecosystem (the habitat), because they are well adapted to living there. We call this ***adaptation to the environment***

Haematite

Haematite is an ***ore*** of iron that is red in colour and is mainly composed of iron oxide. It is sometimes called the kidney ore because of its appearance. Cave artists used powdered haematite as a pigment and red ochre is still used by artists today.

Haemoglobin

This is a red chemical found inside ***red blood cells***. It is important because it can combine with oxygen so that red blood cells carry oxygen very efficiently.

Haemoglobin contains iron (an important ***mineral***), so a lack of iron in the diet means that there are not enough red blood cells, and the person has anaemia.

Blood, Deficiency diseases

Halogens

Group seven elements of the ***periodic table*** are also called the halogens. The halogens are a family of non-metals and include fluorine (F), chlorine (Cl), bromine (Br) and iodine (I). Like any other family, they have many similar features:

- They are coloured elements and are very reactive.
- They are found as compounds in the Earth's crust and in sea water.
- They are found as small molecules of two atoms joined together. These are called diatomic molecules.
- They are all fairly toxic elements and need careful handling.

However, they are not all equally reactive. In fact, fluorine, at the top of the group, is much more reactive than iodine lower down in the group.

> *CHECKPOINT*
>
> Astatine is also a halogen. It is found at the bottom of the group, below Iodine. What state will it be in at room temperature?

The halogens

Symbol	*Formula*	*State at room temperature*	
F	F_2	○○ ○○ ○○	Gas
Cl	Cl_2	●● ●● ●●	Gas
Br	Br_2	●● ●● ●● ●● ●●	Liquid
I	I_2	●● ●● ●● ●● ●● ●●	Solid

Hard water

In some parts of the country you may find that it is very difficult to produce a good soapy lather. When you look inside the kettle you may also find that the heating element is coated in limescale. These are the tell-tale signs that the water supply is hard. Hard water contains calcium and magnesium ***ions***, which mainly get into the water when it runs over limestone rocks. These ions react with soaps and prevent them from being such effective cleansing agents, so that more soap must often be added than would be needed for soft water.

Harvey, William (1578–1657)

William Harvey, a British doctor, was the first to suggest that blood circulates around the body through a system of blood vessels; away from the heart in ***arteries*** towards the heart in ***veins***
Previously it was thought that the blood moved into and out of the ***heart*** in the same vessels, like a tide.

HEALTH

The World Health Organization has defined health as:

> a state of complete mental, physical and social well-being, and not merely the absence of disease.

In order to be healthy we must:

- have a body that is working efficiently,
- have a positive mental attitude to our lives and be able to relax and enjoy ourselves as well as coping with stress,
- look after ourselves properly, by eating a balanced diet and exercising, and not abusing drugs.

There are many factors involved in good health. There are some things it is difficult to avoid, e.g. catching a cold, but there are things we can all do to make sure our lives are generally healthy. For example,

eat a ***balanced diet***,
exercise regularly to keep fit,
get enough sleep,
make sure we have clean food and water,
make time for relaxation and things we enjoy,
avoid ***drugs***,
keep ourselves safe to avoid accidents,
make time to meet friends,
have health problems checked promptly.

Remember: Your body has to last for 60–70 years (or even longer). It makes sense to take care of it!

Disease, Fitness

HEART

This is the pump that keeps the ***blood*** moving through the ***circulatory system***. It has thick walls made of ***muscle***, and when these contract the blood is forced out of the heart through ***blood vessels***. The heart beats (contracts) about 70 times per minute when a person is resting, but faster if they are exercising. This is so that oxygen and food are delivered to the muscles more quickly, and waste products can be taken away.

The heart is divided into right and left sides by a wall (septum) running down the middle:

- the right side pumps blood without much oxygen (deoxygenated blood) to the lungs.
- the left side pumps blood carrying lots of oxygen (oxygenated blood) all around the body.

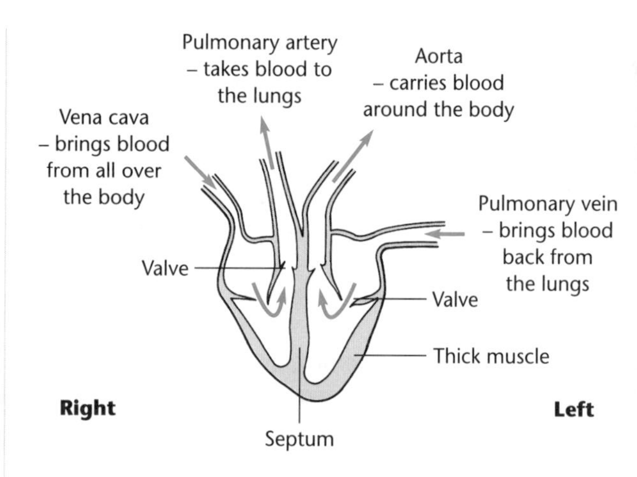

Structure of the heart

What can go wrong with the heart?

The heart muscle needs food and oxygen to stay alive, and to make the energy it needs to carry on beating.

Small blood vessels called *coronary vessels* run over the surface of the heart, bringing food and oxygen to the heart muscle, and carrying away waste products. If these vessels get blocked or damaged, the heart muscle does not get the nutrients it needs and can die. This is a *heart attack*.

Blockage or damage to the coronary vessels is more likely if the person:

- eats a high fat diet,
- is overweight,
- does not exercise regularly,
- smokes.

Arteries, Circulatory system, Fat, Pulse rate

HEAT ENERGY

Heat is another form of ***energy*** and can be measured in ***joules*** ***Solids***, ***liquids*** and ***gases*** are all made from tiny ***particles***. These particles are moving and have ***kinetic energy***. This and the attraction between the particles means that the materials all have internal energy. When we heat a substance we give it more energy and the particles move faster so that they have more energy. We notice this as a rise in ***temperature***. Remember that heat and temperature are connected but they are not the same thing.

Remember: Do not confuse heat and temperature!

Energy, Kinetic theory, Temperature

Heat transfer

There are three main methods by which heat is transferred from one place to another:

1. ***Conduction*** occurs in solids and liquids and is best in metals.
2. ***Convection*** occurs in liquids and gases (fluids) and not at all in solids.
3. ***Radiation*** is infra-red radiation and transfers heat well through gases but is absorbed by solids.

Conduction, Convection, Radiation

Herbivore

This is the second organism in a ***food chain***. It is an animal that eats plants.

Many insects are herbivores, e.g. bees, aphids, caterpillars (butterfly and moth larvae). Many mammals are herbivores, e.g. sheep, rabbits, cows.

A herbivore is also called a primary ***consumer***.

Hertz (Hz)

This is the unit for ***frequency***. A frequency of one event per second is called 1 hertz (1 Hz)

Frequency

Hooke, Robert (1635–1703)

Robert Hooke was the first person to realize that living things are made up of basic units called ***cells*** He used a microscope to observe and describe cells in cork.

Hormones

These are sometimes called 'chemical messengers'. They are chemicals made by glands in the body, which help to coordinate complicated processes. For example,

- the sex hormones (oestrogen and progesterone) are made in the ovary, and they coordinate the events of the ***menstrual cycle*** (ovulation, development of the uterus lining and menstruation).
- adrenaline is made in the adrenal glands, and it coordinates our response to danger, e.g. increased heart rate and breathing rate, increase in blood sugar level, pupils widen.

Pancreas, Puberty

Hydrochloric acid

This ***strong acid*** is found in your stomach to help digest food. It has the chemical formula HCl and is used in industry for cleaning metals and in the manufacture of printed circuit boards and dyes.

Hydroelectric power (HEP)

Hydroelectric power is used in many countries that have rivers large enough to provide the ***energy*** required. In this country, most of the rivers do not fall through enough height or have a large enough flow of water to produce large quantities of energy, but many are used on a smaller scale. The ***gravitational potential energy*** of the water is converted into ***kinetic energy*** as it falls and then into electrical energy by turbines. (See ***energy***.) The original source of the energy is the ***Sun***, which drives the water cycle by evaporating water from the sea. The advantage is that the energy source is not likely to run out (it is renewable), and it will not cause pollution of the air or create waste.

Disadvantages are that it might spoil the appearance of the environment and be costly to build.

Sources of energy

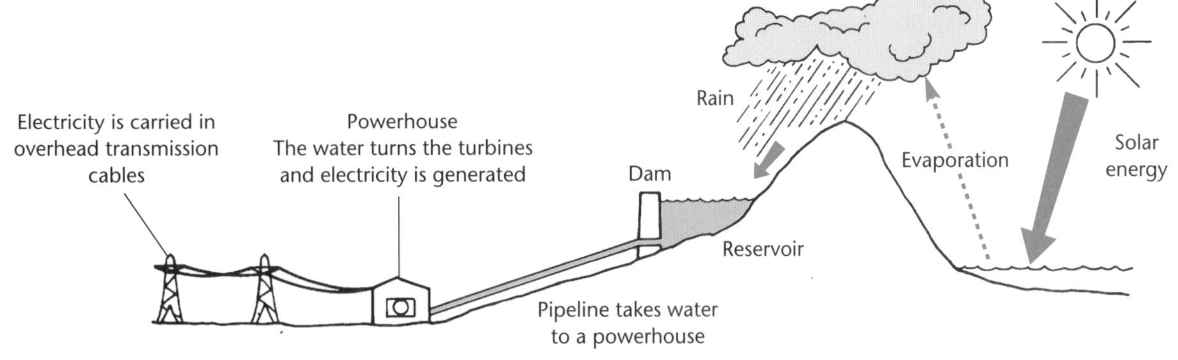

Hydroelectricity

Hydrogen

This is the smallest ***element*** in the ***periodic table*** Hydrogen is a gaseous element, with chemical symbol H. It is the simplest atom possible, containing one ***proton*** in its ***nucleus***. The reaction in which hydrogen atoms are fused together in the Sun, to make helium, is vital to us on Earth. The energy released in the reaction keeps us warm and provides light to the planet.

You may have produced hydrogen in the laboratory by reacting an acid with zinc metal. If you put a lighted splint over the mouth of the test tube, you hear a squeaky 'pop'. Hydrogen is a colourless and odourless gas, the presence of which can be tested for as follows.

Test for hydrogen

Hydrogen + Oxygen $\xrightarrow{\text{lighted splint}}$ Water + a squeaky pop!

Hydrogen is a very light element, but it also very explosive. It is used as a fuel in rockets and is being developed as a clean fuel in Sweden to replace the fossil fuels now being used. The product of burning hydrogen is water.

Hygiene

This is an important part of avoiding ***infectious diseases***. It means keeping things clean to avoid passing on the microbes that cause disease, and includes all of the following:

- washing ourselves and our clothes regularly,
- always washing our hands after using the toilet, and before preparing food,
- storing and preparing food carefully, and keeping kitchens and utensils, e.g. knives, chopping boards, clean,
- regularly vacuuming and dusting, particularly if there are pets in the house,
- keeping pets' feeding bowls separate from human utensils,
- covering food and keeping flies away from it,
- disposing of rubbish quickly,
- making sure that babies' bottles are sterilized properly, and that their toys and surroundings are clean.

Hypothesis

When you do an ***investigation*** you will begin with a hypothesis. This is what you think will happen and your investigation is to see whether you are right.

Begin by thinking of all the things that might make a difference if you changed them. These are the ***variables*** It will help you later if you list them. Choose one that you think will be interesting to investigate. You will get better marks if you pick one that can be changed continuously rather than in separate steps, e.g. if you choose to change the mass or thickness of something you can use whatever values you like. If you choose to change the colour of something or use a different metal then you are limited to changing in fixed steps and your conclusions might be harder to work out.

When you have picked one, think carefully about *what* will happen and *why*. Write down your hypothesis. It often helps to start with 'I think that ...'.

You need to be as exact as you can with your hypothesis. Do not just say that something will change. You will be expected to say whether your independent variable getting bigger will make the dependent variable get bigger or smaller.

If doubling one variable also doubles the other and so on, then you can say that they are *directly proportional*.

If doubling one variable makes the other variable halve then they are *inversely proportional*.

Follow your hypothesis with reasons that are as *scientific* as possible. You will probably need to look for information about the thing that you are investigating. Use books like this one and those in a library. The reasons are important, so do not make them too short, and plan what you write so that what you are saying is clear.

Graph, Investigation, Results

Igneous rocks

Igneous rocks come from the area under the ***Earth***'s crust called the mantle. When the magma from the mantle is forced nearer the surface, it becomes a liquid. If it flows onto the surface it is called lava. Lava flows out of volcanoes and forms igneous rocks such as pumice and obsidian. If the magma solidifies deep in the Earth's crust, the igneous rock formed has large crystals, e.g. granite. Igneous rocks that solidify near the surface have very small crystals, e.g. basalt.

Earth

Immiscible

When two liquids such as oil and water are added together they do not mix but rather separate into two layers. The liquids are then said to be immiscible.

Emulsion

Immune system

This is the name given to the parts of the body that protect us from ***infectious diseases***. It mainly refers to the ***white blood cells***, which make ***antibodies*** to destroy microbes. (See Figure on p. 8.)

This process can be encouraged by ***vaccination***.

Defence against disease

Immunity

This means that a person is protected from a particular ***infectious disease*** because they have ***antibodies*** to destroy the microbes that cause it. This could be because:

- they have been vaccinated against the disease,
- they have already had the disease,
- they have taken in 'ready-made' antibodies – babies do this when they are breast feeding, because breast milk contains antibodies made by the mother.

Defence against disease, Immune system, Vaccination

Indicator

This is a liquid that can change colour and thereby indicate if something is an ***acid*** or an ***alkali***. ***Litmus*** is a commonly used indicator and is made from a plant extract. Phenolphthalein is used to indicate alkalis because it is pink when it is alkaline and colourless in acid or neutral substances. Litmus and phenolphthalein are *narrow* range indicators.

Indicator	*In acid*	*In alkali*	*In water (neutral)*
litmus	red	blue	purple
phenolphthalein	colourless	pink	colourless

Universal indicator is a mixture of dyes and is known as a *full range* indicator, because it can indicate substances from pH 1 to 14.

- If a solution turns the Universal indicator light green, then it is neutral and has a pH of 7.
- If a solution turns the Universal indicator yellow, then it is a weak acid and has a pH of 5 or 6.
- If a solution turns the Universal indicator purple, then it is a strong alkali, pH 14.

pH scale

Inert

Inert is another word for inactive and is often used to describe the ***elements*** in group 8 of the ***periodic table***, the noble gases.

Infectious diseases

These are diseases caused by microbes (***bacteria viruses*** and ***fungi***). They can be caught from other people, and passed on by infected people, so we say they are contagious.

They can often be treated with ***antibiotics*** (to kill bacteria), or anti-fungal drugs. Anti-viral drugs are more rare, and often have bad side effects.

When microbes causing infectious diseases enter the body, our ***white blood cells*** start to make ***antibodies*** to destroy them. Usually the infection is overcome within a couple of weeks, although some infectious diseases can have serious effects and even cause death. ***Vaccination*** is a way of avoiding infectious diseases.

How are infectious diseases transmitted?

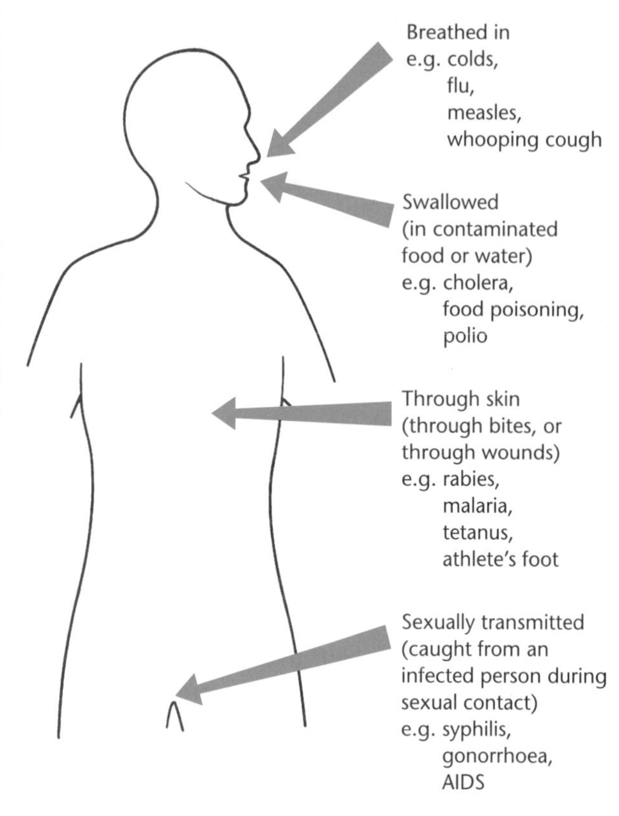

Transmission of diseases

✣ ***Defence against disease, Disease, Immune system, Immunity***

INFRA-RED RADIATION

These ***waves*** are part of the electromagnetic spectrum and are emitted by all hot things. The ***wavelengths*** that are emitted are too long for us to see but do get shorter as the ***temperature*** gets higher. (So hot objects eventually do emit some waves that we can see and glow 'red hot'.) The waves are easily absorbed and their energy becomes heat energy. An electric fire works by having a red-hot element that sends out a lot of infra-red radiation. This can be reflected forward by the metal reflector behind the element and will turn back into heat when it is absorbed by walls, furniture, people, etc.

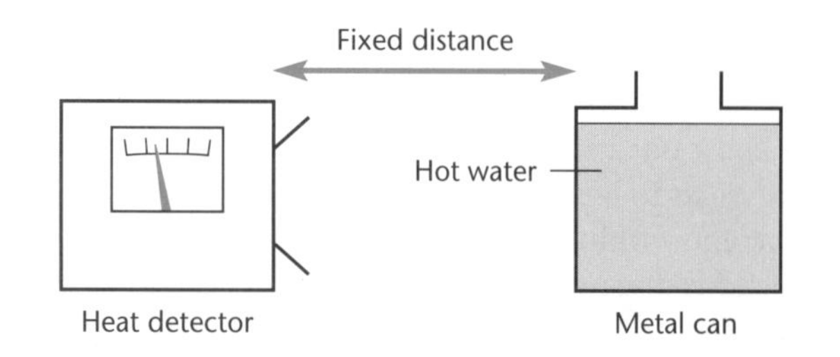

Measuring the radiation

As all objects radiate infra-red at a wavelength dependent on temperature, you can use the infra-red to photograph or detect them. Infra-red detectors are used in night sights for guns and to find people under collapsed buildings after earthquakes or explosions.

The apparatus in the figure below shows the effect of the type of surface on the radiation that is emitted. The metal can is filled with hot water and has four sides that are matt black, shiny black, white and polished metal. These will all be at the same temperature because the can is a good ***conductor***. The radiation (infra-red) detector is pointed at each surface in turn and from the same distance each time to make it a ***fair test***. It shows that the surfaces all radiate heat but that the dull black is best, followed by the shiny black. The polished surface emits very little radiation. If you do not have a radiation detector you can still show the same results by using a set of metal beakers. Paint their outsides in the different colours and finishes that you need and then put the same amount of hot water into each one. Using a stopwatch and a thermometer find the time for each one to cool through the same temperature fall – from 80°C to 60°C may be suitable. The ones that cool fastest are radiating heat fastest. Take care to do a fair test and change only the surface. Marathon runners may be protected by metal foil blankets after the race to prevent them losing more body heat. We use matt black when we paint engines or transistor heat sinks so that they radiate heat as fast as possible. An air-cooled engine, such as a motor cycle engine, will have its cylinders black on the outside to get rid of heat as fast as possible. Coating the surface with shiny chromium plate can cause damage through overheating if the engine is not designed for it. The engine will also have a lot of fins to increase the surface area – this will be able to radiate more heat as well as being in contact with more cool air when the machine is moving.

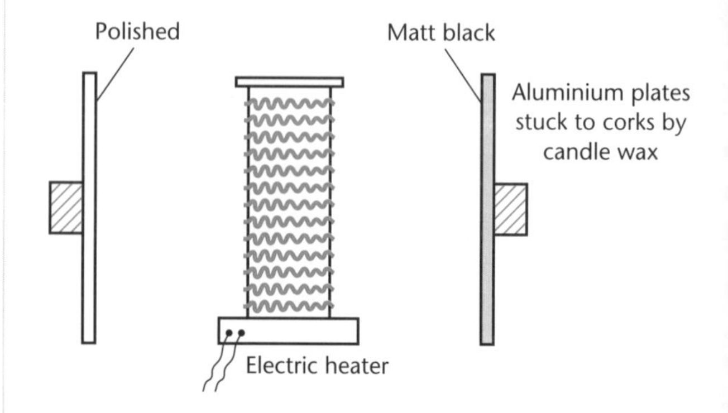

Infra-red radiation

The effect of the surface on the absorption of heat can also be checked using the simple apparatus shown above. The two metal plates are identical pieces of aluminium, with a different surface treatment, and are the same distance from the heater.

The surface that absorbs the heat best will fall off its cork first as the wax melts. This can be done with a variety of surfaces and the matt black surface is the best absorber. Polished surfaces act as a mirror and reflect the waves so that they remain cool.

Remember: The best absorbers are also the best radiators!

Buildings in hot countries are often painted white and have their roofs painted with silver paint so that they absorb less heat and stay cool in the hot sun. Satellites often have a protective layer of metal foil to reflect away radiation from the sun and prevent overheating.

Conduction, Convection, Spectrum, (electromagnetic), Vacuum flask

INSOLUBLE

Cannot be dissolved.

INSULATOR

Electrical

An insulator is a material that does not let electric ***current*** flow though it easily. Most non-metals are insulators. The exception is ***carbon***. Plastics are usually good insulators.

Insulators do not conduct electricity because they don't have free *electrons* to carry the charge along.

Heat

An insulator is a material that does not let ***heat energy*** flow through it easily. Most non-metals are insulators. Plastics are usually good insulators.

All the gases are poor conductors because their ***particles*** are so far apart. If they are trapped in layers or small pockets by solid insulators then the combination is a very good insulator. This idea is used in insulating houses and in layers of clothing.

Non-metals will usually be insulators because they do not have 'free' electrons to carry the heat energy through the material. Plastics are also good insulators because their molecules are very large and interweaved, and so cannot transmit heat energy very easily by vibration.

Gases are poor conductors of heat because of the spaces between the particles, which stops the ***kinetic energy*** being passed from one particle to another. If the gas is kept in small pockets or thin layers it will not be able to transfer heat by ***convection*** and will produce a good insulator. Examples are plastic foams that set solid and contain pockets or bubbles of carbon dioxide or air. These are used in the walls of fridges and on hot water cylinders. Layers of clothing trap layers of air between them and two thin layers are often warmer than one thick one. Roof insulation works in the same way, preventing heat loss from the warm air, which rises to a layer under the ceiling as a part of the convection process. Mineral fibres between the bricks of a cavity wall stop heat loss through the walls of a house and carpets on the floors may also prevent some heat loss.

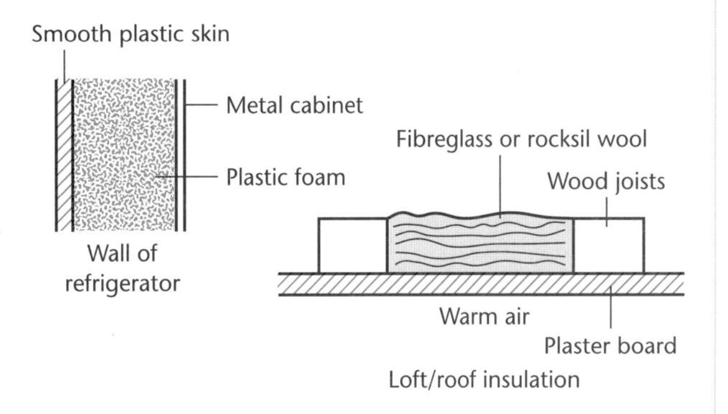

Using insulation

Clothing for cold weather and 'lagging' on water pipes also trap air to make good insulation.

> *CHECKPOINT*
>
> Why are gases poor conductors?
>
> What must you do to make a gas into a good insulator?
>
> Name four ways of insulating your house.

Conductor, Conduction of heat, Convection, Current

INTESTINE

This is the largest part of the ***digestive system***. It is divided into two main areas: the small intestine and the large intestine.

Small intestine

This is a long, narrow part of the gut, made up of the duodenum and ileum. Here, food is mixed with ***enzymes*** made by the ***pancreas*** and the gut wall, and proteins, carbohydrates and fats are digested. In the ileum, the digested food is absorbed into the blood. The wall of the ileum is covered in finger-like spikes called ***villi***. These give it a large surface area, so ***absorption*** is very efficient. The walls of the ileum contain lots of blood vessels ready to pick up the digested food. This is taken directly to the ***liver*** to be processed.

Large intestine

This is the wider part of the gut between the appendix and the anus. The colon and rectum are both parts of the large intestine. Once food reaches this part of the gut, all useful substances have been digested and absorbed, so only the ***faeces*** remain inside the gut. As they pass through the large intestine, water is absorbed. Faeces are stored in the rectum before being pushed out of the body at the anus.

INVERTEBRATES

These are ***animals*** that do not have an internal ***skeleton***

Some are soft bodied, e.g. earthworms. Some have a shell, e.g. snails. Some have a hard, external skeleton, e.g. insects.

Over 90 per cent of all animals are invertebrates. Invertebrates are usually classified in eight main groups:

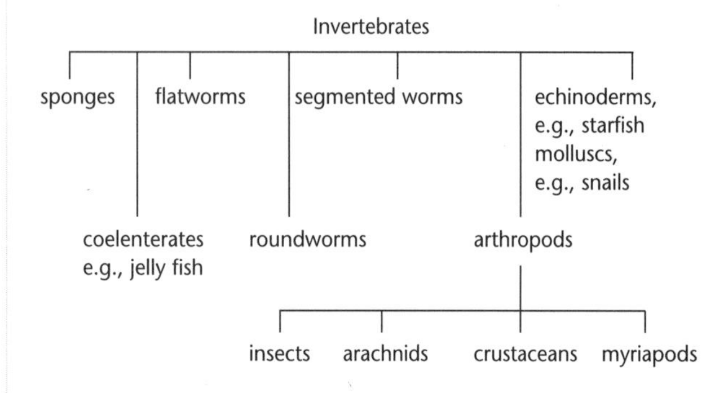

We will look at some of these groups in more detail.

Segmented worms, e.g. earthworms:

- soft body,
- body is divided into segments,
- no legs,
- the body surface is damp.

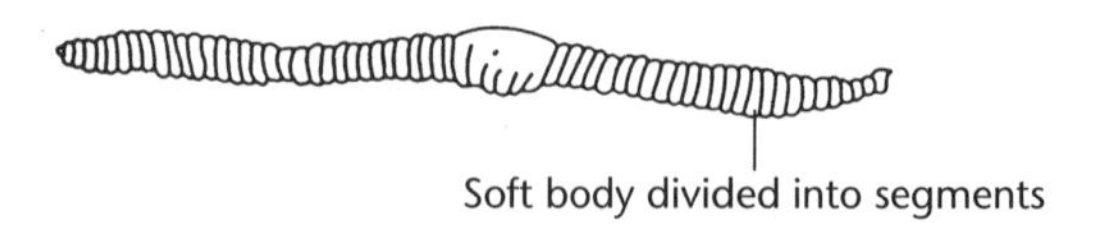

Insects, e.g. housefly, bee, mosquito:

- body has a hard covering (exoskeleton),
- body has three parts (head, thorax and abdomen),
- three pairs of legs,
- usually two pairs of wings,
- one pair of antennae.

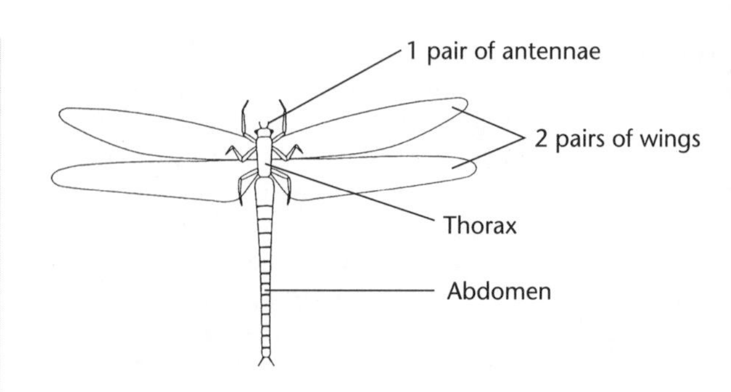

Some insects are very useful to humans, e.g. because they pollinate plants, but others cause ***disease***

Crustaceans, e.g. woodlice, crabs, shrimps:

- body has a hard covering (exoskeleton),
- many legs or 'leg-like structures',
- two pairs of antennae.

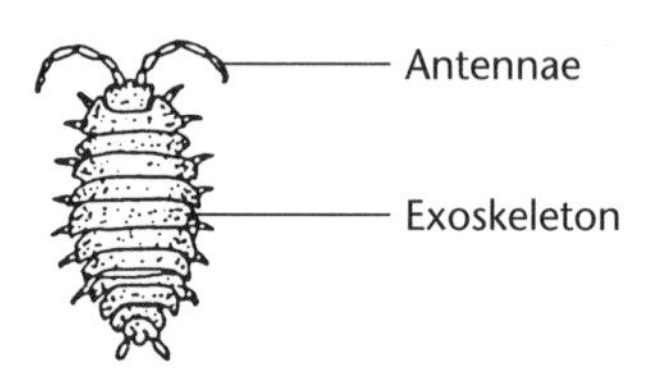

Arachnids, e.g. garden spider, mites, ticks:

- body has a hard covering (exoskeleton),
- four pairs of legs,
- no antennae.

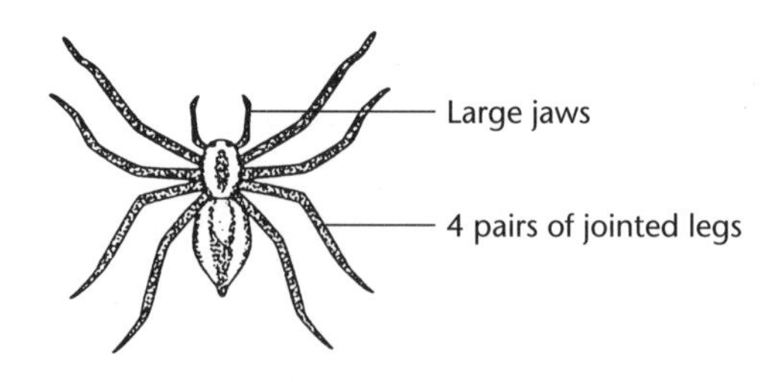

Myriapods, e.g. centipede, millipede:

- body has a hard covering (exoskeleton),
- body is divided into many segments,
- one or two pairs of legs on each segment,
- one pair of antennae.

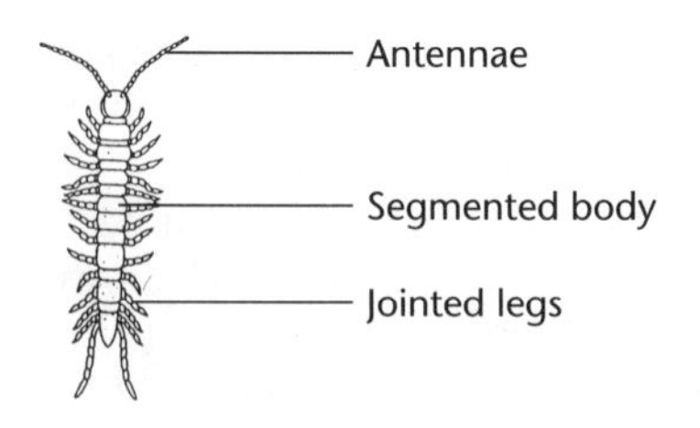

Molluscs, e.g. snails, limpets, mussels:

- soft body,
- no legs,
- body may be protected by one or two shells.

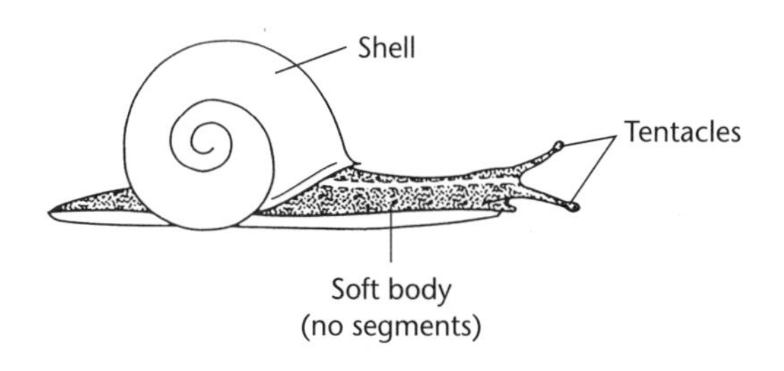

Classification

Investigation

As a part of your assessment at the end of year nine you must have done some investigations and your teachers will have recorded the results when you did them. They go together with your SAT result to give your National Curriculum level in Science.

In the first stage you will decide *what* you are going to investigate, make predictions (probably as a ***hypothesis***) and design the ***fair test*** that you are going to do.

In the second stage you will carry out your tests, making careful measurements and repeating things when you need to do so. You will put all of your ***results*** in a neat and tidy table and write carefully about what you did.

Next you should draw a ***graph*** of the results if you can and look for patterns and trends in the results. Use this information to draw ***conclusions*** and try to explain your results with scientific reasons.

Finally do an ***evaluation*** of your investigation. Look through your experiment again and see if you really did get good clear evidence. Look at any odd results and explain how they might have happened and then see if you can suggest ways in which the investigation might have been improved.

It is important that you check that you have included everything before you hand in the work to be marked. Do make sure that you have said what makes your tests fair and that you have not accidentally left out something that you did!

Appendix on p. 173, Conclusion, Fair test, Graph, Hypothesis, Results, Variable

Ion

An ion is a charged particle. ***Atoms*** such as sodium or chlorine do not have a charge. They have an equal number of positive ***protons*** and negative ***electrons*** However, sodium prefers to give away the spare electron in its outer electron orbit. When this happens it now has more positive charges (protons) than negative electrons and becomes a *positive ion.* Chlorine, on the other hand, prefers to take in extra electrons and so has more negative electrons than positive charges (protons). It becomes a *negative ion.*

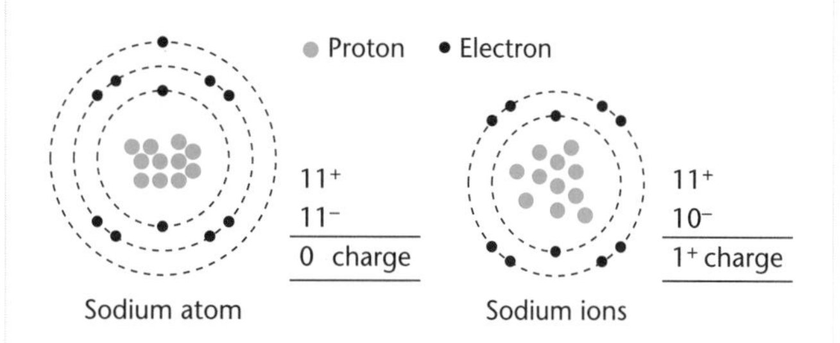

Ions

Periodic table

Jenner, Edward (1747–1823)

Edward Jenner was the first western doctor to safely ***vaccinate*** a patient against a disease. Smallpox was a serious disease, which often caused death. Jenner deliberately infected a boy with cowpox, and when the boy had recovered, he infected him with smallpox. The boy did not become ill, because the cowpox had made him immune to smallpox – we know now that his white blood cells had made ***antibodies*** to fight the disease.

Joints

A joint is part of the skeleton where two or more bones meet, e.g. elbow joint, knee joint. Joints are important because they allow the skeleton to move.

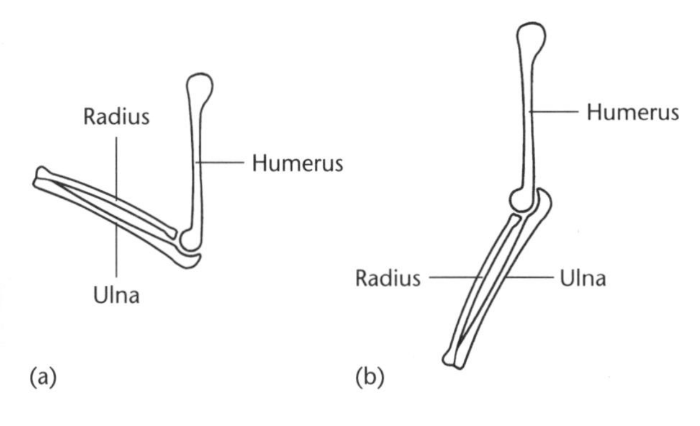

The elbow joint: (a) bent, (b) straight

There are two main types of joint:

1. Fixed joints, where bones are held tightly together and cannot move. These are found in the skull.
2. Movable joints, where bones can move when they are pulled by ***muscles***.

Some movable joints can only move in one direction. They are called hinge joints, e.g. knee, elbow, finger.

Some movable joints can move in several directions. They are called ball and socket joints, e.g. hip, shoulder.

The ends of the bones inside a joint are covered in a smooth, slippery material called ***cartilage***. This reduces friction and allows the bones to move smoothly. There is an oily liquid called ***synovial fluid*** that lubricates the joint. Fibres called ***ligaments*** hold the bones in place.

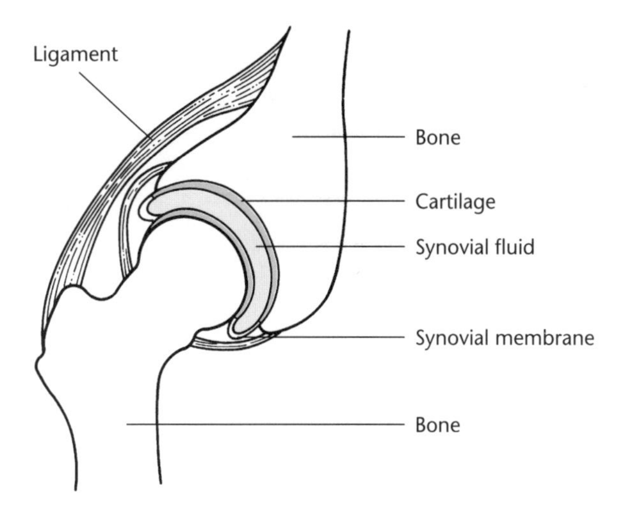

Inside a movable joint

Sometimes the ends of a bone become damaged and rub together. This restricts movement, and is very painful. It happens mainly in older people, and in weight-bearing joints, e.g. hip, due to natural wear and tear.

The ends of the bones can be replaced by a synthetic material, e.g. metal or plastic, so that the joint can work properly again. This is called a replacement joint, or artificial joint.

✣ ***Bones, Movement, Muscles, Skeleton***

Joule

A joule is an exact amount of ***energy***.

As ***work*** is done when the same amount of energy is changed from one form to another, it is also the unit for work. The symbol for one joule is J.

> *Remember:* All *the different forms of energy will be measured in joules.*

The joule is too small for many practical measurements and the kilojoule is often used instead (1,000 J = 1 kJ). Electricity is measured in ***kilowatt hours*** because a larger unit is needed.

✣ ***Energy, Joulemeter***

Joulemeter

This is a meter for measuring ***electrical energy***. It is connected between the mains and the appliance that you are testing. Usually there is a small light on it that flashes each time 100 J of energy goes through it. All you have to do is count the flashes and multiply by 100. If the light is flashing too quickly there is often a switch to make the light flash after each 1,000 J instead.

✣ ***Energy, Joule***

Kelvin

This is a unit on a special ***temperature scale*** that starts at ***absolute zero***. It is the same size as 1°C. Its symbol is K. Remember that it is *not* called a degree. Since absolute zero is at –273°C you can change a temperature in °C into kelvin by adding 273.

For example:

- Water freezes at 0°C, which is 273 K and boils at 100°C, which is 373 K.
- Body temperature is 37°C, which is 310 K.

> *CHECKPOINT*
>
> 1. Convert 127°C to kelvin
> 2. Convert 1,000 K to °C.

Temperature, Temperature scale

Keys

These are used to help biologists identify living things. There are hundreds of thousands of different types of living things on Earth, so nobody could possibly remember all their names. A key is a table or chart to help you with identification. While using the key, you must look at the animal or plant very carefully.

There are two main types of keys:

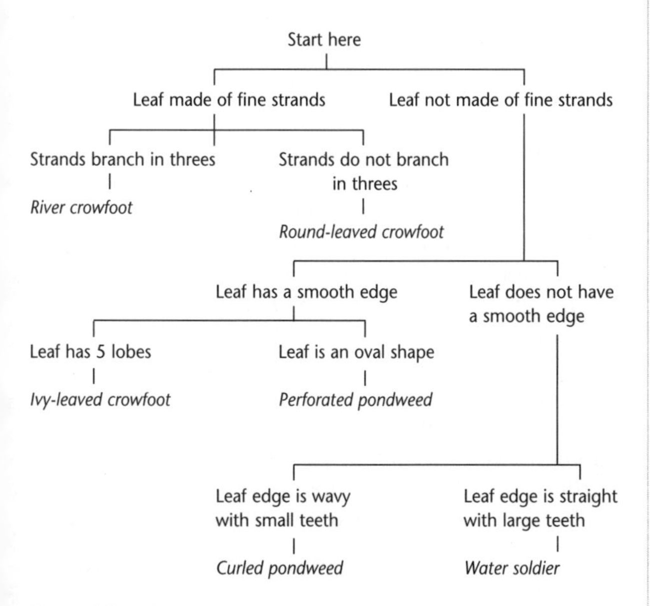

Branching key

Branching key

This is set out as a flowchart. At each stage there is a simple question, and only one of the answers can be correct. See above.

Number key

This is set out as a list of questions. For each question there is a simple choice, and an instruction about what to do next.

1.	(a) Leaf has many fine strands	– go to number 2
	(b) Leaf has a flat blade	– go to number 3
2.	(a) Strands branch into threes	*River crowfoot*
	(b) Strands branch without a set pattern	*Round-leaved crowfoot*
3.	(a) Leaf has a toothed edge	– go to number 4
	(b) Leaf has a smooth edge	– go to number 5
4.	(a) Leaf is flat with sharp teeth	*Water soldier*
	(b) Leaf is wavy with very small teeth	*Curled pondweed*
5.	(a) Leaf has no lobes (oval shapes)	*Perforated pondweed*
	(b) Leaf has five lobes	*Ivy-leaved crowfoot*

> *CHECKPOINT*
>
> Use the keys to identify the plants in the box.

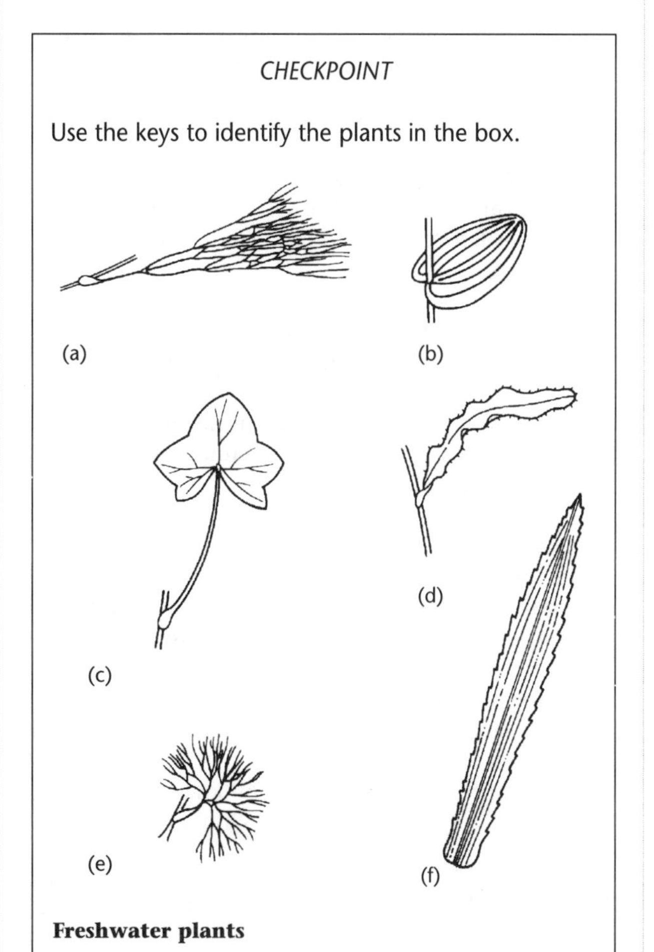

Freshwater plants

Kidney

Mammals have two kidneys. They filter the blood to remove *urea*, a very poisonous waste substance. They also remove excess salts and water, so that fluid balance in the body is right. *Urine* is made by the kidneys – it contains urea, salts and water. The kidneys are excretory organs, because they get rid of waste substances.

If the kidneys stop working properly, urea builds up and the person becomes ill. They will need to have kidney dialysis to remove the urea from the blood, and may have a kidney transplant.

Kilowatt hour (kWh)

This is the unit that we use to measure the electrical *energy* for our electricity bills. The *joule* is the unit for energy but it is so small that the numbers would be far too large to be sensible. (It takes 4,200 joules to raise the temperature of 1 kg of water by 1°C.) The kilowatt hour is a better size and this is the energy used when a power of 1kW is used for one hour. On my last electricity bill, 1 kWh of electricity cost 7p. To find the cost of using electricity, work out the number of kWh by multiplying the power in kW by the time in hours. Then multiply the answer by the cost per unit. Remember to change numbers of watts to kilowatts by dividing by 1,000.

Energy in kWh = Power in kW × Time in hours

For example :

Mr Speed left the computer system at work switched on by mistake. The system is rated at 400 W and was left on for 10 hours. What did this cost at 7p per unit?

number of kWh = $0.4 \times 10 = 4$
cost = units × cost per unit = $4 \times 7 = 28$p

You can add together the power ratings for appliances that are all on for the same time and find the cost in one calculation.

For example:

A school uses 120 lights for an average of 6 hours each day. If each light is rated at 100 W, and a unit of electricity costs 7p, what does this cost for a week?

number of units = $0.100 \times 120 \times 6 \times 5 = 360$
{only 5 days per week!}

cost = units × cost per unit = $360 \times 7 =$
2520p = £25.20

Energy, Power

Kinetic energy

Kinetic energy is *energy* that an object has because it is moving.

An object that has more *mass* will have more energy at the same speed than one with a smaller mass. The *speed* is even more important. The kinetic energy increases rapidly with speed and doubling the speed will mean four times as much kinetic energy.

A car can do more damage in a crash if it is being driven faster because it has more kinetic energy and a bigger stopping distance. This is the reason for the safety poster that says 'speed kills'.

A bike will have less energy than a car at the same speed because it has less mass – so there will be less energy to turn to heat in its brakes when you stop.

Heavy wheels called flywheels spin quickly and store a lot of kinetic energy.

400 m/s

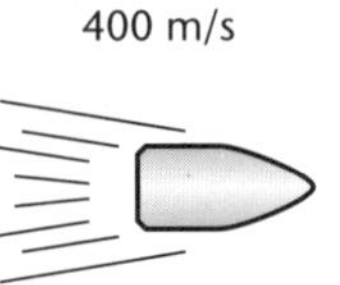

(a) A bullet has a lot of kinetic energy because of its speed

25 000Kg

(b) A lorry has a lot of kinetic energy because of its large mass

Some kinetic energy

CHECKPOINT

Objects that are ________ have kinetic energy. Increasing ________ or ________ will also increase kinetic energy, but increasing __________ has the biggest effect.

Energy

Kinetic theory

When you warm up an ice cube, it *melts*. If you walk past a coffee shop you can smell the coffee outside the shop. When you get out of a swimming pool you feel cold, even if it is quite a warm day. All these things can be explained by the kinetic theory.

The kinetic theory says that matter is made up of tiny *particles* that move all the time. The particles are often called *atoms* or *molecules*. It is very difficult to imagine just how small these particles are because nobody has actually seen them. There are thought to be as many as 50,000,000,000,000,000,000 particles in a thimbleful of air.

The key points of the kinetic theory are as follows:

- All matter is made up of tiny, invisible, moving particles.

- These particles move all the time. The higher the temperature, the faster they move.
- Heavier particles move more slowly than light ones at the same temperature.

Changing states

KINGDOMS

When biologists classify (sort out) living things, they put them into groups. First they must decide which kingdom they belong to. There are five kingdoms:

Animals
Plants
Fungi
Monera (bacteria)
Protoctists (simple single-celled organisms)

Classification

KOCH, ROBERT (1843–1910)

Robert Koch was a German scientist who identified which types of ***bacteria*** were responsible for causing particular diseases. He also developed techniques for growing and studying bacteria e.g. using nutrient agar to grow them, and dyes to stain them so they could be seen clearly under the microscope.

Lavoisier, Antoine Laurent (1743–1794)

In the eighteenth century, combustion was called the phlogiston theory. According to this theory, when combustion took place the substance that was burning lost phlogiston in the flame. Lavoisier did not believe this to be true and set about to show that substances actually *gained* mass when they burned rather than lost mass. At the same time, the English chemist, Joseph Priestly, was heating things too. Both men are said to have been involved in the discovery of oxygen.

Lavoisier was a very wealthy landowner and also a politician. He was guillotined during the French Revolution.

Leaf

Leaves are usually thin and flat so that they have a large surface area to absorb light. They are green because many leaf cells contain ***chloroplasts***. The main function of the leaf is ***photosynthesis*** (making sugar). The underside of the leaf contains thousands of tiny holes called ***stomata***, to let gases in and out.

The leaf also contains veins to carry water to the leaf cells, and sugars away.

Levers

A lever is a ***machine*** that we use to change the size of a ***force***.

In most cases, the force is made bigger and the lever is a *force multiplier*.

The force that is put in is called the *effort* and the force that is produced acts against the force called the *load*. Both of these forces act on something that is able to turn on a pivot.

There are three general types of lever that depend on exactly where the effort and the load are placed.

Type 1

If the effort and load are on opposite sides of the pivot and the effort is a bigger distance from the pivot than the load then the lever is a useful force multiplier. An example is the crowbar, which is often used to move large or heavy objects.

If the distance from the effort to the pivot is twice the distance from the load to the pivot then the effort can lift a load that is twice as big. In a real

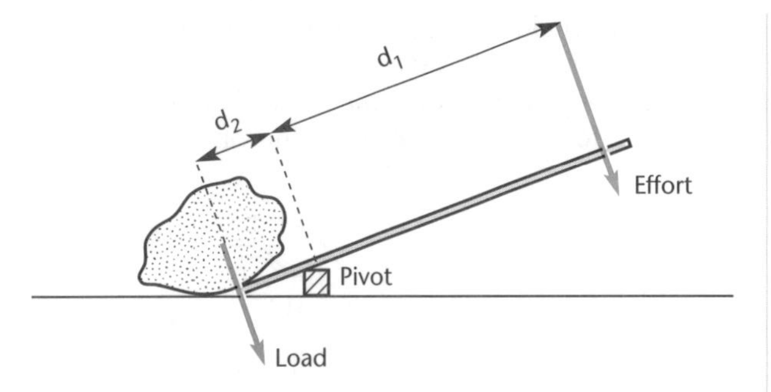

The crowbar

case, the distance from effort to pivot may be at least ten times as big as the load to pivot distance and the machine is multiplying your effort force by ten. The force made can move quite heavy objects.

Scissors and pliers are pairs of this first type of lever on the same pivot.

> *Remember: You can never create energy. You have made a bigger force but it will move the object by a correspondingly smaller distance. You have not got 'something for nothing'!*

Type 2

Sometimes the forces are both on the same side of the pivot but the effort is still a bigger distance from the pivot than the load. This will also be a force multiplier in exactly the same way as the first set of levers.

An example of this is the wheelbarrow where the load in the carrier and the effort on the handles are both on the same side of the axle of the wheel.

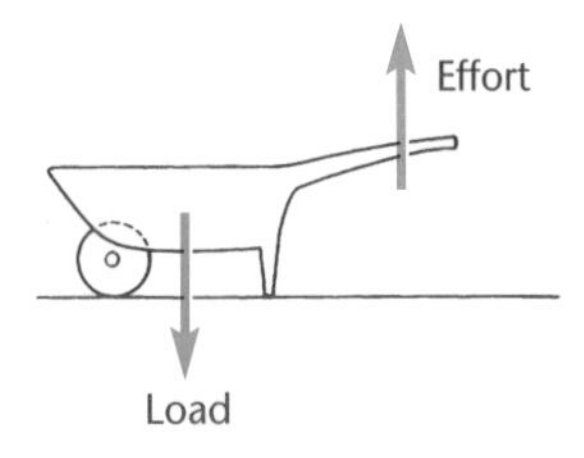

The wheelbarrow

To make the effort smaller you should move the load as close as possible to the axle so that the distance to the effort is as much bigger than the distance to the load as it can be.

The arms of a pair of nut crackers would be two of this type of lever on the same pivot.

Type 3

The third type has the effort and the load on the same side of the pivot but with the effort closer to the

pivot than the load. This means that the effort will be bigger than the load. A system like this does have some uses where it is convenient but do remember that the effort force has not been increased.

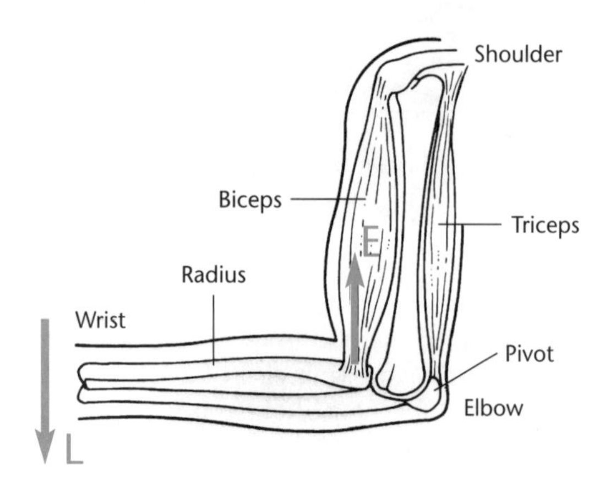

The forearm

When you use your biceps muscle to move your forearm you will use this type of lever. This is why you cannot hold a heavy weight outwards in your hand for very long – the effort supplied by the muscle has to be a lot larger than the weight!

A pair of tweezers or tongs is made from two of these levers acting on the same pivot.

It is possible to work out the forces on levers by using the ***Principle of Moments***. Use the distances from the pivot to the load and the effort when the forces are just balanced. You will then know that the system will move if the effort is increased by even a tiny amount.

If the distance from the effort to the pivot is d_1 and the distance from the load to the pivot is d_2 then

$$\text{Effort} \times d_1 = \text{Load} \times d_2$$

This means that

$$\frac{\text{load}}{\text{effort}} = \frac{d_1}{d_2}$$

This is a measure of how good the lever is and is called the *mechanical advantage*.

You may now be able to see more clearly why making d_1 much bigger than d_2 in the crowbar meant that the load was much bigger than the effort.

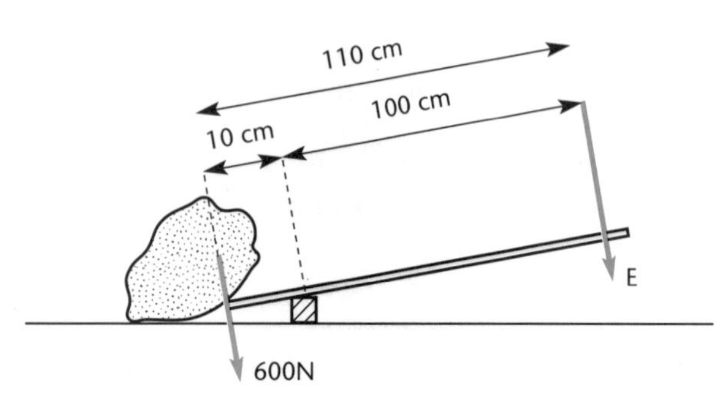

Lifting the rock

For example:

What is the effort needed to lift a rock that weighs 600 N if the length of the crowbar is 110 cm and the pivot is 10 cm from the end?

Effort = E — Load = 600 N

Distance pivot to effort = 100 cm — Distance pivot to load = 10 cm

$$\text{Effort} \times d_1 = \text{Load} \times d_2$$
$$E \times 100 = 600 \times 10$$
$$E = 60\ \text{N}$$

Machine, Moment, Principle of moments, Turning forces

LIFE PROCESSES

These are sometimes called the ***characteristics of living things***. They are the ways that living things (organisms) are different from non-living things.

All living things carry out the following seven life processes:

1. ***Movement***
2. ***Respiration*** (making energy from food)
3. ***Sensitivity*** (being aware of, and responding to, surroundings)
4. ***Growth***
5. ***Reproduction***
6. ***Excretion*** (getting rid of waste)
7. ***Nutrition*** (getting food)

To help you to remember this important list, it is useful to use a mnemonic, e.g. MRS GREN (from the first letters of each word).

LIGAMENTS

These are strong, flexible fibres that hold ***bones*** together and stabilize ***joints***. If they are damaged, e.g. during a sporting injury, the person may suffer a sprain, or even a dislocation of the joint.

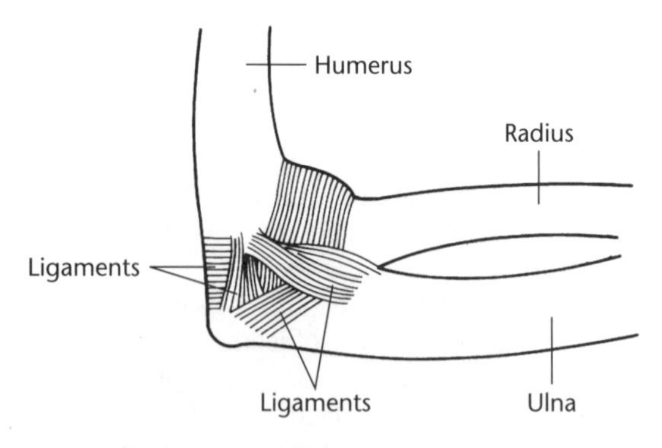

Ligaments of the elbow joint

LIGHT

Light is a sort of **wave** that can be detected by our eyes.

You will already know some facts about light, which probably include the following:

- Light travels outwards from a source. The source is often a very hot object such as the Sun, a flame or the hot wire in a light bulb. We can see a source because the light comes straight from it to our eyes.
- Light can be reflected from many things with many different surfaces. We can see these things, even though they do not give out light like a light source, by looking at the light that they reflect. You can see grass because it reflects the green part of sunlight and some of the reflected light reaches your eyes. Remember that you will only see the colours that reach your eye. A red rose appears to be red because it reflects red light.
- A thin, narrow beam of light is called a *ray*.
- Light will travel in straight lines. You can test this with a simple experiment. Take three pieces of card and make a small hole in each one. Look through the holes in the cards at a source of light such as a bulb. You can only see the light when all three holes are in a straight line.
- The fact that light travels in straight lines causes it to make shadows because it does not bend round objects that get in its way. The shadow is in the area behind an object that the light cannot reach.

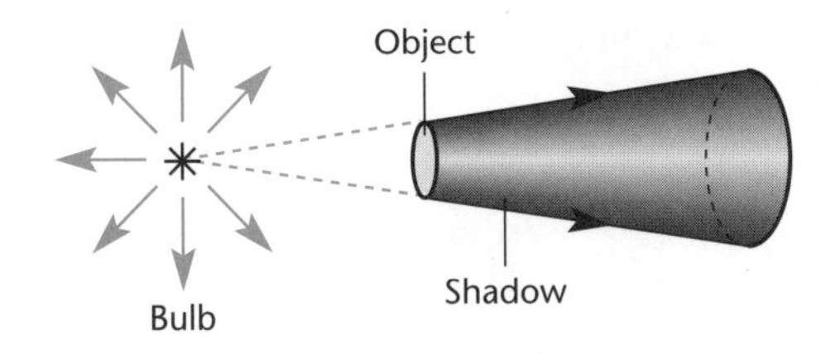

A simple shadow

The diagram shows the edges of the **shadows** marked by the rays that can just get past the edges of the object. When the light source is small or a long way away, the shadow has sharp exact edges.

- Light travels at a very fast speed. This is about 300,000,000 m/s in a vacuum and almost the same in air. This is *much* faster than sound, which can only travel at about 300 m/s in air and cannot travel through a vacuum, such as space, at all. This is why you often see things before you hear them. In other transparent materials, such as glass or perspex or water, the light is slowed down.
- It is easy to see what happens when light is reflected if you look at very shiny, polished, flat surfaces like glass mirrors or polished metal.

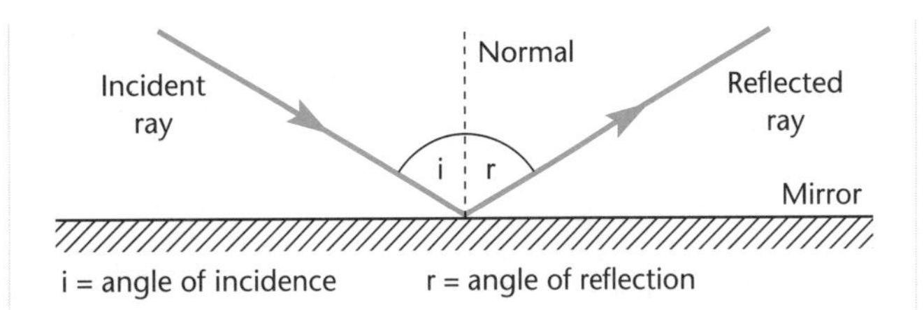

Reflection

Imagine a line at 90° to the mirror at the place where a ray of light hits it. This line is called a *normal*. The angle between the ray going towards the mirror and the normal is called the *angle of incidence*. The ray will be reflected off so that it makes an angle the same size on the other side of the normal. This is the *angle of reflection*.

The angle of reflection = the angle of incidence.

You can test this with a ray box and a mirror and measure the angles. Do it for a range of angles and make sure that it is always true.

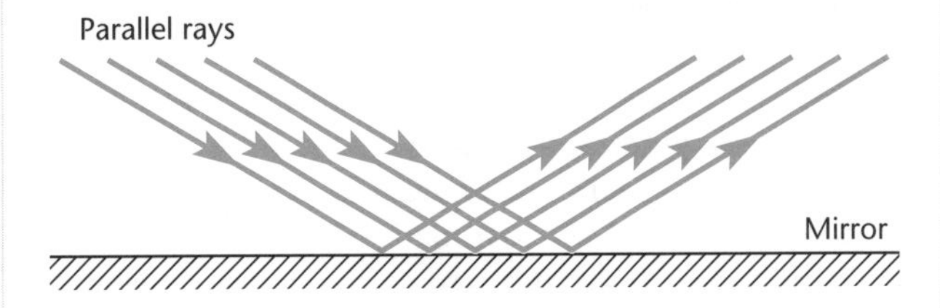

Reflecting a beam of light at a mirror

Rays of light are always reflected like this but a mirror can also reflect a wide beam of light rays in one particular direction because its surface is so smooth. All waves obey this same law when they are reflected.

- Light will always obey the law of reflection but it will still be scattered by a rough surface because it hits the surface at all sorts of different angles. Many objects scatter light in this way. White paper is a good example. This sort of reflection does not make an image like a mirror.

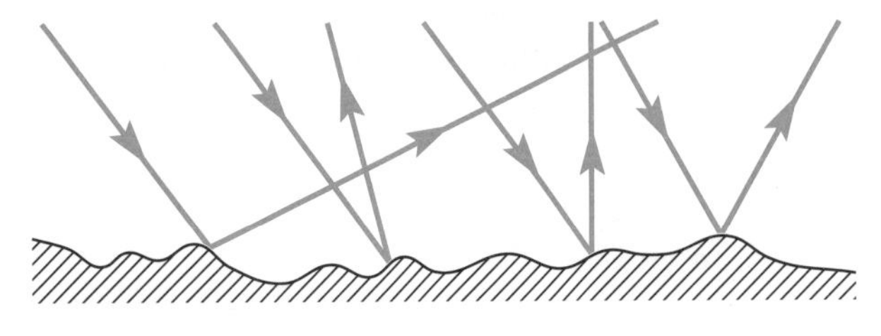

Diffuse reflection

- Light is a **wave** that is partly an electrical vibration and partly a magnetic vibration. It is part of a set of waves that are called the *electromagnetic* spectrum. Our eyes can only see the visible part of the **spectrum**. The different **wavelengths** are seen as different **colours**.

Colour, Refraction, Shadows, Spectrum, Wave

Reaction	$CaCO_3$	Heat → CaO + H_2O / Heat → + H_2O →	$Ca(OH)_2$ Lime water
Product name	Limestone lumps	Quick lime	Slaked lime
Uses	• Roadstone • Making glass	• Neutralizing acid	• Limewater • Mortar

Limestone chemistry

LIME

Calcium oxide is the chemical name for lime. Lime is used to ***neutralize*** acids in soil and in lakes polluted by ***acid rain***.

LIMESTONE

Limestone is a sedimentary rock formed from the bodies of sea animals that have died and have been compressed over millions of years. It is also a very important ***mineral*** and raw material. Limestone, like chalk and ***marble***, is a form of calcium carbonate and is quarried in many areas of the country. The eastern part of Britain has large deposits of limestone, formed over 300 million years ago when Britain was covered by a tropical sea.

The limestone in Derbyshire is particularly pure and is such a valuable mineral that it is even quarried in the Peak District National Park.

LIMEWATER

Calcium hydroxide solution is more commonly called limewater. When carbon dioxide is bubbled through it, a fine white precipitate is formed of (insoluble) calcium carbonate. The limewater is said to go cloudy. You have probably used limewater in the laboratory to test for the presence of carbon dioxide.

Carbon dioxide

LINNAEUS, CAROLUS (1707–1778)

Carolus Linnaeus was a Swedish scientist who realized the importance of ***classifying*** living things, and invented the binomial system of ***scientific names*** we use today. He gave Latin binomial names to thousands of types of plants and animals – he even gave a Latin binomial name to himself! (His real name was Carl von Linné.)

LIQUID

When ice melts, it turns into liquid water. In fact the majority of ***solids*** will, when heated, melt to form liquids. As the temperature increases, the particles move further apart and are able to slide over each other. Liquids take the shape of the container they are poured into. They are not compressible.

Changes of state

LISTER, JOSEPH (1827–1912)

Joseph Lister was a Scottish doctor who realised how important it was to use antiseptic before operations. Previously about half the patients who had surgery died from infections, but Lister found that if the operating theatre and instruments were clean, and if the wound was sprayed with antiseptic, far less patients died.

LITMUS

When lichens are ground up, a pigment is extracted which is called litmus. This changes colour when it comes into contact with acids and alkalis.

Litmus colour changes

	Colour of red litmus paper	*Colour of blue litmus paper*
Acid	Red	Red
Water	Red	Blue
Alkali	Blue	Blue

Indicator

LIVER

This is the largest *internal* organ of the body. It has several very important functions:

- absorbed food travels here to be processed, e.g. ***carbohydrates*** can be changed to ***fats***, ***minerals*** can be stored,
- it makes *bile*, which helps to break down fats,
- it destroys poisons, e.g. alcohol and drugs,
- it makes ***urea*** from excess ***proteins***,
- it contains stored carbohydrates, which are used to keep the blood sugar level steady.

If the liver stops working properly, due to damage or disease, then the person may become very ill and need a liver transplant. Too much ***alcohol*** is known to cause liver damage.

LOCOMOTION

This means that the whole animal moves from one place to another. There are different methods of locomotion, depending on the type of animal involved, and where it lives. Each type of animal is ***adapted for its environment***. For example:

fish have fins and a tail to allow them to move easily through water. Most fish have a swim bladder, so that they float at the right depth. They are covered in scales and have a streamlined shape to reduce drag.

frogs have long, powerful back legs so that they can jump, and short front legs to act as shock absorbers. When they are in water they swim, so they have webbed feet.

birds have wings and powerful breast muscles so that they can fly. They have hollow bones so that they are not too heavy, and a streamlined shape to reduce wind resistance. Not all birds can fly – penguins are adapted so that they are very good underwater swimmers, and ostriches are adapted to run fast.

cheetahs are the fastest land mammals. They have very powerful leg muscles and a flexible backbone, so they can run at speeds of more than 50 miles per hour.

→ ***Movement***

LOUDNESS

The loudness of a ***sound*** depends on the ***amplitude*** of the wave. The loudness is measured in units called decibels (dB). The units are quite different to the other units that you have met because the loudness that you hear will *double* each time you increase by 10 dB. The scale starts at 0 dB, which can only just be heard by someone with good hearing. The table may help you to see how the scale works.

Noise	*dB*
Whisper	30
Normal conversation	60
Vacuum cleaner	70
Door slam	80
Noisy factory	95
Loud personal stereo	125
Permanant ear damage	140

As you can see, the scale is useful for measuring noise to see if it is a nuisance or could cause ear damage. A car silencer can lower the noise by 60 dB.

A normal ear does not hear all sounds equally. It will hear sounds with a frequency of about 2 kHz as loudest. Special noise meters are made that take into account the effect of frequency.

→ ***Amplitude, Sound***

LSD (ACID)

This is an illegal, mind-altering drug.

It is normally sold as tablets or on small pieces of blotting paper, which dissolve on the tongue

The effects start about 30 minutes after taking it, and last for up to twelve hours. They include seeing and hearing things differently, and a feeling of being outside the body; the person may feel dizzy or depressed and may panic.

It is very difficult to control the dose, since only tiny amounts are needed to get an effect.

→ ***Drugs***

LUNGS

The lungs are the site of ***gas exchange*** in humans.

Air moves in and out of the lungs through a large tube called the ***trachea*** (windpipe). This divides to form two ***bronchi***, one bronchus leading to each lung. These divide repeatedly to form smaller tubes called ***bronchioles***, which spread through all parts of the lung. At the ends of the bronchioles are groups of ***alveoli*** (air sacs) where gas exchange actually occurs.

→ ***Breathing, Diaphragm, Smoking***

MACHINE

It is quite difficult to define a machine because the word has so many slightly different meanings in everyday use. In science, a machine is a device that does some ***work***. While it is doing this, it will transform some ***energy*** from one form to another.

A ***lever*** is an example of a machine.

The machine is often a *force multiplier*, which means that it takes a ***force*** put in, called the *effort*, and makes it bigger so that it can act against a larger force called the *load*.

A car engine is a machine that converts the ***chemical energy*** in the petrol into ***kinetic energy***.

✣ ***Energy, Force, Lever, Work***

MAGNETIC FIELD

This is the ***force*** that is exerted on a ***magnetic material*** in the space surrounding a magnet. The strength of the field gets weaker as the distance from the magnet increases.

We can show a picture of a magnetic field by drawing *lines of force*. Each line is the path that would be taken by a free N pole. (As you cannot have a N pole without a S pole it is impossible to have a truly free N pole, but the idea is useful because it helps you to 'see' the field.) Each line of force will be going away from N poles and towards S poles. The lines cannot cross as the N pole can only be moved in one direction by the field.

There are several ways to plot these lines of force and the quickest and easiest way is to use iron filings sprinkled evenly onto a piece of paper placed over the part of the field that you wish to examine. Each iron filing becomes a tiny magnet and will turn to line up with the field if you gently tap the paper. The method is not very good in strong fields because the iron filings get pulled across the paper towards the nearest strong pole! (It makes the magnets easier to clean if you wrap them in 'cling film' first!)

A better method is to use a 'plotting compass', which is a small magnetic compass. Put a piece of plain white paper on your desk, put the magnet on the paper and draw round it. Place the compass on the paper close to the magnet and put a pencil dot on the paper as close as possible to the N of the compass. Move the compass so that the S of the compass is next to the dot and draw a second dot near to the N end. Continue this process as far as needed and then join the dots. Do this beginning in different places until you have enough lines to show the field.

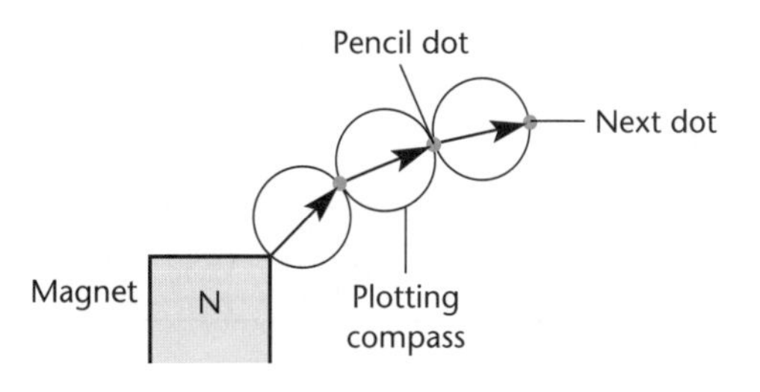

Plotting fields

Some examples of the fields that you might obtain are shown in the diagrams. Notice how the lines are closer together where the field is stronger.

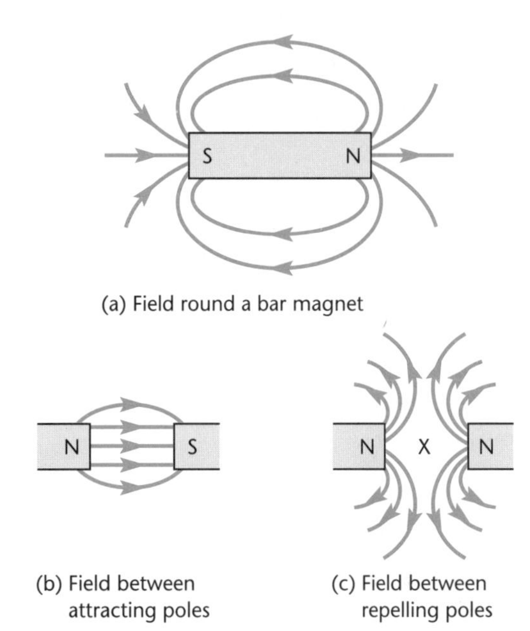

(a) Field round a bar magnet

(b) Field between attracting poles

(c) Field between repelling poles

Magnetic fields

At a *neutral point* all the magnetic forces 'cancel' because there are two equal and opposite forces. The point labelled X will be a neutral point where the repelling forces from the magnets are equal.

Magnetic fields from electric current

When you send an electric current along a wire it makes a magnetic field. The field is circular round the wire.

When the wire is wound into a coil, the field that you get is very similar to that of a bar magnet. The main difference is that you can also use the field inside the coil.

A long narrow coil like this is sometimes called a solenoid. The magnetic field will be made several hundred times stronger if you put an iron core in the centre of the coil so that the core is magnetized. This then has uses as an ***electromagnet***.

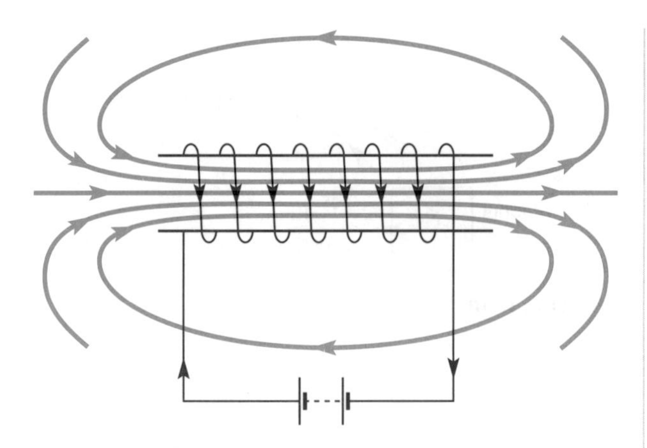

The field round a coil

Using magnetic fields from electric current

Making an electromagnet

Put a soft iron core in the coil and it becomes magnetized, making the magnetic field from the coil much stronger and producing an ***electromagnet***. You can sort out which pole is which if you follow the rule illustrated in the diagram. Look into the ends of the coil and imagine the current flowing from + to –. The direction of the current fits one of the N or S symbols as shown.

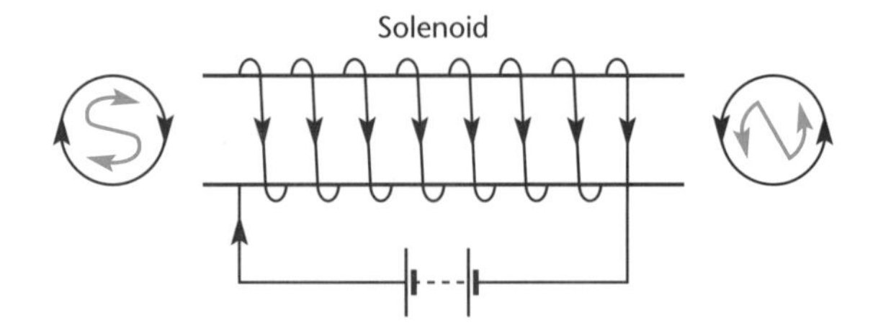

The poles of an electromagnet

An electromagnet like this is used in the ***relay*** and in large electromagnets for lifting scrap metal.

In some cases, the direction of the field does not matter and you can use an alternating current (ac) instead of direct current (dc). An electromagnet will still attract scrap metal even though its poles are 'swapping over' rapidly!

Making a magnet

If you set up a solenoid as in the diagram and put a piece of magnetic material inside it, then the material becomes magnetized. It works better if you put a variable resistor in the circuit and slowly increase the current (and the field) up to a maximum and then decrease back to zero rather than suddenly switching the current on and off. This is the best way to make a magnet. If you do not have a coil and a power supply you can weakly magnetize a material such as a needle by stroking it repeatedly in one direction with a permanent magnet.

The magnetic material has areas called *domains* where the atoms are in the correct pattern to make each domain like a small magnet with two poles. Before magnetizing, the material has the same number of domains pointing in all directions so that they cancel out. When you magnetize the material you pull on the domains so that most of them turn their field to point in the same direction.

Demagnetizing materials

If you use the same circuit with an ac supply, the material inside the coil can be demagnetized. This works better if you slowly withdraw the material from the coil to a distance with the ac turned on or slowly make the current smaller. Many delicate instruments – even mechanical watches – need to be demagnetized in this way so that they work accurately. The magnetic field is changing over so rapidly that the domains are mixed up again.

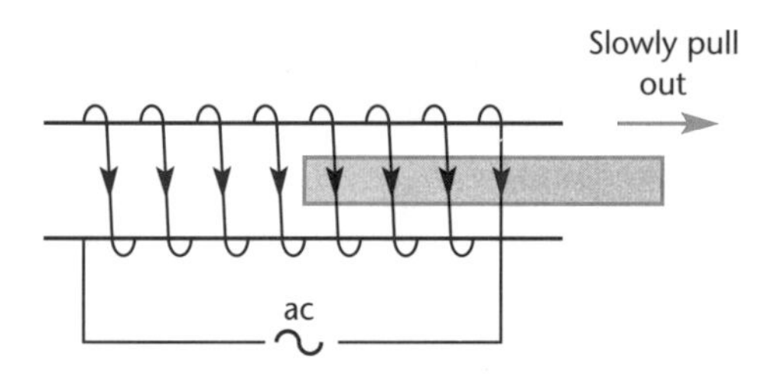

Demagnetizing a rod

Magnetic field, Magnetic materials, Relay

MAGNETIC MATERIALS

A magnetic material is one that can be magnetized and be picked up by a magnet. There are only three ***metals*** that are magnetic. These are *iron, nickel* and *cobalt*. Any material that is magnetic must contain at least one of these. The commonest one is iron.

Remember: Mixtures of metals used to make special magnetic materials will be alloys.

Until 1993 all of our coins were made from an alloy that was not magnetic, but some of the new 'copper' coins are now made from a central disk that is magnetic, with a coating on top. You can find these by testing with a magnet. In a similar way you can test soft drink cans to see if they are aluminium, which is not attracted by a magnet. Only the aluminium ones are collected for recycling. Take care with the use of words in this section – a *magnetic material* will only become a *magnet* when it is *magnetized*, but it WILL always be attracted to a magnet.

Hard magnetic materials are hard to magnetize but, once magnetized will also be difficult to demagnetize. They are mostly used to make

permanent magnets for things like electric motors and loudspeakers or even 'fridge magnets'. Steel is usually a hard magnetic material. Lots of research goes into producing alloys that make strong permanent magnets.

Soft magnetic materials are easy to magnetize but also lose their magnetism quickly and easily. They are mainly used for the core of electromagnets in ***relays***, ***electric bells***, the heads in tape recorders, the cores of transformers and large ***electromagnets*** for lifting scrap metal. Iron can be made into a soft magnetic material.

Electric bell, Magnetic field, Magnets, Relay

MAGNETS

On each magnet there will be two places where the magnetic force is at its strongest. These places are often at opposite ends or sides of the material and they are called *poles*. If the magnet is suspended on a thread so that it can turn freely it will turn until the poles are approximately North–South. The poles are then called a *north seeking pole*, which we shorten to north pole or N, and a *south seeking pole*, shortened to south pole or S. There will always be one pole of each type, you cannot have a single magnetic pole.

If we suspend two magnets close to each other we find that they obey two simple rules:

1. If we put two poles the same next to each other then they repel.
2. If we put two opposite poles next to each other then they attract.

> *Like poles repel.*
> *Unlike poles attract.*

- Both poles of a magnet will attract an unmagnetized piece of magnetic material.
- A magnet will attract magnetic materials through thin layers of some other materials such as paper or wood but its effect always gets smaller quite quickly as distance from the magnet increases.

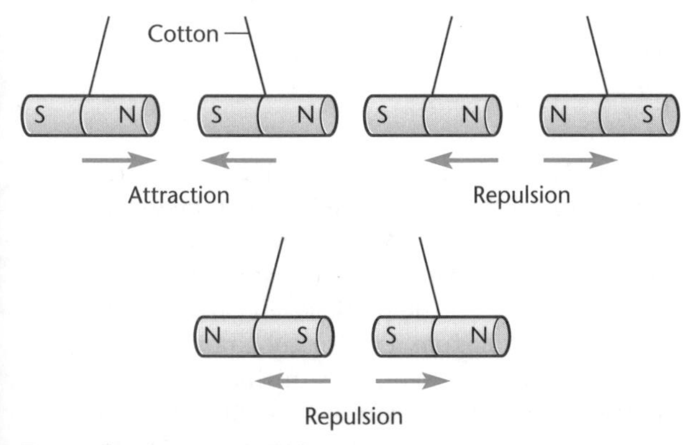

Forces between magnets

A magnet does not need to be in air to attract things and will work quite well in a vacuum or in space.

- You can shield things from a magnetic field by surrounding them with magnetic material such as iron. The magnetic effect (called the field) goes round through the magnetic material instead of straight through the middle.
- A *compass* works because the ***Earth*** has a fairly strong ***magnetic field*** with poles that are quite close to the geographic poles. A small magnetic needle that is free to turn will always point towards the magnetic north pole and can be used to find the direction of true north if you are careful and know the angle between the directions of magnetic north and geographic north. (This is printed on large scale maps as well as the direction of true north. It is about 5°W of true N in the north of the country at the moment and is getting a little bit smaller each year because the magnetic north pole is moving slowly.)
- You can find out which pole is which on a magnet by using a small compass. Make sure that you know which is the N pole of the compass needle and bring it close to each end of the magnet. Watch to see which pole *repels* it. This is the N pole of the magnet. Be careful because a compass needle will be attracted to both ends of an unmagnetized piece of magnetic material so you must look for repulsion and *not* attraction.

> *CHECKPOINT*
>
> Two north poles will ______________ .
> A N pole and a S pole will ______________ .
> Describe how to identify the N pole of a permanent magnet. (Hint: there is more than one way!)

Magnetic field, Magnetic materials

MAGNIFICATION

This tells you how much bigger an object looks when you are using a ***microscope***, binoculars, a telescope or a magnifying glass.

To calculate magnification, you need to look for the numbers printed on the microscope lenses, e.g. 5×, 10×.

> *Total magnification*
> *= eyepiece lens × objective lens*

Malnutrition

This is a general term which means that a person is not getting a ***balanced diet***. This may happen in several ways:

They might not have enough food

This happens when food is in short supply, e.g. in a famine, and causes weakness and slow growth. Severe starvation can cause death.

They might have too much food

This often happens in developed countries, e.g. Britain, USA, where people can afford to eat more food than they need (particularly sugary and fatty foods). This can lead to ***obesity***, ***heart disease*** and ***tooth decay***.

They might have a diet lacking in some food groups

This might happen because some foods are difficult to obtain, e.g. fresh fruit and vegetables, or because they are expensive, e.g. meat. Sometimes, people choose to eat a limited diet because they prefer the taste of particular foods. This can cause health problems,

e.g. scurvy if there is not enough Vitamin C in the diet (fresh fruits and vegetables),
anaemia if there is not enough iron in the diet (red meat and green vegetables).

Balanced diet, Deficiency diseases

Marble

This is a ***metamorphic rock***. It is formed when limestone is heated to very high temperatures. It is much harder and denser than limestone.

Mass

Mass is a measure of the amount of matter in something. It is measured in kilograms (kg) and a block of a platinum alloy kept at Sevres in France is the standard kilogram for SI units. Mass is usually measured on a *balance*. It is important to remember that mass is *not* the same as ***weight*** and is *not* a ***force***. The total mass of an object will remain the same wherever you take it. Even when a space probe is a very large distance from any star or planet and becomes completely weightless it will still have the same mass.

We sometimes use an additional unit, the tonne, for large objects.

1 tonne = 1000 kg

If you find it difficult to imagine a 1 kg mass remember that it is the mass of a bag of sugar from the supermarket!

A larger mass will need a larger force to produce the same acceleration on it. (Think of pushing a Mini or a large Volvo along the same road.)

Density, Weight

Measuring cylinder

This is a simple cylinder with a scale on its side so that you can measure the ***volume*** of ***liquids***. It is important to use the narrowest possible cylinder to get the best results. The narrowest cylinder will have the most sensitive scale – perhaps to 0.1 ml instead of 1 ml on the next largest cylinder – because small changes in volume will move further up a narrow cylinder.

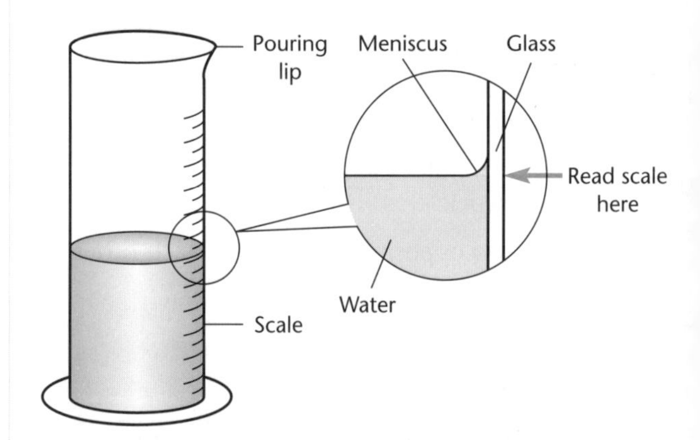

Measuring cylinder

For really accurate results you will notice that many liquids, especially water in glass, form a curved surface called a *meniscus* where they touch the glass. You should put the cylinder on a level surface and read the scale at the bottom of the meniscus.

Volume

Melting

Melting is the term used to describe the changing of state from solid to liquid. Melting can be explained by the ***kinetic theory***. When a solid is heated, vibrations of the particles in the solid increase but the forces between the particles are sufficient to hold the structure together. Eventually a point is reached when the vibrations are so great that the forces between the particles cannot hold the structure together and the particles start to move. At this

point, we say a liquid has been formed and the temperature at which this occurs is called the melting point.

Changes of state

MENDEL, GREGOR (1822–1884)

Gregor Mendel was an Austrian monk who carried out a series of very carefully organized experiments in ***genetics***. He studied how pea plants pass on their characteristics from one generation to the next e.g. height, flower colour, seed shape, etc. He developed the rules of genetics that we still use today, e.g.

- Parents have two copies of a particular gene, but gametes have only one.
- Individuals can be homozygous or heterozygous.
- Some alleles are dominant and others are recessive.

MENDELEYEV, DIMITRI IVANOVICH (1839–1907)

The ***periodic table*** that is used today was devised by Dimitri Mendeleyev. His fellow chemists scoffed at him because he left gaps in his table, as he believed that there were elements that had not yet been discovered. He was later to be proved correct when germanium and silicon were isolated.

He was an excellent chemistry teacher and was frowned on even more when he insisted on teaching women at the university. He had come from a very poor background and always tried to help people worse off than himself.

Periodic table

MENOPAUSE

This is the time in a woman's life when her ***menstrual cycle*** stops. Her ***ovaries*** no longer release eggs, and she does not have ***periods***, so she cannot become ***pregnant***. It usually happens between the ages of 40 and 55 years, and is sometimes called the change of life.

MENSTRUAL CYCLE

These are all the changes occurring in a woman's reproductive system each month. Two main things are happening:

1. the ***ovary*** releases an egg,
2. the lining of the ***uterus*** gets ready to receive the egg if it is fertilized. If the egg is not fertilized, the lining breaks up and the woman has a ***period*** (menstruation).

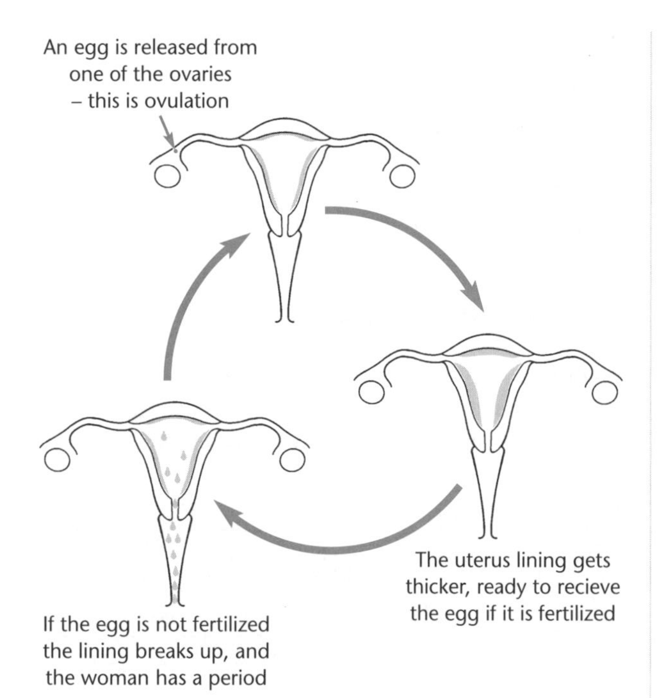
An egg is released from one of the ovaries – this is ovulation
The uterus lining gets thicker, ready to recieve the egg if it is fertilized
If the egg is not fertilized the lining breaks up, and the woman has a period

The menstrual cycle

The whole menstrual cycle lasts for about 28 days, and then it is repeated. It first starts when a girl reaches ***puberty*** (at about 9–16 years of age), and is repeated until she reaches the ***menopause*** (at about 40–55 years old). After this she has no more menstrual cycles and cannot become pregnant. When a woman is ***pregnant*** the menstrual cycle stops, and will start again after the birth of the baby.

Reproduction

MENSTRUATION

This is another word for a ***period***. It is the part of the ***menstrual cycle*** where the uterus lining breaks up and passes out through the vagina. It lasts for about five days.

> *CHECKPOINT*
>
> Make sure you understand the difference between ***menstruation*** and the ***menstrual cycle***.

METAL

Eighty-one of the ninety-two naturally occurring elements are metals.

Metals

- are good conductors of heat and electricity.
- can be beaten into shapes. This is called *malleability*.
- can be pulled out into a thin wire. This is called *ductility*.

- are very hard.
- are strong.
- have high melting points and boiling points.
- are shiny.
- give a ringing sound when hit.

Metal extraction

Metals are very important raw materials extracted from the Earth's crust. As technology has improved, it has become easier to get at the metals in the ores.

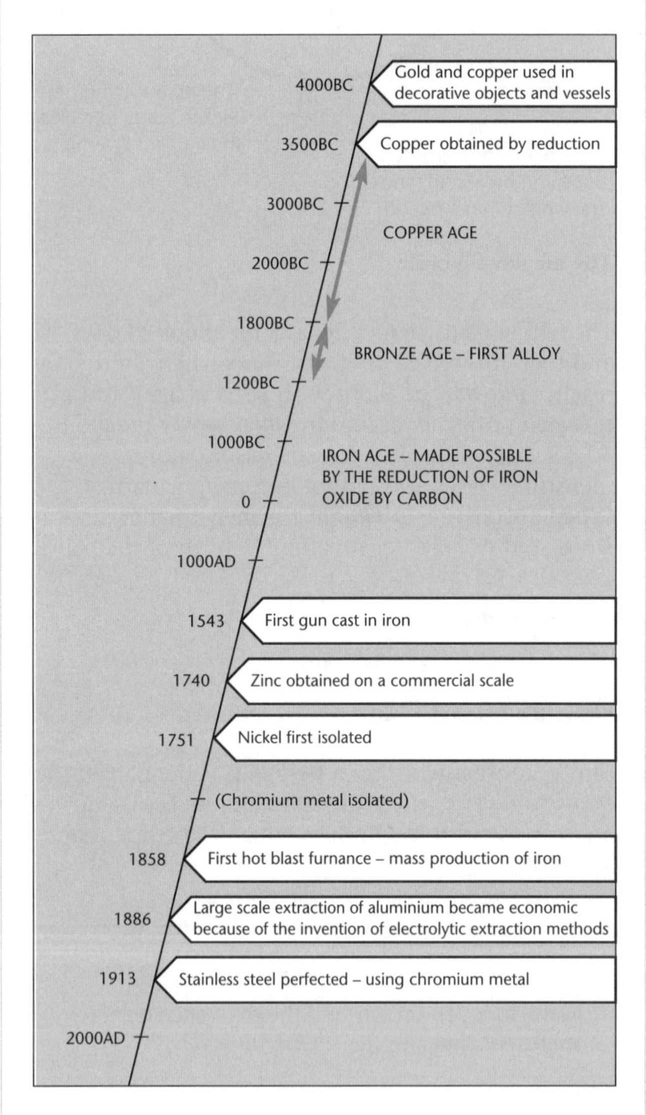

Metal extraction through the ages

It is possible to trace this development and link it to the metals available.

- The oldest metal items on display in the Fitzwilliam Museum in Cambridge are made from very unreactive metals, such as gold and silver. These metals were found uncombined with other elements and early chemists could simply collect them and shape them into jewellery and other objects.
- When fire was discovered, early chemists could heat rocks, for example allowing copper to be extracted from malachite rocks.
- A few centuries later, the early chemists probably realized that using charcoal helped to make fire burn better, making the smelting of ores possible. Iron, zinc, tin and lead then became available. The range of implements could now increase and alloys were developed to combine the best properties of these metals.
- Napoleon was probably the first world leader to have an aluminium dinner service. A chemist working in France used a displacement reaction to extract aluminium from its ore. However, aluminium only became easily available when electrolysis was developed, around 1866.

Metal reactivity series

Although metals have common properties, they are not exactly the same. Some metals are more reactive than others; i.e. have a greater tendency to form ***ions*** than others. Gold, silver and copper are very unreactive. Jewellery is often made from these metals. They have been available for thousands of years because they were easily extracted from the Earth. Sodium and potassium, on the other hand, are very reactive. It would not be a good idea to make jewellery from these metals.

An easy way of remembering the reactivity series is:

Place	Potassium	K	Most reactive metal
Charlie's	Calcium	Ca	
Monkeys	Magnesium	Mg	
And	Aluminium	Al	
Zebras	Zinc	Zn	
In	Iron	Fe	
The	Tin	Sn	
Lead	Lead	Pb	
Cages	Copper	Cu	
Most	Mercury	Hg	
Securely	Silver	Ag	
Guarded	Gold	Au	Least reactive metal

Metamorphic rocks

Metamorphic rocks are formed when ***igneous*** and ***sedimentary*** rocks are changed by intense heat and pressure. For example, limestone, a sedimentary rock, is changed into ***marble*** by intense heat and pressure.

Microbe

This is a general name for any organism too small to be seen with the naked eye. Microbes (micro-organisms) can only be seen using a ***microscope***.

Bacteria ***Fungi*** ***Viruses*** ***Protoctists***	are all examples of microbes.

Some microbes are useful to humans, and some are harmful.

Useful microbes

- bacteria and fungi that make dead material rot (decomposers),
- bacteria and fungi used in food manufacturing, e.g. to make yoghurt, cheese, vinegar, bread, alcohol,
- bacterial and fungi used in sewage treatment,
- fungi used to make ***antibiotics***,
- protoctists that are an important part of ***food chains***.

Harmful microbes

- bacteria, fungi and viruses that cause human ***diseases***,
- bacteria, fungi and viruses that cause diseases in other animals and plants,
- bacteria and fungi that make food go off, and can cause food poisoning.

MICROSCOPE

We use this when we want to look at very small things, e.g. individual cells, bacteria. Most microscopes contain two types of lenses (eyepiece lenses and objective lenses) to magnify objects (make them look bigger).

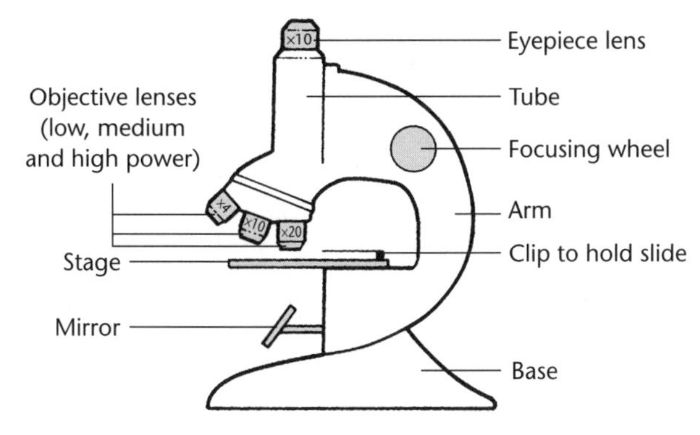

The parts of a microscope

How to use the microscope

1. Place the material you want to look at (the specimen) on a piece of glass called a microscope slide, with a smaller, thinner piece of glass (the coverslip) on top. This helps to keep the specimen flat and protects the lenses from damage.
2. Place the slide on the stage and adjust the mirror so that light shines through the specimen.
3. Turn the focusing wheel so that you can see the specimen clearly when you look through the eyepiece lens.

To calculate the ***magnification***, you will need to look at the numbers printed on the two lenses (these tell you how many times bigger each lens will make the object look).

Total magnification = eyepiece lens magnification × objective lens magnification

Most microscopes have three objective lenses, so you can look at objects using low power, medium power or high power.

MILKY WAY

Our ***Sun*** is a ***star*** that belongs to a ***galaxy*** called the Milky Way. We are on the edge of this galaxy and you can see it at night as a bright band of stars across the sky. It looks like this because we are looking at it edge on. It is a giant spiral shape containing about a hundred million stars. It is about 100,000 light years across and about 10,000 light years thick at the centre. (Light travels at 300,000,000 m/s and a light year is the distance that light travels in one year.)

The Milky Way is one of a cluster of galaxies called the *Local Cluster*.

Galaxy, Star, Sun

MINERALS

These are naturally occurring ***compounds*** that have been formed in the ***Earth's*** crust. For example, limestone is chemically calcium carbonate.

Minerals are also nutrients, which are needed in small amounts to keep living things healthy. If an organism does not get enough of a particular mineral, it will suffer from a ***deficiency disease***.

Mineral requirements in animals

Animals obtain minerals from the food they eat. This table shows three of the minerals needed by humans.

Some of the minerals needed by humans

Mineral	*Found in...*	*Needed for...*	*Problems if you do not have enough*
Iron	Red meat, cocoa, green vegetables	Making new red blood cells	Anaemia (lack of red blood cells). The person feels tired and weak and may look pale
Calcium	Cheese, milk, fish	Healthy teeth and bones	Tooth decay Weak bones
Sodium	Salt and all salty foods	Muscle contractions Nerve impulses	Muscle cramp

Mineral requirements in plants

Plants obtain minerals from the ***soil***. They are absorbed through ***root hairs***. Minerals can be added to the soil in ***fertilizer***. The following table shows three of the minerals needed by plants.

Three of the minerals needed by plants

Mineral	*Needed for...*	*Problems if the plant does not have enough*
Nitrate	Making protein Making chlorophyll	Plant cannot grow properly. It is small and stunted, with yellow leaves
Magnesium	Making chlorophyll	Plant looks yellow and cannot photosynthesise properly
Phosphate	Efficient growth Making energy (respiration)	Plant cannot absorb other minerals from the soil properly

Miscible

This is where two or more liquids mix together.

Mixture

Elements can be mixed together to form a mixture. You will probably have mixed iron filings with sulphur in the laboratory. This mixture is easily separated by using a magnet because the iron filings are magnetic. Mixtures are easily separated. Other examples of mixtures include ***crude oil***, ***sea water*** and ***air***.

Mohs's scale

Geologists are able to identify minerals by measuring their relative hardness. The Mohs's scale of hardness was developed by a German geologist called Friedrich Mohs. On the scale of hardness from one to ten, Mohs classified talc mineral as number one, the softest, with diamond, as number ten, the hardest.

Molecule

All matter is made up of ***particles***; there are three different types; ***atom***, molecule and ***ion***. The molecule is a particle that contains two or more atoms chemically joined together. Molecules can contain the same type of atom, or different atoms chemically joined (bonded).

Each molecule has a name and a ***chemical formula*** to represent which atoms are joined together. For example, glucose (a sugar) – $C_6H_{12}O_6$ – contains six atoms of carbon, twelve atoms of hydrogen and six atoms of oxygen.

Moment

This is a measure of the size of a turning ***force***.

The moment will depend on the size of the force being applied and also on the distance of the force from the centre of rotation. The centre of the rotation could be an axle, a balancing point, a hinge or anything else that the object turns on and it is often called a *pivot*.

Imagine tightening a nut using a spanner. To make the nut tighter you could either use a bigger force (push harder) or move the force further from the pivot (use a longer spanner). Sometimes, the wheel nuts on a car are very tight and difficult to remove. Car spares shops sell a telescopic spanner that you can slide outwards and make it longer so that you can turn the nut with a reasonable force.

It is important to measure the shortest distance from the pivot to the line showing the direction of the force. When you do this, the line from the pivot will meet the line showing the direction of the force at 90°. In most cases you do not need to worry too much about this because the problems in Key stage 3 are usually chosen so that they are at 90° anyway.

You can calculate the moment of a turning force by using this equation:

$$\text{Moment} = \text{Force} \times \text{distance to pivot}$$

The force will be in newtons and the distance will be in metres, so the units for the moment will be Nm.

In all of the following cases, the moment will be F × d.

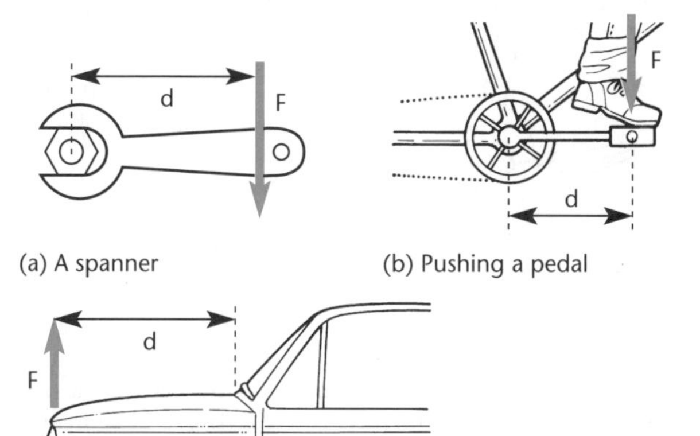

(a) A spanner (b) Pushing a pedal

(c) Opening a car bonnet

Some turning moments

Remember: The distance that you measure must be at 90° to the force.

For example:

- John pulls on a door handle with a force of 5N. The handle is 70cm from the hinge. What is the turning moment?

  Moment = Force × distance to pivot
  = 5 × 0.70
  = 3.5 Nm

- When Mika lifts the handles of a wheel barrow the force needed is 400N. The handles are 1.5m from the axle of the wheel. What is the turning moment?

  Moment = Force × distance to pivot
  = 400 × 1.5
  = 600 Nm

If there is more than one turning force, such as two children on the same side of a seesaw, then do F × d for each one and add together those that turn *in the same direction* to find the total.

CHECKPOINT

A moment is the size of a t ________ f ________ . The moment depends on the ________ and on the ________ of the force from the pivot.

Write down the equation for working out a moment.

Levers, Principle of moments, Turning forces

Monera

This is one of the five kingdoms in ***classification***. ***Bacteria*** and blue-green algae are put into this kingdom. They are microscopic, single-celled organisms with a cell wall and cytoplasm, but no nucleus.

Moon

A moon is a fairly large object that has passed close to a ***planet*** and has been captured by it. The planet and the moon attract each other because of the force of ***gravity*** and the moon becomes a ***satellite*** orbiting round the planet. ***Earth*** has only one moon but some of the other planets in the ***solar system*** have several moons.

The moon orbiting the Earth is about 3,400 km across and 384,000 km from the Earth.

Planet, Satellite, Solar system

Mould

This is the general name for multicellular ***fungi***. They often grow on food (e.g. bread, jam, cheese), on dead material (e.g. old wood), or in soil.

Some types of mould make ***antibiotics***.

Movement

This is an important ***life process***. All living things can move at least part of themselves.

e.g. plants can turn their leaves towards the Sun,
some plants can close the petals of their flowers at night,
barnacles can open the plates of their shells when the tide covers them,
humans can walk around to get from one place to another

Movement is very useful because it allows organisms to:

- find food,
- find a suitable place to live,
- make the best use of conditions available, e.g. light,
- spread out to avoid overcrowding,
- communicate with each other (think about dogs wagging their tails, or baring their teeth).

In humans, the skeletal system ***(skeleton)*** is concerned with movement. This is made up of ***bones***, which can move when ***muscles*** contract.

Locomotion

Muscles

Muscles are very important in the process of ***movement*** in animals, because they can contract (get shorter) and relax. If a muscle is joined to two bones, the bones will be pulled closer together when the muscle contracts.

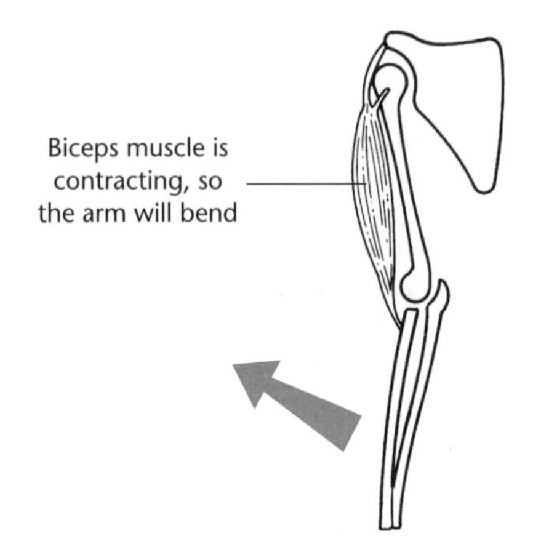

When a muscle contracts, bones are pulled closer together

Muscles cannot push bones apart when they relax, so muscles always work in pairs, called ***antagonistic muscle pairs***. The muscles have *opposite* effects to each other, e.g. *biceps* and *triceps* are an antagonistic muscle pair:

- biceps bends the arm, triceps straightens the arm,
- when biceps is contracted, triceps is relaxed,
- when triceps is contracted, biceps is relaxed.

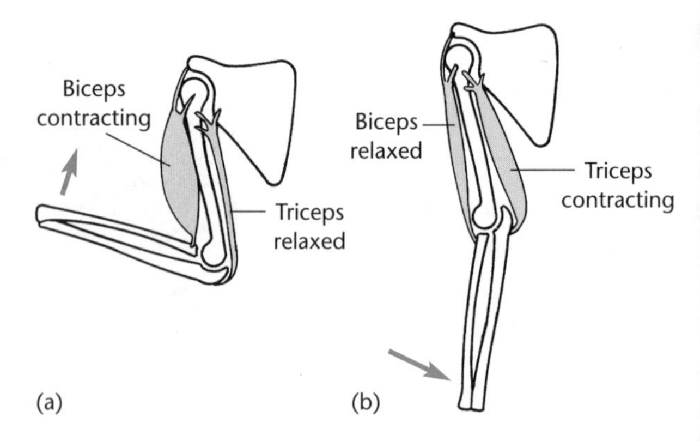

Antagonistic muscles: (a) biceps is contracting, so the arm will bend; (b) triceps is contracting, so the arm will straighten.

Remember: Not all muscles are joined to bones,
e.g., muscle in the uterus wall contracts during birth,
muscle in the heart wall contracts when the heart beats,
muscle in the gut wall contracts during peristalsis,
but all muscle can contract.

Joints

NAMING COMPOUNDS

✦ *Compounds*

NATURAL GAS

Natural gas is a fossil fuel often formed alongside ***crude oil***. Both are formed by the decay of animals and plants. Gas and oil are often found together. Natural gas is the gas you use in the laboratory and is mostly made of *methane*.

NATURAL SELECTION

This idea was first put forward by Charles Darwin and Alfred Wallace in 1858. It tries to explain how living things have changed over a long period of time. There are five main points to the theory:

1. lots of organisms produce very large numbers of offspring,
2. there are not enough resources to go round, so organisms have to compete,
3. some organisms have characteristics that will help them to compete successfully (this is called a ***selective advantage***). These will survive, and other organisms will die,
4. the individuals that survive are more likely to breed and produce offspring like themselves,
5. gradually more and more of the organisms will have these useful characteristics, i.e., the ***population*** will change.

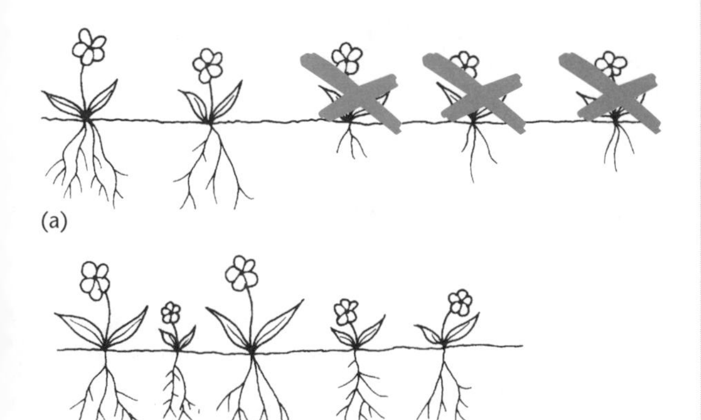

Natural selection: (a) if there is a shortage of water, the plants with the longest roots are most likely to survive; (b) they will produce offspring like themselves

Since Darwin suggested this theory, scientists have found some evidence to support it. For example,

- white peppered moths survive best in country areas, and black peppered moths survive best in industrial areas,
- rats that are resistant to rat poison have a selective advantage, and are more likely to survive and breed,
- bacteria that are resistant to antibiotics have a selective advantage, and are more likely to survive and breed.

✦ ***Competition for resources, Survival of the fittest***

NEUTRALIZATION

A neutral solution is one that has a pH of 7; for example, pure water. Neutralization is a chemical reaction that involves an acid and a base, the result of which is a salt. The base in the reaction could be either a metal oxide or a metal hydroxide.

Here is an example of neutralization:

$$HCl + NaOH \longrightarrow H_2O + NaCl$$

Hydrochloric acid + Sodium hydroxide ⟶ Water + Sodium chloride

Neutralization happens all around you:

- If you have ever suffered from stomach ache, you will probably have had too much hydrochloric acid in your stomach. You may have been given an antacid tablet. This alkali will have neutralized the acid.
- Bee stings are acidic. If you treat the sting with bicarbonate of soda (sodium carbonate), you will neutralize the sting.
- Wasp stings are alkaline, so you should put a weak acid, such as vinegar, on it.
- When soil becomes too acidic, it limits the crops that can be grown. Farmers therefore add alkali in the form of lime.
- Many of the Scottish lakes are polluted by acid rain, so that some of the fish have died. Lime has been added to some of the lakes in an attempt to neutralize the acid.
- When new houses are built, a very important neutralization reaction takes place between the bricks that hold them together. The mortar is alkaline and it reacts with the acidic carbon dioxide in the air to form a solid substance, calcium carbonate.

Lime mortar + Acidic gas ⟶ Solid cement

NEUTRON

An electrically neutral particle of similar mass to a ***proton***. It consists of an ***electron*** and proton in close association.

NEWTON (N)

A newton is the unit for ***force***.

A force of one newton can accelerate a ***mass*** of one kilogram at one m/s^2.

It might help you to 'picture' the size if you remember that a bag of sugar will weigh 10N.

Force

NOBEL, ALFRED (1833–1896)

Each year scientists, peace campaigners and writers are awarded prizes for their work. These prizes are awarded from a legacy left in the will of Alfred Nobel. He was a Swedish industrialist who made his fortune from the manufacture of explosives. He was horrified at the uses to which his products were put and set up a fund to enable prizes to be awarded.

NOBLE GASES

Group eight, or the ***inert gases***, of the ***periodic table*** are sometimes called the noble gases. These gases show no chemical reactivity (with a few exceptions) because they have stable filled outer electron shells or orbitals. They do not form ***molecules*** but exist as separate ***atoms***.

NOISE

Noise is unwanted sound. It may be musical (and too loud?) but is often an irregular or random mixture of sounds. It can be nuisance and may cause ear damage if it is loud enough.

Loudness, Sound

NON-METALS

These ***elements*** are found on the right-hand side of the ***periodic table***. Non-metals do not conduct electricity (carbon is the exception to the rule). The main differences between metals and non-metals are shown in the table overleaf.

Properties of metals and non-metals

Property	*Non-metal*	*Metal*
State at room temperature	Solids	Solids and gases
Melting and boiling points	Usually high	Often low
Conductivity: electricity	Usually high	Do not conduct
Conductivity: heat	Good	Poor
Strength	Strong, and can be shaped	Often weak/brittle
Density	Usually high	Often low

NORMAL

A normal is a line at 90° to a surface.

It is drawn to show the angles when a ***wave*** is reflected or refracted.

Reflection, Refraction

NUCLEUS

This controls all the activities of the ***cell***, e.g. cell division, making new proteins. It contains ***chromosomes*** (made of ***DNA***), which carry genetic information.

NUTRITION

This is an important ***life process***. All living things need food to stay alive, and nutrition means getting food.

Nutrition in animals

Animals get the food they need by eating other living things (plants or animals), so animals are called ***consumers***. Once the food is inside the animal's gut it is digested by ***enzymes***.

Nutrition in plants

Plants get the food they need by making it in their leaves by ***photosynthesis***, so plants are called ***producers***. Carbon dioxide and water are used to make sugar and this process can only happen in the light.

Nutrition in simple organisms (bacteria and fungi)

Most of these absorb food substances from their surroundings. Some will make ***enzymes*** to digest the food before they absorb it. Many bacteria and fungi feed on dead material so they are called ***decomposers***.

OBESITY

This means that a person is seriously overweight. It is usually defined as being more than ten per cent above the ideal weight for your height and build.

It happens because the person takes in more ***food*** (and therefore more ***energy***) than they need for their daily activities. It is most common where people have a diet containing too much ***fat*** and ***carbohydrate***. Fat is stored under the skin and around the body organs, e.g. heart and kidneys.

Too much body fat is linked to the following conditions:

- ***heart*** disease: a type of fat called *cholesterol* builds up in arteries and blocks them, leading to heart attacks,
- high blood pressure and strokes,
- damage to ***joints***, e.g. hips and knees, due to the extra weight they are carrying.

Obesity can be reduced by lowering the food intake, i.e., eating less food, particularly high fat foods.

-‡- ***Balanced diet, Energy in food***

OIL

-‡- ***Crude oil***

OMNIVORE

This is an animal that eats plants and other animals, e.g. humans, thrushes, voles, pigs.

ORE

An ore is a deposit of a useful ***mineral*** or ***metal***, which is found in large enough quantities to make it economic to mine or quarry.

ORGANS

An organ is a collection of ***tissues*** that work together to carry out a particular function.

Organs in humans

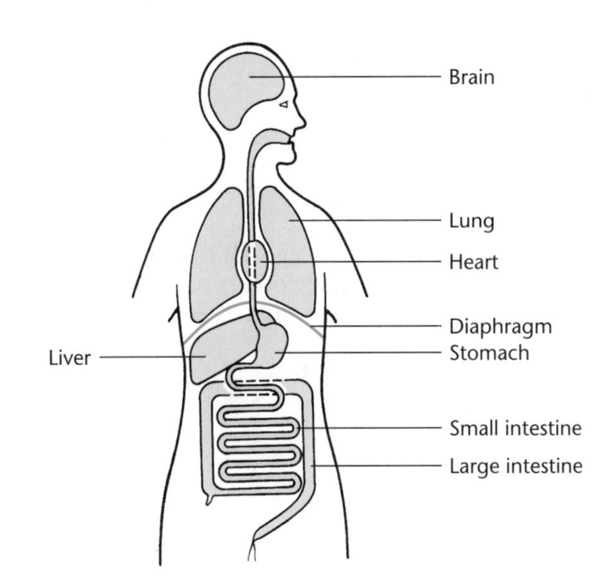

Organs in humans

Organs in plants

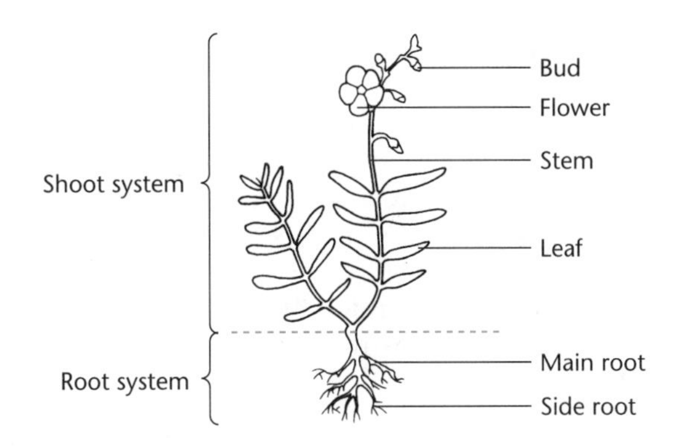

Organs in plants

-‡- ***Bladder, Eye, Ovaries, Pancreas, Systems, Testes, Uterus***

OVARY

Human

Women have two of these small organs. There are thousands of ova (egg cells) inside each one. When a girl reaches ***puberty***, the ova start developing and one ***ovum*** is released each month – this is ***ovulation***.

The ovaries also make the female sex ***hormones*** oestrogen and progesterone.

Plants

This is the part of the ***carpel*** that contains the ***ovule***.

After ***fertilization*** has occurred, the ovary develops into a ***fruit***, which protects the seed and helps ***dispersal*** to occur.

✦ ***Reproduction***

OVULATION

This means that an ***ovum*** (egg cell) is released from one of the ***ovaries***. It usually occurs once a month from the time a girl reaches ***puberty*** until she reaches the ***menopause***.

✦ ***Reproduction***

OVULE

This is the female ***gamete*** (sex cell) in plants. It is found inside the ***ovary***, where it is ***fertilized*** by the ***pollen*** grain nucleus. It develops into a ***seed***.

✦ ***Reproduction***

OVUM (EGG CELL)

The function of this cell is to develop into a baby once it has been fertilized by a ***sperm*** cell.

It is a very large cell (so sperm can find it more easily) and the nucleus contains 23 ***chromosomes*** (half the normal number).

The cytoplasm contains lots of stored food to provide energy for the early stages of the baby's growth.

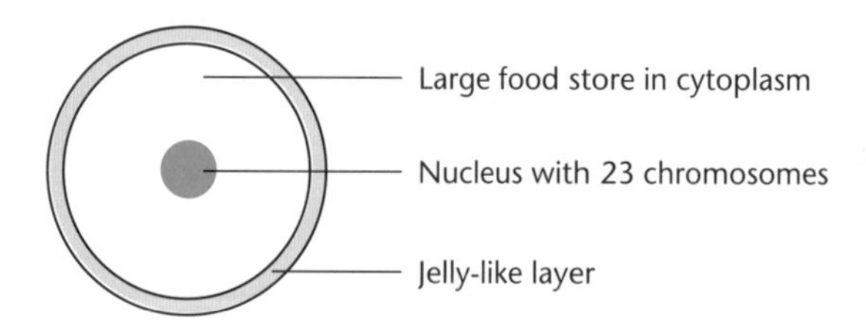

Ovum (egg cell)

✦ ***Fertilization, Gamete, Reproduction***

OXIDATION

When a substance combines with oxygen, we say it has been oxidized. ***Reduction*** is the opposite of oxidation. Both reduction and oxidation reactions usually happen together, which we then call a ***redox*** reaction.

An example of an oxidation reaction is when magnesium is burned in air so that a white powder magnesium oxide is then formed.

Magnesium + Oxygen ⟶ Magnesium oxide

Oxidation reactions also happen when apples and other fruit turn brown, after being exposed to the air.

OXYGEN

Oxygen is very important to living things

- it is used in the process of ***respiration*** to make ***energy***

  Glucose + Oxygen ⟶ Energy + Carbon dioxide + Water.

  This reaction occurs in all cells of all types of living things all the time

- it is made during ***photosynthesis***

  Carbon dioxide + Water $\xrightarrow{\text{light}}$ Oxygen + Glucose.

  This reaction occurs in plant cells containing ***chlorophyll***, e.g. ***palisade*** cells of the leaf, during the day.

- oxygen re-lights a glowing splint.

OZONE

Ozone, O_3, is an unstable form of oxygen. It is a very reactive gas and when it is formed near the surface of the Earth it can cause problems, especially for people who suffer from asthma. *Low level* ozone, as this is known, is caused by the reaction of gases given out from car exhausts.

There is also a layer of ozone around the Earth high up in the atmosphere. This high-level ozone is very useful because it acts as a large sunscreen, blocking out cosmic and harmful ultraviolet rays from space.

James Lovelock, an independent scientist, detected pollutant gases off the coast of Ireland, which made him worry about the state of the ozone layer. His fears were confirmed in 1984 when Joe Farman from the British Antarctic survey based in Rothera in the Antarctic discovered a hole in the ozone layer. Dr Farman realized that the CFC (chlorofluorocarbon) gases released from aerosols were breaking down the reactive ozone. Many countries have agreed to stop using these substances and new, less harmful, substitutes are being developed by chemists.

PALISADE CELLS

These cells are found close to the surface of the ***leaf***. They are cylindrical and are packed tightly together. They contain lots of ***chloroplasts*** to trap light energy. Most ***photosynthesis*** occurs in these cells.

✦ *Cells*

PANCREAS

This important organ has two main functions:

1. it makes digestive ***enzymes*** to help you to digest your food,
2. it makes ***hormones*** to control your blood sugar level (insulin and glucagon). Some people do not make enough insulin, so they are diabetic and may need insulin injections.

Your pancreas is close to your small ***intestine***.

✦ *Digestive system*

PARALLEL

Parts of a ***circuit*** will be in parallel if the ***current*** in the circuit divides, some of it going through each part, and then joins up again later to complete the circuit.

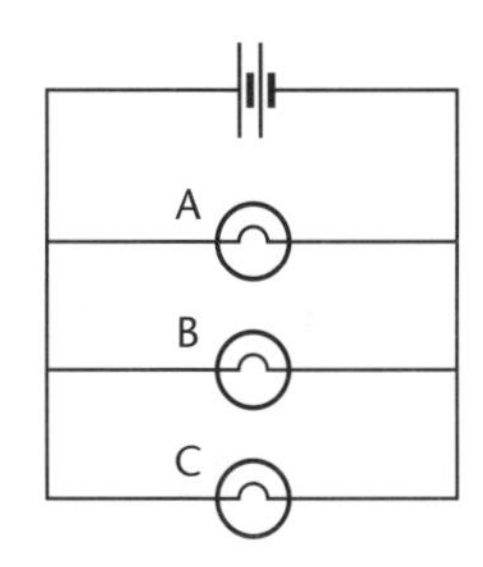

Bulbs in parallel

In the figure, the bulbs A, B, and C are all in parallel. This circuit is useful because if one bulb fails the other bulbs remain on. Each bulb gets its own current from the battery so they are all at their 'normal' brightness. If a switch in a room controls more than one light bulb they will be connected in parallel.

Putting identical cells in parallel does not change the ***voltage*** (like putting them in ***series***) but it does make a bigger battery that can supply more current if it needs to.

> *CHECKPOINT*
>
> A circuit has a battery, bulb and a switch in series.
>
> What will you see happen to the bulb if another bulb is placed in parallel with it?
>
> What has happened to the size of the current taken from the battery?

✦ *Current, Resistor, Series*

PARASITES

These are living things that live on or in another living thing (the host) and cause it harm.

Humans may be affected by several types of parasite:

- some parasites live on the outside of the host, and feed on blood, e.g. headlice, fleas, mosquitoes (***insects***).
- some parasites live inside the host, and absorb nutrients, e.g. tapeworms, athlete's foot (***fungus***).
- some parasites live inside cells and eventually kill the cells, e.g. ***viruses***.

Other animals and plants are also affected by parasites.

PARTICLES

It is useful to imagine that ***atoms***, ***molecules*** and ***ions*** are the particles that make up all matter. They are so small that they cannot be seen, even through the most powerful microscope. It is then possible to account for the behaviour of solids, liquids and gases using a particle model.

✦ *Kinetic theory*

PASTEUR, LOUIS (1822–1895)

Louis Pasteur was a French scientist who spent most of his time investigating ***microbes***. He discovered

- that ***yeasts*** were responsible for ***fermentation*** (anaerobic respiration) to make alcohol;
- that ***bacteria*** could interfere with this process, and could make food go off;
- that bacteria could be killed by heating them (this is the basis of pasteurization, which was then used to keep milk fresh);
- how to make vaccines for anthrax, rabies and other diseases.

✦ *Vaccination*

Penis

During ***sexual intercourse*** the penis fits inside the woman's vagina so that ***sperm*** are released as close to the ovum as possible. The penis must be erect for this to happen, so spaces in the erectile tissue fill up with blood.

The tube running through the penis (the urethra) carries ***semen*** from the sperm ducts and ***urine*** from the bladder, but it cannot carry both at once.

Reproduction

Periodic table

The periodic table is a complete list of all the ***elements*** and therefore the ***atoms*** that exist. However, the list is arranged in a definite grid or pattern of rows and columns. Each row is called a *period* and each column is called a ***group***.

- As you go across the table in each row (period), the atoms get bigger, since there are more ***electrons***. The atoms also get heavier, since there are more ***protons*** and ***neutrons***.
- As you go down the table in each column (group), the atoms also get bigger and heavier. For each of these groups, the elements in them have similar chemical properties. This is because the atoms in each group have the same number of electrons in their outer shell, and it is the arrangement of these electrons that determines how atoms behave in chemical reactions.

Periods

As part of the ***menstrual cycle***, the ***uterus*** lining will break up and pass out of the vagina: this is a period (menstruation). Periods usually last for about four to seven days and happen about once a month. When a woman is ***pregnant*** her periods will stop until the baby is born.

Reproduction

Peristalsis

These are the muscle contractions that move food along the gut. There are rings of ***muscle*** inside the gut wall, and when these contract the gut gets narrower, so food is pushed along.

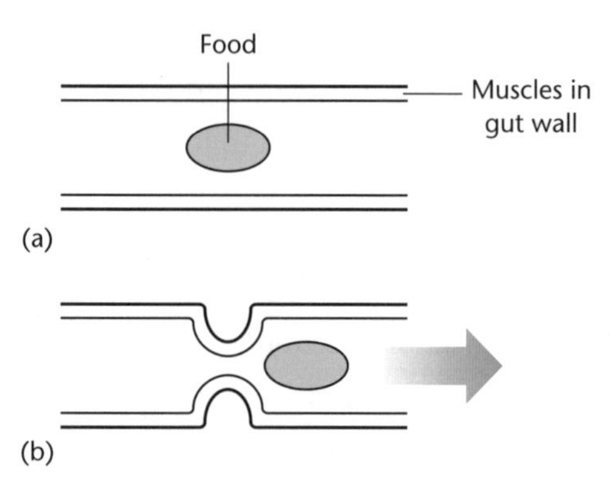

Muscle contraction moves food along the gut: (a) muscles relaxed; (b) muscles contract and food is pushed along

Digestive system

Group 1 = Alkali metals **Group 2** = Alkaline earth metals **Group 7** = Halogens **Group 0** = Noble gases

	Group 1	Group 2											Group 3	Group 4	Group 5	Group 6	Group 7	Group 0
Period 1							Hydrogen H 1											Helium He 2
Period 2	Lithium Li 3	Berylium Be 4											Boron B 5	Carbon C 6	Nitrogen N 7	Oxygen O 8	Fluorine F 9	Neon Ne 10
Period 3	Sodium Na 11	Magnesium Mg 12											Aluminium Al 13	Silicon Si 14	Phosphorus P 15	Sulphur S 16	Chlorine Cl 17	Argon Ar 18
Period 4	Potassium K 19	Calcium Ca 20	Sc 21	Ti 22	V 23	Chromium Cr 24	Manganese Mn 25	Iron Fe 26	Cobalt Co 27	Nickel Ni 28	Copper Cu 29	Zinc Zn 30	Ga 31	Germanium Ge 32	Arsenic As 33	Selenium Se 34	Bromine Br 35	Kr 36
Period 5	Rb 37	Sr 38	Y 39	Zr 40	Nb 41	Mo 42	Tc 43	Ru 44	Rh 45	Pd 46	Silver Ag 47	Cadmium Cd 48	In 49	Tin Sn 50	Sb 51	Te 52	Iodine I 53	Xe 54
Period 6	Cs 55	Ba 56	Lanthanides see below	Hf 72	Ta 73	W 74	Re 75	Os 76	Ir 77	Platinum Pt 78	Gold Au 79	Mercury Hg 80	Tl 81	Lead Pb 82	Bi 83	Po 84	Astatine At 85	Rn 86
Period 7	Fr 87	Ra 88	Actinides see below															

Lanthanides	La 57	Ce 58	Pr 59	Nd 60	Pm 61	Sm 62	Eu 63	Gd 64	Tb 65	Dy 66	Ho 67	Er 68	Tm 69	Yb 70	Lu 71
Actinides	Ac 89	Th 90	Pa 91	U 92	Np 93	Pu 94	Am 95	Cm 96	Bk 97	Cf 98	Es 99	Fm 100	Md 101	No 102	Lr 103

Short version of the periodic table

pH SCALE

The pH scale is a measure of acidity. It was devised by Carl Sorensen who was a brewer working in Copenhagen. Acids have pH values of less than seven and alkalis of over 7.

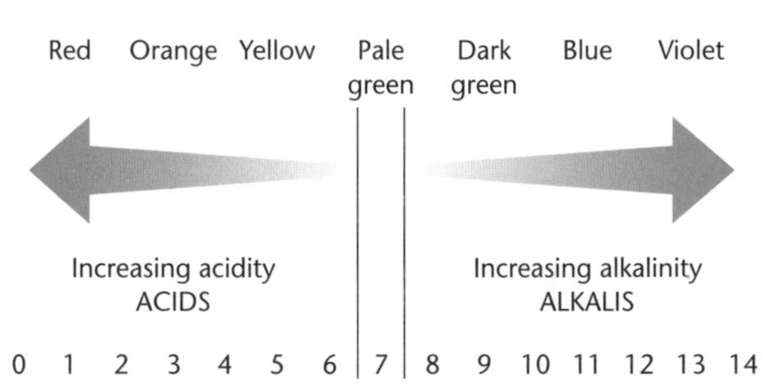

Indicators: the colour changes of universal indicator on the pH scale

pH scale

PHLOEM TUBE

These are tubes inside plants that carry sugar solutions (pronounced *flow-em tubes*).

The sugar is made in the leaves by ***photosynthesis*** and is moved to other parts of the plant through the phloem tubes, for example:

- to the roots to be changed into starch and stored,
- to the buds to give them energy to grow,
- to the fruits so that they will taste sweet.

PHOTOSYNTHESIS

This is how plants get the food they need to survive.

Photosynthesis is a chemical reaction that takes place in the ***leaves*** of plants in sunlight. Plants use water (from the soil) and ***carbon dioxide*** (from the air) to make sugar and oxygen. The ***word equation*** is:

$$\text{Water} + \text{Carbon dioxide} \xrightarrow{\text{light energy}} \text{Sugar} + \text{Oxygen}$$

The plant can change the sugar into starch and store it, or it can use the sugar as an energy source for growth. It can also be used to make other substances, e.g. protein and chlorophyll. As the plant stores starch or grows it will weigh more, so there is an increase in ***biomass*** (biomass is the amount of matter in an organism).

Some plant cells, e.g. ***palisade cells*** contain ***chlorophyll***, inside ***chloroplasts***. Chlorophyll is a green chemical that can trap light energy for photosynthesis. This is why photosynthesis can only occur in the green parts of plants.

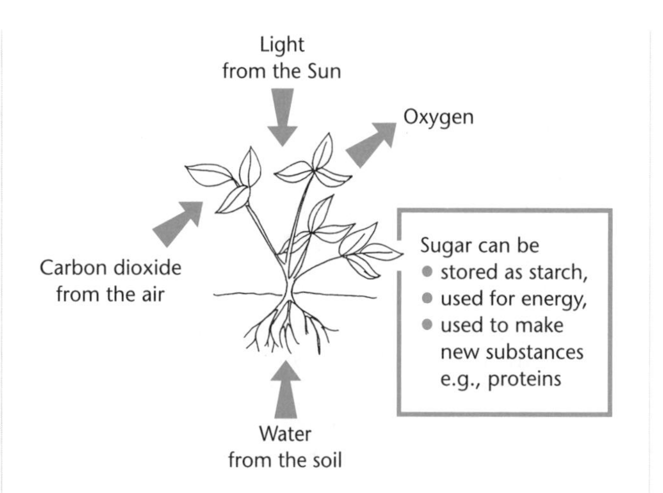

Photosynthesis

If leaves are *variegated* (have green areas and white, yellow or pink areas), only the green areas can photosynthesise.

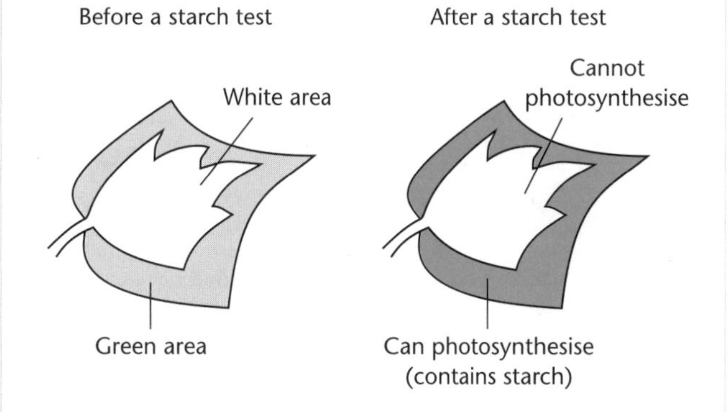

Variegated leaves

The main tests for photosynthesis are:

1. the ***starch test*** – the parts of the leaf that go black contain starch, so we can tell that photosynthesis has occurred here.
2. production of oxygen by ***pondweed*** – this is often used to investigate the rate of photosynthesis, because the amount of oxygen produced in a set time can be measured.

Appendix on p. 173.

PLACENTA

This is a very important organ during ***pregnancy*** – it acts as a life support system for the ***foetus***.

The placenta is attached to the ***uterus*** wall and it helps to keep the foetus alive by exchanging materials between the mother's blood and the foetal blood. The two types of blood are very close together, so substances can be exchanged easily, but they never mix.

Food substances and oxygen pass from the mother to the foetus, and waste products pass from the foetus to the mother.

Unfortunately some harmful things can pass from the mother to the foetus through the placenta, for example:

- ***drugs***, e.g. nicotine, alcohol, heroin
- ***viruses***, which cause disease, e.g. rubella (german measles).

These can damage or even kill the developing foetus, so the mother must avoid them if possible.

Once the baby has been born, the placenta comes off the wall of the uterus and is pushed out by contractions of the muscles. This is the third stage of ***birth*** (sometimes called afterbirth).

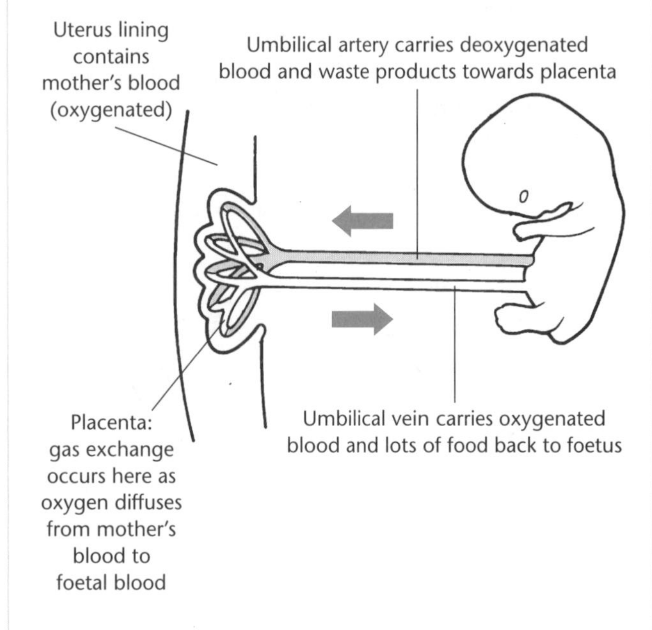
Uterus lining contains mother's blood (oxygenated)
Umbilical artery carries deoxygenated blood and waste products towards placenta
Placenta: gas exchange occurs here as oxygen diffuses from mother's blood to foetal blood
Umbilical vein carries oxygenated blood and lots of food back to foetus

The placenta

Reproduction

PLANET

A planet is an object that orbits around a ***star***. It will not be hot enough to give out light and is therefore seen by reflected light from the star. Each planet is attracted to the star at the centre by ***gravity*** and this attracting force keeps the planet in its orbit.

The planets in our ***solar system*** are of two main types. The four closest to the ***Sun*** are smaller than the ones further out and are *rocky* and more dense. They mostly have cores of iron and nickel. The planets further out are much colder and larger. They are *icy* with a rocky core. Pluto, which is furthest away, is icy but smaller. Many other stars may have a planet system like the Sun.

Solar system

PLANTS

All plants have two things in common:

1. their cells have a ***cell wall*** made of cellulose,
2. they make their own food by ***photosynthesis***.

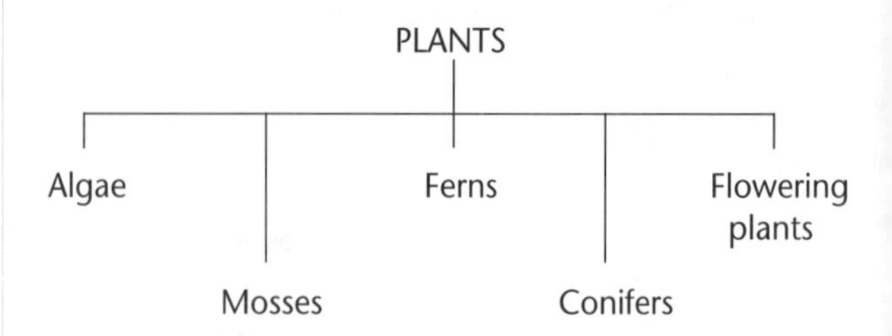
PLANTS
Algae
Ferns
Flowering plants
Mosses
Conifers

Plants are normally classified into five groups, but most of the information in this book is about flowering plants.

Algae, e.g. seaweeds

- simple plants with no proper roots, stems or leaves,
- live in water,
- no flowers, or seeds,
- reproduce by spores.

(See Figure on p. 4.)

Mosses, e.g. sphagnum

- simple plants with no proper roots,
- live in damp places,
- no flowers or seeds,
- reproduce by spores released from capsule.

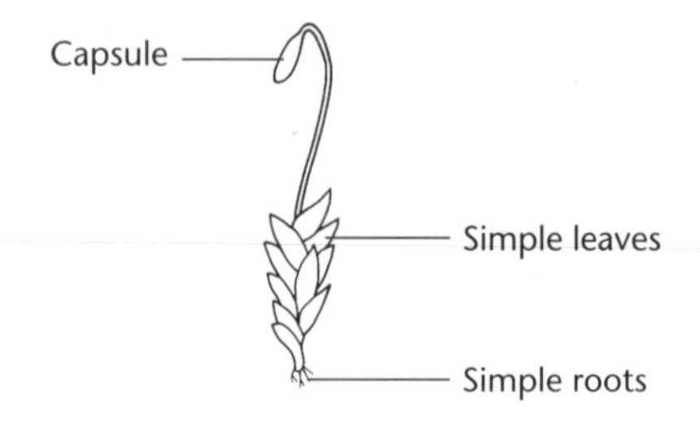
Capsule
Simple leaves
Simple roots

Ferns, e.g. bracken

- plants with simple roots, stems and leaves (called fronds),
- live in damp, shady places,
- no flowers or seeds,
- reproduce by spores.

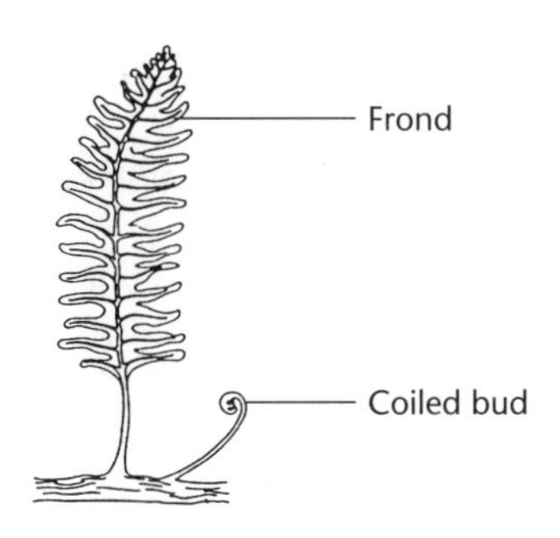

Conifers, e.g. pine

- large trees or shrubs with proper roots, stems and leaves,
- often live in dry areas,
- leaves are needle shaped,
- no flowers,
- produce seeds inside cones.

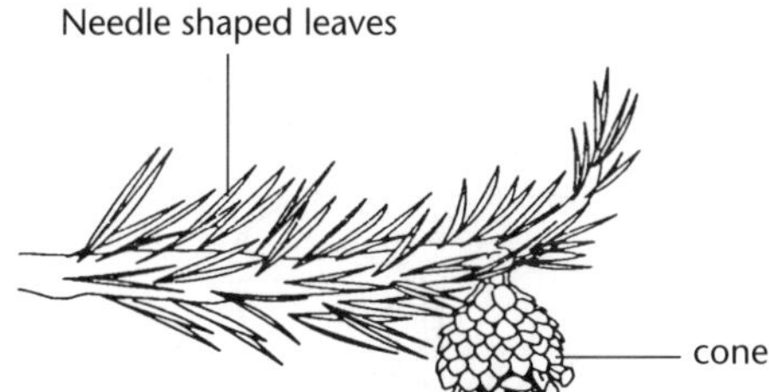

Flowering plants, e.g. grass, bluebell, daisy, oak

- plants have proper roots, stems and leaves,
- leaves may be long and thin (monocots) or broad (dicots),
- live in lots of habitats (land and water),
- have flowers containing reproductive organs,
- make seeds enclosed inside a fruit.

(See Figure on p. 3.)

✦ *Classification, Organs, Reproduction*

PLAQUE

This is a sticky film of ***bacteria*** and sugar, which coats the surface of the teeth and tongue. It is a problem because the bacteria feed on the sugar and produce acid, which can cause ***tooth decay***. Plaque can be removed by brushing and flossing the teeth thoroughly, but if it is allowed to harden it may be necessary for a dentist to remove it by polishing the teeth.

PLASMA

This is the pale, watery liquid found in the ***blood***. It is very important because it carries the following substances around the body:

- carbon dioxide,
- food substances,
- waste products, e.g. urea,
- hormones,
- drugs.

It also contains important plasma proteins, which help the blood to clot when we are injured, and which help to fight disease.

✦ *Circulatory system*

PLASTIC

✦ *Polymer*

PLATELETS

These are tiny cell fragments found in the ***blood***. They are important because they help the blood to clot when we are injured. This is necessary to:

- stop us losing large amounts of blood from a wound,
- form a scab that stops dirt and bacteria getting into the wound, and allows it to heal properly.

POLE (MAGNETIC)

A pole is an area on a ***magnet*** where the ***magnetic field*** is strongest.

✦ *Magnetic field, Magnets*

POLLEN

This is the male ***gamete*** (sex cell) in plants. It is made in the ***stamens*** of the plant, and transferred to the stigma in the process of ***pollination***. Some pollen grains are very small and light so they can be blown by the wind. All of us breathe them in during the spring and summer, but some people are allergic to them and so they suffer from hayfever.

✦ *Reproduction*

POLLINATION

This is the transfer of ***pollen*** from the anthers to the stigma. It is an important part of ***sexual reproduction*** in plants. Pollen cannot move by itself, so there are two main methods of pollination.

Insect pollination

Insects, e.g. bees, are attracted to ***flowers*** by their brightly coloured petals, pleasant scent and sugary nectar. They visit the flowers to feed on the nectar, and will accidentally brush against the anthers. Pollen grains stick to the insect's body and, when the insect visits another flower, they may be brushed off onto the stigma.

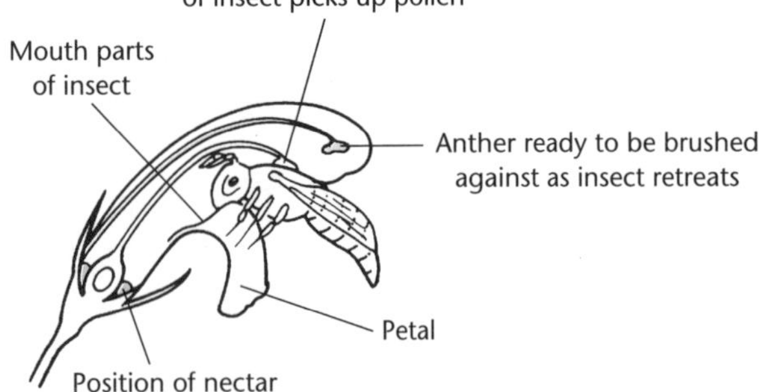

Insect pollination

Wind pollination

The anthers are large and hang outside the flower. When they burst open, pollen grains will be blown around by the wind. The pollen grains are very small and light, so they can be blown for long distances. The stigma of wind-pollinated plants is feathery, like a net, so pollen may be trapped in it. Wind-pollinated plants have to produce very large amounts of pollen because most of it will never reach the stigma.

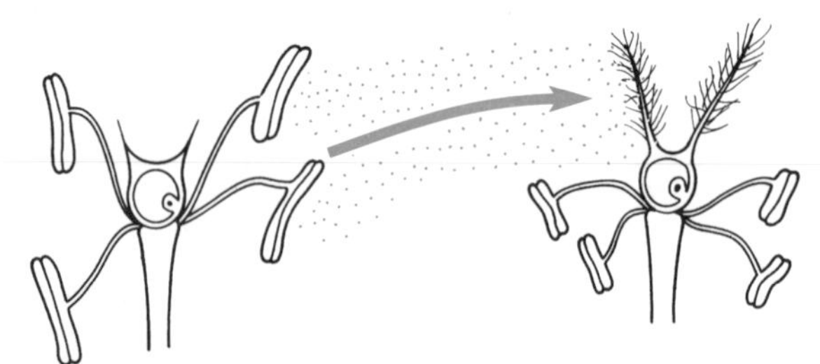

Wind pollination

Self-pollination means that the pollen is transferred from the anther to the stigma of the same plant.

Cross-pollination means that the pollen is transferred from the anther of one plant to the stigma of another plant. Cross-pollination helps to increase ***variation***.

Comparison of insect- and wind-pollinated plants

Insect-pollinated plants	*Wind-pollinated plants*
Large, brightly coloured petals	Small, green petals (or petals may be completely absent)
Nectar to attract insects	No nectar produced
May have a pleasant smell	No pleasant smell to attract insects
Stamens are short and enclosed within the petals	Stamens are long and hang outside the flower
Stigma is not feathery	Stigma is feathery like a net to trap pollen
Pollen grains are quite big and spiky, so that they will be stick to insects	Pollen grains are very small and light, so they will blown easily
Smaller amounts of pollen produced	Very large amounts of pollen produced

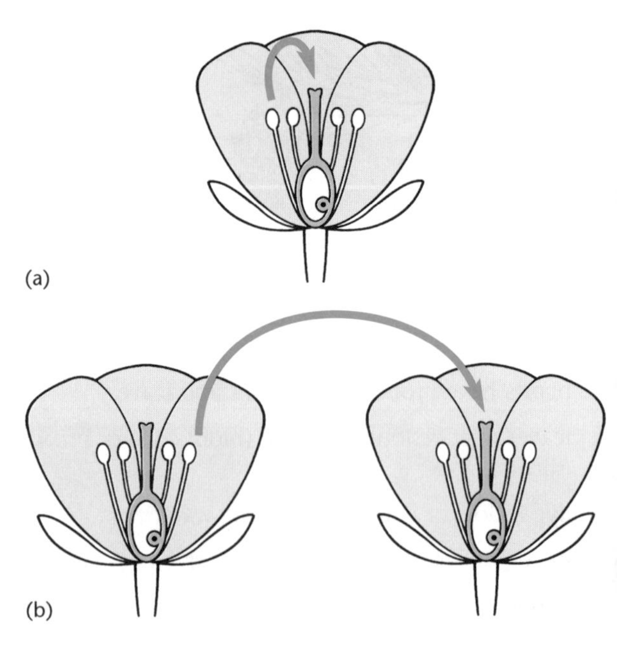

Types of pollination: (a) self-pollination; (b) cross-pollination

Reproduction

POLLUTION

A pollutant is a substance that contaminates its environment. The two most worrying types of pollution involve air and water.

- Air pollution is mainly caused by the burning of ***fossil fuels***, either in power stations or in cars. Gases such as sulphur dioxide, nitrogen dioxide and ozone react with the air and cause ***acid rain***.

- Drinking water is also polluted by a range of substances that are hazardous, such as nitrates from nearby arable land which has had fertilizer on it. Nitrates are very soluble and run off into the ground water. In some parts of East Anglia, tap water contains nitrate levels near to the World Health Organization recommended limits. High levels of nitrate may cause stomach cancer.

POLYMER

Plastics are more correctly called polymers. These are long chains made by joining small molecules called monomers. When the monomer ethene is joined by a polymerization reaction, polyethene is produced. This is more commonly called polythene. There are a wide range of polymers available and all of these have originally come from ***crude oil*** and have been produced by polymerization reactions. To help with the recycling of plastic material, most items now have the international recycling symbol stamped on them.

Society of Plastics Industry
(SPI) Identity Mark

Polyethylene terephtalate

High density polyethylene

Polyvinyl chloride

Low density polyethene

Polypropylene

Polystyrene

Abbreviations in common use in the UK for PVC (V) and PET (PETE) are not consistent with the SPI code.

Polymers

PONDWEED

This is often used in experiments to investigate the rate of ***photosynthesis***. When it is submerged in water, bubbles of oxygen come from the cut end of the stem.

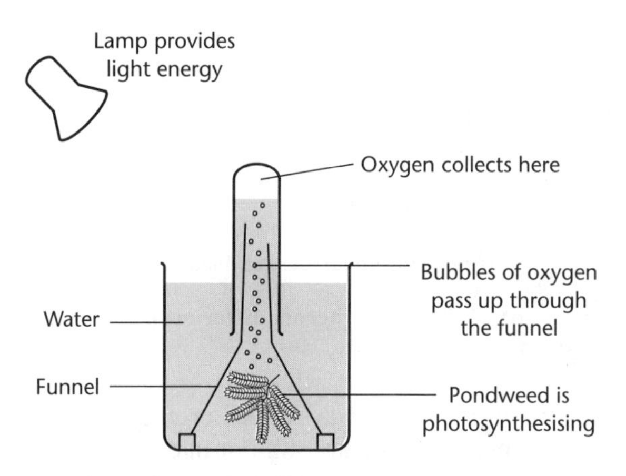

Measuring the rate of photosynthesis with pondweed

The *rate* of photosynthesis can be calculated in two ways:

1. count the number of bubbles released each minute,
2. collect the oxygen released in one hour in a measuring cylinder and read off the volume.

It is easy to prove that the gas collecting at the top of the tube is oxygen, because it will re-light a glowing splint.

These factors will change the rate of photosynthesis:

- amount of light,
- temperature,
- amount of carbon dioxide.

Appendix on p. 173.

POPULATION

This is all the organisms belonging to the same ***species*** that live in the same ***habitat***, e.g. you could study the population of:

- limpets in a rock pool,
- squirrels in a wood,
- buttercups in a field,
- dragonflies on a pond.

POTENTIAL DIFFERENCE (pd)

The potential difference between two places in an electric circuit is what drives current between them. pd is measured in ***volts*** (V). If you make the pd between the two places bigger (by using a battery with a bigger voltage) then more current will flow. The size of the current that flows also depends on the ***resistance*** between the two points.
In order to measure a pd you need to connect a ***voltmeter*** *across* the two points, i.e., in ***parallel*** with that part of the circuit. (See ***voltmeter***.)

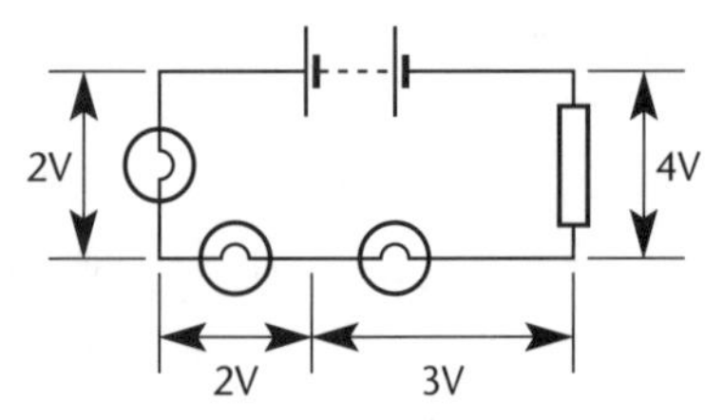

The pd across the battery terminals is 11V

The potential difference across different parts of a circuit in series will add

The idea of potential always causes problems when you first meet it. If you are still not happy about it, try thinking of the potential as equivalent to pressure in a piped water system. Just as the water flows from high pressure to low pressure, the current flows from high potential to low potential. As the water flows from higher to lower pressure it releases energy that can drive turbines. As the current flows from higher to lower potential it also releases energy that can be turned into other forms such as heat and light. The pump that drives the water is the source of both the pressure and the energy. The battery in the circuit is the source of both the potential and the energy.

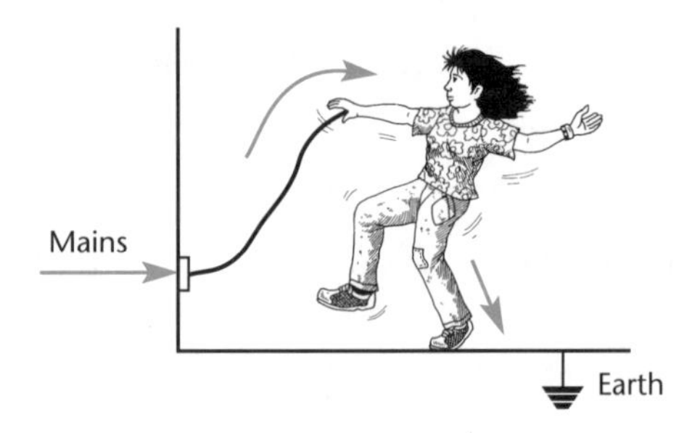

Electric shock as current goes to earth

You should also remember that the earth is at zero voltage (0V). Higher voltages will try to drive current down to this zero potential, which is why there is a danger of electric shock as 'mains' voltages try to drive current through you to earth.

Remember: Always remember that it is the current that moves and the pd that makes it go. Do not make nonsense statements in tests about voltages flowing round circuits!

CHECKPOINT

What would you use to measure pd?

What other factor, as well as pd will decide the current that flows?

Current, Electromotive force, Volt

POTENTIAL ENERGY

Potential energy is the ***energy*** that an object has because of its position or its condition.

If you stretch a spring then you store energy in it that is released when the spring is allowed back to its original length. In a similar way stretched elastic, a bent beam, a wound up spring or a taut bow all contain some potential energy that can quickly be transformed into other forms of energy.

Two magnets that are close to each other have the ability to do work as they attract or repel and have magnetic potential energy. Two electric charges will also have electrical potential energy when they are close together as the forces between them can be used to do work.

If you lift an object upwards then you store energy in it and that same quantity of energy can be recovered by allowing the object to return to its original level. The additional energy that the object contained at the higher position is called ***gravitational potential energy***.

Energy, Gravitational potential energy

POWER

Power is a measure of how *fast* you use ***energy***.

A power of one ***joule*** every second is called one watt (1W)

Energy

PRECIPITATE

This is an ***insoluble*** substance that appears in a solution. Precipitates can form when hot liquids cool down and a previously dissolved substance solidifies from the solution. If you have ever tried to make crystals, you will have produced the seed crystals in this way.

Another example of a precipitate is when you bubble carbon dioxide into ***limewater***. A fine white powder appears and the limewater goes cloudy as this precipitate of calcium carbonate is formed.

PREDATOR-PREY RELATIONSHIPS

A *predator* is a ***carnivore*** that feeds on other animals. The *prey* is the animal it eats.

If a predator relies mainly on one particular animal as its prey, the populations will be strongly affected by each other. For example, think about a simple food chain:

Algae ——► Limpets ——► Oystercatchers (birds)

If the number of oystercatchers decreases they will eat less limpets, so the number of limpets will increase.

When this happens, there will be lots of food available for the remaining oystercatchers, so they will breed and produce many young. All of these have to be fed, so the number of limpets will decrease.

Oystercatchers will be short of food and some of them will die. This gives the limpet numbers a chance to increase again. This cycle will be repeated over and over again.

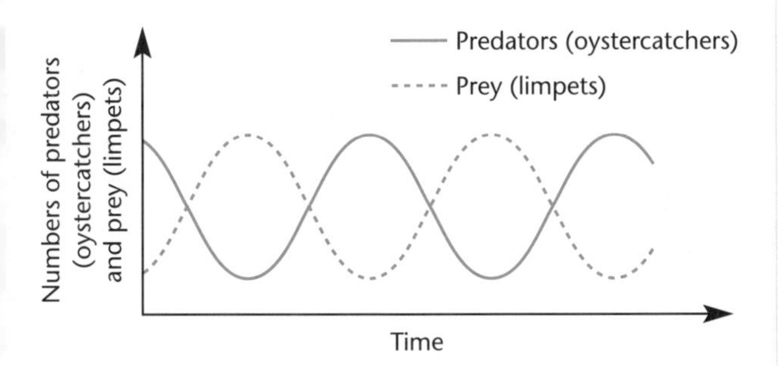

How numbers of predators and prey change over a period of time

CHECKPOINT

This graph shows how the numbers of plants, slugs and frogs changed over a period of time:

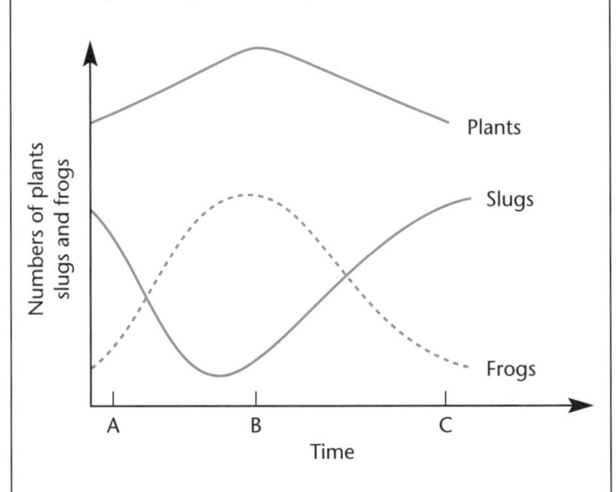

Can you

- explain why the number of slugs falls at time A?
- explain why the number of plants starts to rise at time A?
- explain why the number of frogs falls at time B?
- explain what would happen at point C?

Pregnancy

This is the time that a baby is developing inside the mother's ***uterus*** before birth. In humans, pregnancy lasts for about nine months.

During pregnancy a woman should make sure she does the following things so that she is more likely to have a healthy baby:

- eat a ***balanced diet*** with plenty of protein, vitamins and minerals,
- take regular ***exercise*** and get enough sleep,
- go to regular ante-natal check ups,
- do not ***smoke,***
- do not take ***drugs*** or medicines,
- do not drink ***alcohol,***
- avoid catching viral diseases, or make sure she has been ***vaccinated*** against them before getting pregnant.

Birth, Placenta, Reproduction

Pressure

Pressure is the effect of a ***force*** acting on an area.

A force acting on a small area makes a bigger pressure than the same force acting on a large area.

For examples:

- When you press in a drawing pin, the force acts on the tiny area at its point and the pressure is great enough to push into the board.
- Animals with a large weight will have large feet so that the pressure under the feet is small enough to stop them sinking into the ground.

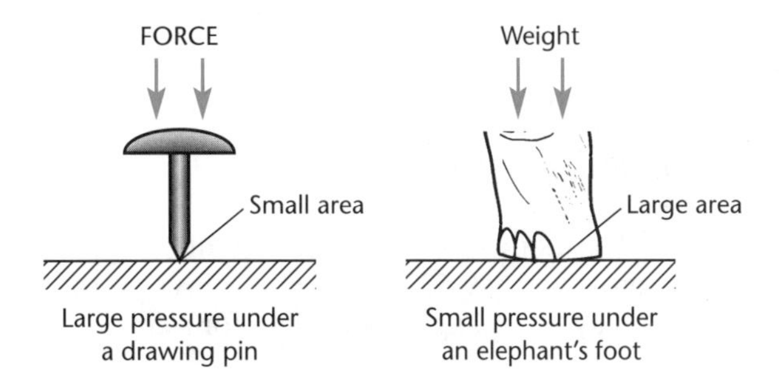

Some pressures

- The weight of a skier is spread out over a larger surface area so that he or she can stay on top of the snow. Snow shoes also spread weight over a bigger area.
- A knife will be sharp when its edge is very thin. When you push on the blade the area is small and the pressure is very high so that it cuts.

You can calculate the size of the pressure by using this equation.

$$\text{Pressure} = \frac{\text{Force}}{\text{Area}}$$

The force must be in newtons (N) and the area in m^2 or cm^2. The pressure will then be in N/m^2 or N/cm^2. 1 N/m^2 has a special name, the *pascal* (*Pa*), because we use it so often.

The force that you measure should always be at 90° to the area. It is called a *normal force.*

For example: a man weighs 780 N and stands on one foot so that the weight is on an area of 195 cm^2. What is the pressure on the floor?

$$\text{Pressure} = \frac{\text{Force}}{\text{Area}}$$

$$= \frac{780}{195}$$

$$= 4\ \text{N/cm}^2$$

(there are 10,000 cm^2 in 1 m^2 so 1 N/cm^2 = 10,000 Pa and the pressure under the foot is 40,000 Pa.)

If he stands on both feet, the area is doubled so that the pressure is halved and becomes 2 N/cm^2.

Standing on a stiletto heel with a small area can easily make a big enough pressure to damage a hard wooden floor.

For example: the pressure in a tyre is 160,000 Pa and it stands on 150 cm^2 of road. What is the force (weight) acting on the road?

160,000 Pa = 16 N/cm^2

$$\text{Pressure} = \frac{\text{Force}}{\text{Area}}$$

$$16 = \frac{\text{Force}}{150}$$

$$\text{Force} = 16 \times 150 = 2400\ \text{N}$$

If the car has four wheels, the total weight of the car is approximately 9,600 N, which means that the car has a mass of 960 kg – about right for a small family car.

> *CHECKPOINT*
>
> When you hammer a nail into wood the force at its point is the same as the force of the hammer on its head but the ________ on the wood is ________ because the area is smaller.
>
> Write down the equation for pressure.
>
> What is the name of the special unit for pressure?

In many of these problems the force is a ***weight*** and causes the pressure by acting downwards on a certain area. In ***gases*** this is *not* true and small weights of gas can make large pressures. A gas is made from a large number of ***particles*** that are small but move very fast. Each time one of these particles hits a surface it pushes on it a little bit. Because there are such huge numbers of the particles this becomes a continuous force making a pressure on the surface. This means that air pressure is NOT caused by the weight of air above you pressing down but by the particles of the gases in the air bumping into things. As the particles are moving in all directions the pressure also acts in all directions and not just downwards.

Force

PRIESTLY, JOSEPH (1733–1804)

Joseph Priestly was a church minister who was very interested in science. He discovered *nitrogen* in 1772 and two years later is thought to have discovered the gas that Lavoisier had also experimented with, namely ***oxygen***. English textbooks usually say that Priestly was the person who discovered oxygen.

PRINCIPLE OF MOMENTS

This says that when an object is balanced so that it is not turning, the clockwise ***moment*** will be equal in size to the anticlockwise moment.

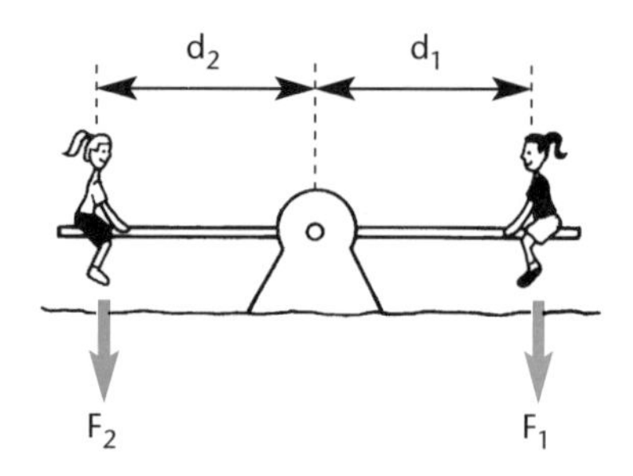

Playing on a see-saw

The two children on the see-saw will only balance each other when the clockwise moment ($F_1 \times d_1$) is the same as the anticlockwise moment ($F_2 \times d_2$) so that

$$F_1 \times d_1 = F_2 \times d_2$$

Clockwise moments = Anticlockwise moments

If the child on the right is heavier than her friend (F_1 is bigger than F_2) then she can still balance her friend as long as she can move further along the see-saw towards the middle so that d_1 is smaller than d_2 and the equation works again.

If there is more than one turning force, such as two children on the same side of the see-saw, then do F × d for each one and add those that turn in the same direction to find the total.

For example: Helen sits 1.5m from the centre of a see-saw and weighs 400 N. Her friend Julia sits on the other side balancing the see-saw. How far is she from the centre if she only weighs 300 N?

Helen's moment = Force × distance
= 400 × 1.5
= 600 Nm

Julia's moment = Force × distance
= 300 × d

These must be equal for the see-saw to balance so:

300 × d = 600
d = 2 m from the centre

> *CHECKPOINT*
>
> Amit lays his pencil on the desk and then balances his ruler on it. He puts a 10 g mass on the ruler 10 cm from the pencil and balances it with his rubber, which is only 8 cm from the pencil. What is the mass of his rubber?
>
> Hint: Draw the system first and mark the measurements on the diagram – it always helps!

Lever, Moment, Turning forces

PRODUCER

This is the organism at the start of a ***food chain***. It makes its own food by ***photosynthesis***.

All plants are producers.

PROTEIN

This is one of the food groups making up a ***balanced diet***. It is needed for:

- making new cells (for ***growth*** or replacement), so it is sometimes called a body building food,
- normal body functioning, e.g. making ***enzymes*** and ***hormones***.

It is found in meat, fish, pulses (peas and beans), nuts, milk, eggs and cheese.

If we eat too much protein, the excess is broken down in the ***liver*** and changed into ***urea***. This urea is removed from the body in ***urine***.

If we eat too little of protein, this can cause serious problems, particularly in children. Children will not grow properly and they will feel weak and tired. In severe cases they have a ***deficiency disease*** called kwashiorkor.

PROTOCTISTS

In some books these are called Protozoa or Protists.

They are all microscopic, single-celled organisms. Some live in water or soil, e.g. *Amoeba*, and some live inside other organisms and cause disease, e.g. *Plasmodium* causes malaria.

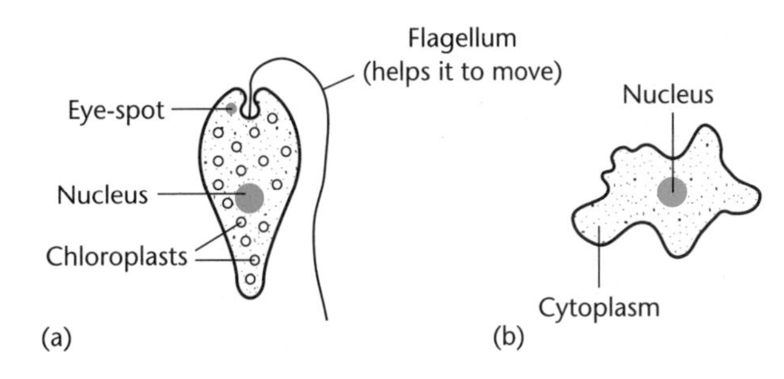

Protocists: (a) Euglena; (b) Amoeba

Some Protoctists are like plants, and make their own food by ***photosynthesis***, e.g. *Euglena*.

Some Protoctists are like animals, and feed on particles from their surroundings, e.g. *Amoeba*. They are usually 0.1–1mm long, and reproduce ***asexually*** to form a ***clone***.

PROTON

This is one of the particles found in the ***nucleus*** of atom. Protons have a positive charge and their mass is very small. Each proton has a mass of one atomic mass unit.

Atom

PUBERTY

This is the time around adolescence when the sex organs become fully developed. It occurs between the ages of nine and sixteen, usually earlier in girls than boys, and it is controlled by sex ***hormones***. Many physical and mental changes occur at this time:

Girls

- ovaries start to produce eggs,
- periods start,
- breasts develop,
- hips widen,
- vagina and uterus grow bigger,
- body hair grows (underarm and pubic hair),
- grows taller,
- may develop spots,
- more likely to have body odour,
- feel more mature,
- starts to be sexually attracted to others,
- may have pre-menstrual tension,
- can become pregnant.

Boys

- testes start to produce sperm,
- may have wet dreams,
- testes and penis grow bigger,
- body hair grows (underarm, pubic and chest hair),
- facial hair grows (beard and moustache),
- shoulders broaden,
- voice breaks (deepens),
- grows taller,
- may develop spots,
- more likely to have body odour,
- feel more mature,
- starts to be sexually attracted to others.

Reproduction

PULSE RATE

You can feel a pulse when an ***artery*** runs close to the skin. Counting the pulse rate is an easy way of measuring the person's heart rate.

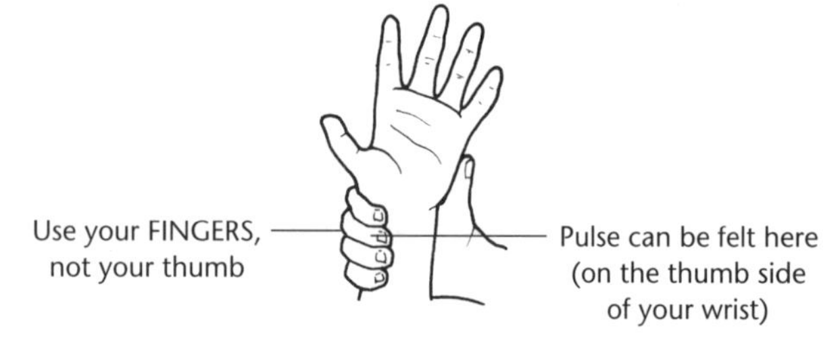

Measuring pulse rate

When a person is resting, their heart rate is normally about 70 beats per minute, but this increases if they are exercising or if they are frightened.

The time for a person's pulse rate to go back to normal after exercise is called the recovery time. The fitter a person is, the shorter their recovery time will be.

Circulatory system, Exercise, Fitness, Heart

PUMPED STORAGE

This is a way of storing ***energy*** until it is needed.

It is cheaper to run electrical generators in power stations all the time rather than starting and stopping them on demand, especially since the demand for electricity varies a lot during the day. In this system there are two large lakes that are used as reservoirs. One is at quite a large height above the other. When demand is low, the electricity is used to pump water from the lower reservoir into the higher one. The energy will have been stored as ***gravitational potential energy*** in the water. When there is a greater demand for electricity, the water flows back down a pipe from the higher to the lower reservoir and passes though a turbine as it goes. The turbine drives a generator that changes the energy into ***electrical energy***.

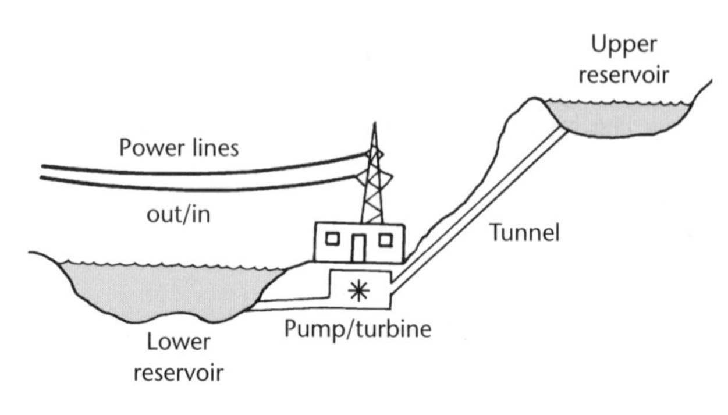

A pumped storage system

If you live near enough, or go for a holiday, there are two of these in north Wales that are worth a visit.

Biomass, Energy, Geothermal energy, Hydroelectric power, Solar energy, Tidal energy, Wave power, Wind power

PYRAMID OF BIOMASS

This shows the ***mass*** of organisms at each stage of a ***food chain***. For example:

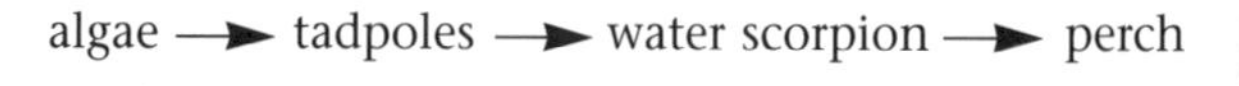

If all the organisms at each stage were collected and weighed you could draw a pyramid where the length of the bar was proportional to the mass of organisms at each stage of the food chain.

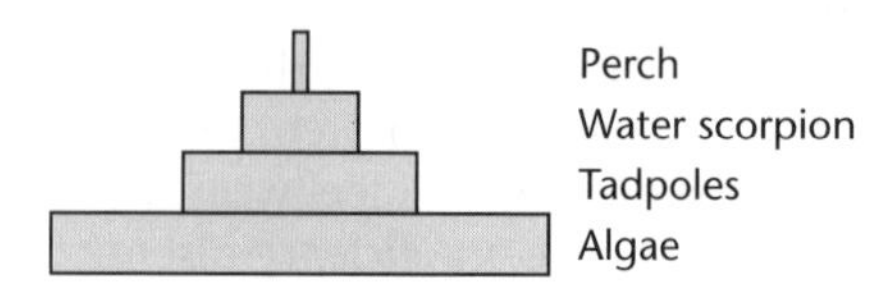

Pyramid of biomass

Pyramids of biomass are always the right shape, because they take account of the size of the organisms involved.

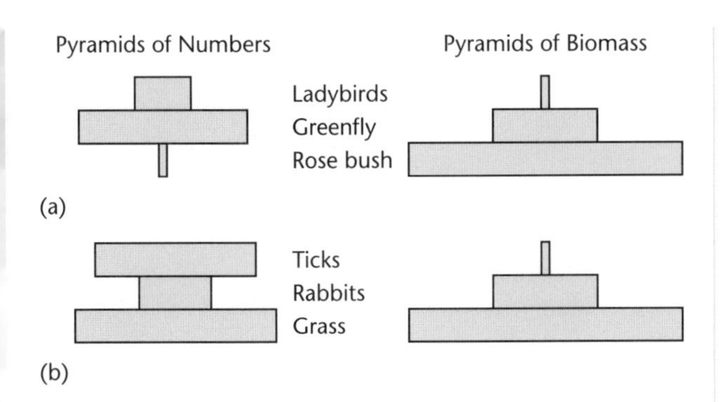

Pyramids of biomass: (a) involving a large plant; (b) involving parasites

Energy in the environment, Pyramid of numbers

PYRAMID OF NUMBERS

This shows the *number* of organisms at each stage of a food chain. For example:

algae ⟶ tadpoles ⟶ water scorpion ⟶ perch

In this typical pond food chain, there might be thousands of algae (microscopic plants), hundreds of tadpoles, about 50 water scorpions and two perch, so the pyramid of numbers would look like that shown on the page opposite.

The length of each bar is proportional to the numbers of organisms at that stage of the food chain.

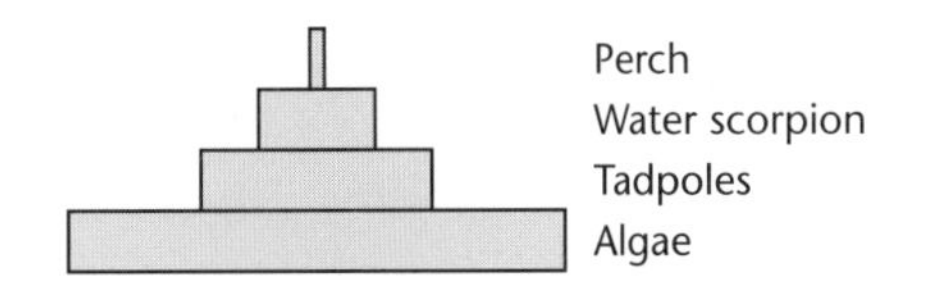

Typical pyramid of numbers

Sometimes the pyramid is the 'wrong shape', for example:
A pyramid is this shape (a) when lots of animals live on one large plant.

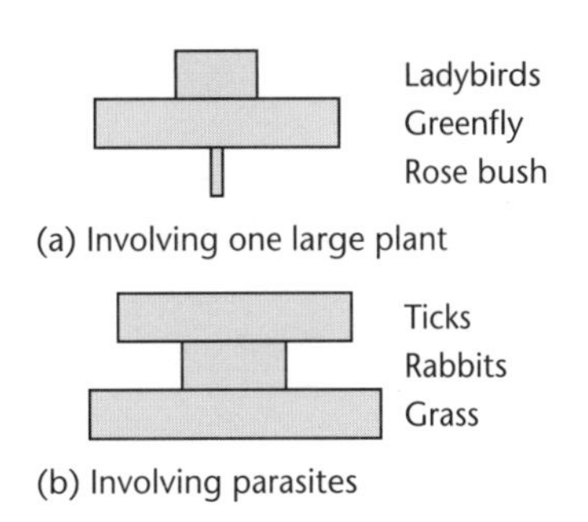

Oddly-shaped pyramids of numbers

A pyramid is this shape (b) when lots of parasites, e.g. ticks, fleas, lice, live on one animal.

Pyramids of numbers do not take account of the size of organisms in the food chain.

Energy in the environment, Pyramid of biomass

QUADRAT

This is a frame, usually made of thin metal, which is used to collect data in ecology.

It is placed on the ground, and the plants or animals inside it are identified. It can be used to:

- find out about the *variety* of organisms, i.e., how many species there are,
- find out about the *number* of organisms,
- find out about the *distribution* of organisms, i.e., where they are.

Quadrats are used to sample the area you are studying. It is not normally possible to count all the plants in a field, but you can place the quadrat *randomly*, e.g. by throwing it 20 times, and count the plants inside the quadrat.

Most quadrats are 0.5m × 0.5m in size, so they have an area of $0.25m^2$.

They are most useful when studying animals that do not move, e.g. limpets, barnacles, and plants.

CHECKPOINT

A student threw a quadrat ten times and counted the number of daisy plants inside the quadrat each time. Here are the results.

Quadrat number	1	2	3	4	5	6	7	8	9	10
Number of daisy plants	0	6	11	3	2	10	0	0	1	4

What was the average number of daisy plants?

The quadrat has an area of 0.25 m^2. If the student is investigating a garden with an area of 100 m^2, can you estimate the number of daisy plants in the whole garden?

Distribution, Ecology

Radiation

Radiation is when ***particles*** or ***waves*** travel outwards from a source carrying ***energy***. There are a lot of times when this happens and it is *not* always dangerous!

Radiation	*Source*	*Detector*
Sound	Vibration	Ear
Light	Hot objects	Eye
Gamma rays	Radioactive materials	Geiger tube
Radio waves	Radio transmitters	Radio

Light, Sound

Radiation of heat

Heat is radiated from hot objects as infra-red radiation.

Infra-red radiation

Rate of reaction

Some chemical reactions take place very slowly. Rusting, for example, is quite a slow reaction, although hydrogen reacting with oxygen is a very rapid reaction. Chemical reactions take place when the reactant particles collide with each other.

There are a number of ways of *speeding up* a chemical reaction. Each of the following conditions help reactants collide more frequently.

- *Increase the temperature*. The particles move faster when they are hotter and so they are likely to bump into each other more frequently.
- *Increase the concentration*. If there are more particles in total in a given space, then they are more likely to collide.
- *Increase the surface area*. If solid or 'lumpy' particles are spread out over a greater surface area, this provides more opportunities for particles to collide.
- *Use a catalyst*. A catalyst helps speed up the reaction but does not react itself. It is possible to think of a catalyst as a waiting or holding area. One reactant is held still, which increases the likelihood of reactants colliding.

Reactions happen when particles collide

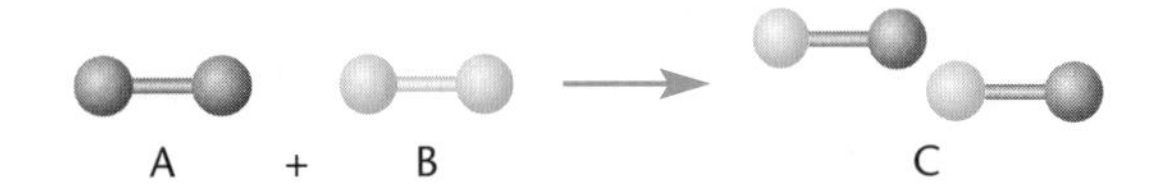

* Increasing temperature

COLD

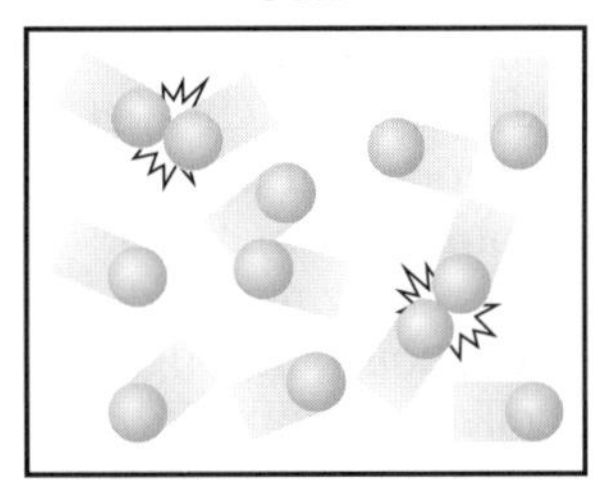

Slow moving particles, few collisions and low energy collisions
SLOW REACTION

HOT

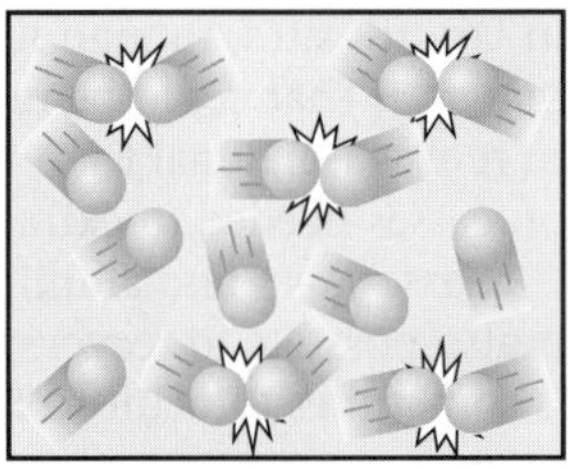

Fast moving particles, many collisions and high energy collisions
FAST REACTION

* Increasing concentration

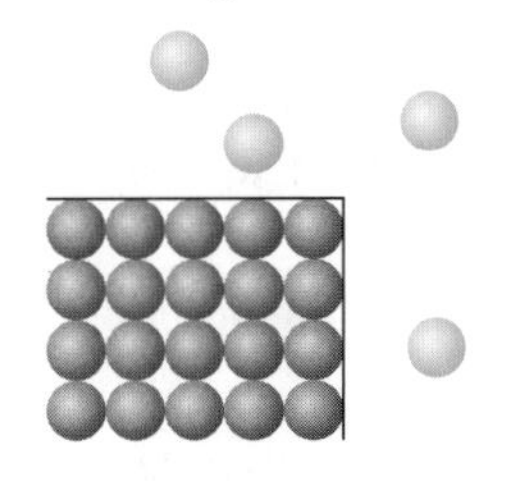

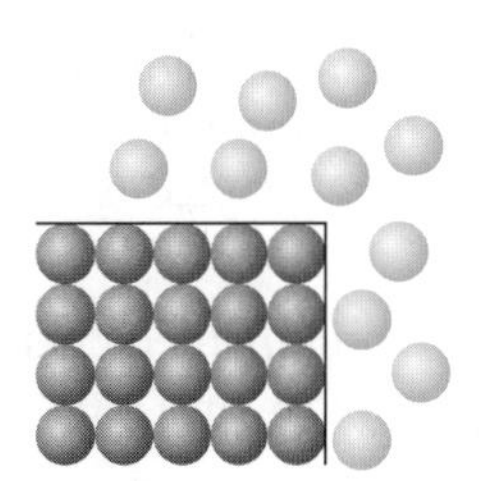

* Increasing surface area

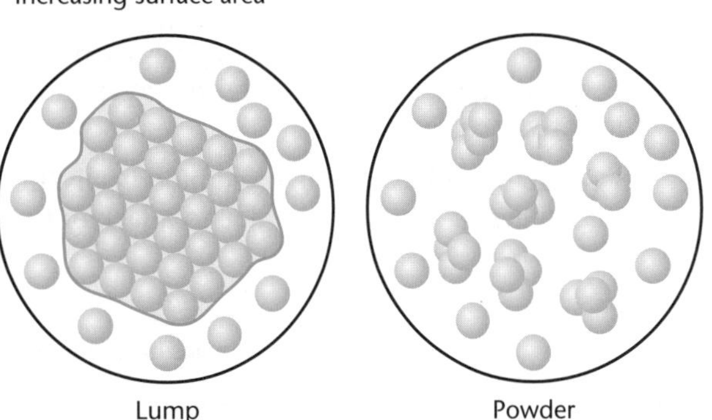

* use a catalyst

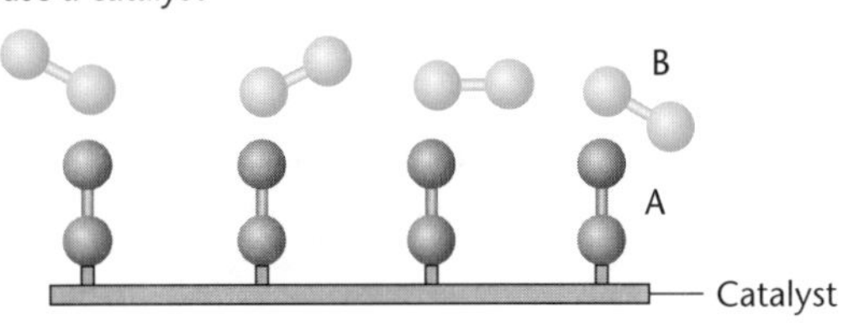

Increasing the rate of reaction

Reaction

Chemical reaction, Rate of reaction

Reactivity series

Metal reactivity series

Recycling

The ***Earth*** is our main source of materials. It is important that we recycle materials because they will eventually be used up.

Every year, about 30 million tonnes of rubbish are thrown away in the UK alone. Most of this is buried in landfill sites, though it contains very valuable materials that could be recycled. It is often cheaper to re-use a material than to go through all the processes needed to extract it from a raw material.

Glass, paper and aluminium are easily recycled. It is also possible to recycle plastic rubbish although it is sometimes difficult to find collection points.

Red blood cells

These are tiny, disc-shaped cells and there are very large numbers of them in the ***blood*** (about five million per ml of blood).

Their function is to carry oxygen around the body, and they are adapted (suitable) for this in several ways:

- they contain a red chemical called ***haemoglobin***, which joins with oxygen,
- they have no nucleus, so they can contain large amounts of haemoglobin,
- their shape (biconcave disc shape) gives them a large surface area, so they can absorb oxygen more efficiently.

If a person does not have enough red blood cells, he or she has anaemia. This is often due to a lack of iron in the diet.

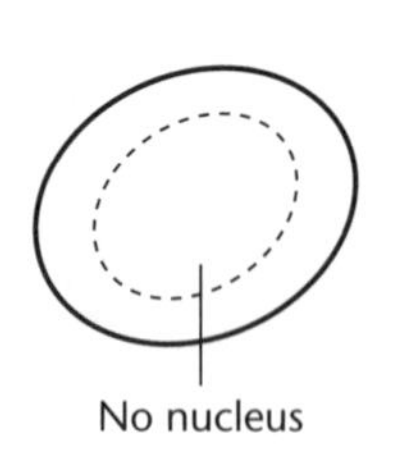

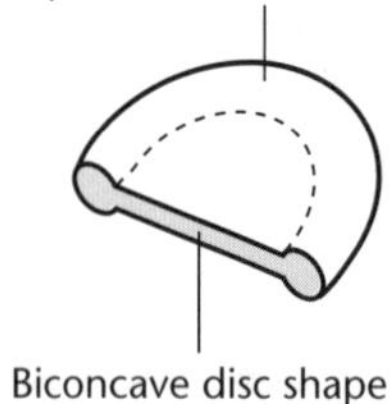

Red blood cells

Circulatory system, Deficiency diseases

Redox

A reaction involving ***reduction*** and ***oxidation***.

Reduction

A reduction reaction often involves the removing of oxygen. It is the opposite of ***oxidation***, but both reactions may occur together, in a ***redox*** reaction.

Reflection

Waves can be reflected from a suitable surface.

Hard surfaces will reflect sound waves and the waves come that back are heard as an ***echo***.

Polished, shiny surfaces will reflect light. Coloured surfaces reflect the colour of light that you see and absorb the other colours.

When waves are reflected they obey the *laws of reflection*. Each narrow straight beam will be reflected so that:

1. the angle of incidence = the angle of reflection,
2. the angle of incidence and the angle of reflection both lie on the same plane.

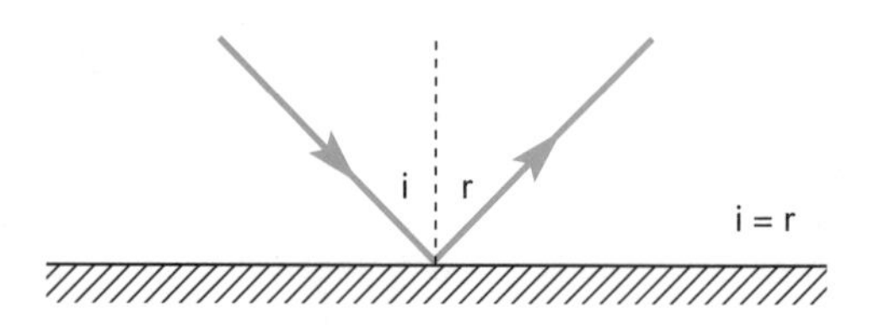

Laws of reflection

i = r

You must remember that both angles are measured from the ***normal***, which is a line at 90° to the surface of the reflector. In the diagram, i is the angle of incidence and r is the angle of reflection. You can check that all this is true by using a strip of plane mirror and a ray box to reproduce the rays in the diagram on a piece of plain paper. To make diagrams simple, mirrors are drawn as a line with lots of small 'hatch' lines on the *back* of the mirror to show the silvering.

When light rays from an object reflect from a plane mirror, the reflected rays will produce an image. We can work out where this must be from the laws of reflection.

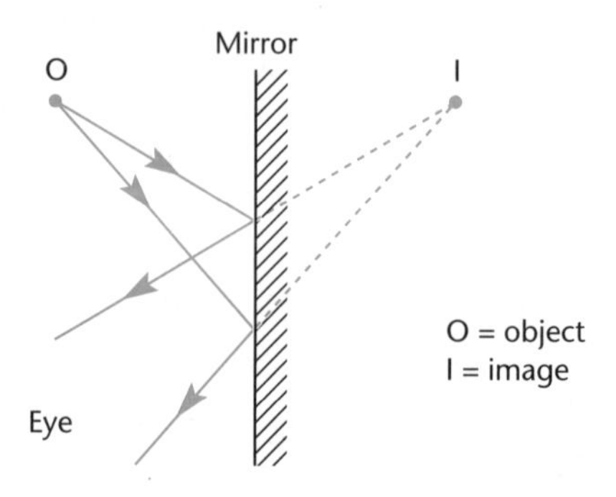

The image in a plane mirror

The diagram shows that the eye will see an image of the object that will always obey the following rules:

1. a line from the image to the object will cross the mirror at 90°,
2. the object and the image are both the same distance from the mirror,
3. the image is a *virtual* image.

Applying these rules to a more complicated shape such as my initial (K) in the diagram shows that the image will always obey some more rules!

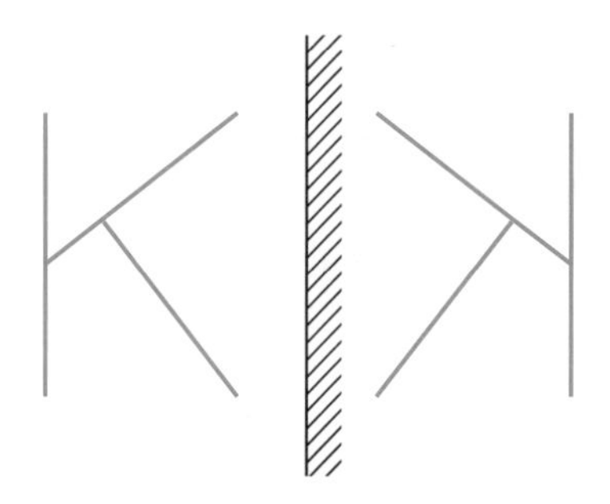

Reflecting letters

4. the image is the same size as the object. It sometimes *seems* to be smaller because it is further away!
5. the image is laterally inverted. This means that it is turned sideways but not upside down. You should check these rules by drawing some images for yourself – perhaps your initials are suitable? – remember to draw the plane mirror with the symbol that has been used in these diagrams.

Light

Refraction

Refraction is a change of direction of a ***wave*** when it goes from one material into another. It is caused by the change of ***velocity*** of the wave.

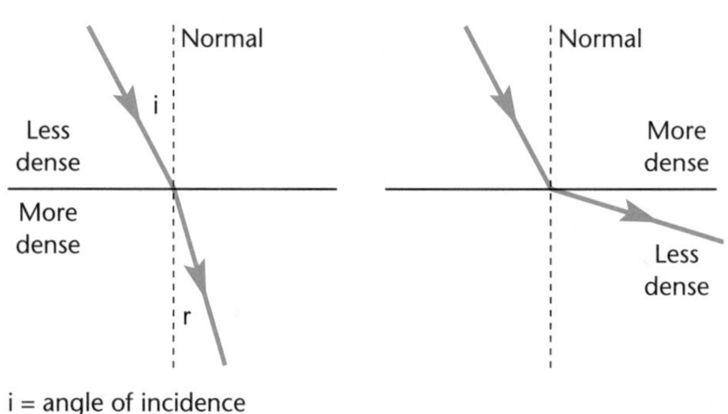

Refraction

You will see this happen with light waves. When a light wave goes from one material into a more dense material it is bent towards the ***normal***. When it goes from a more dense into a less dense material it is bent away from the normal.

When light goes through a glass block as in the diagram it will leave parallel to the direction that it entered. It will have been bent towards the normal when it went in and away from the normal when it came out.

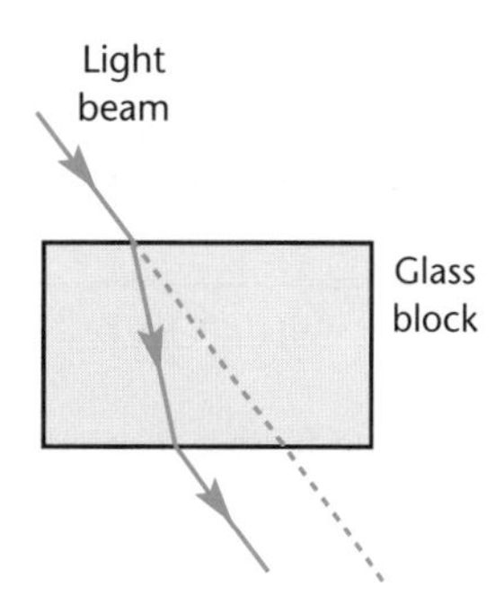

Refraction in a glass block

You can easily see this if you put a glass block on a piece of paper and send a narrow beam of light through it from a ray box.

The beam is refracted because one edge of it is slowed down before the other edge so that each wave is turned as it crosses the surface.

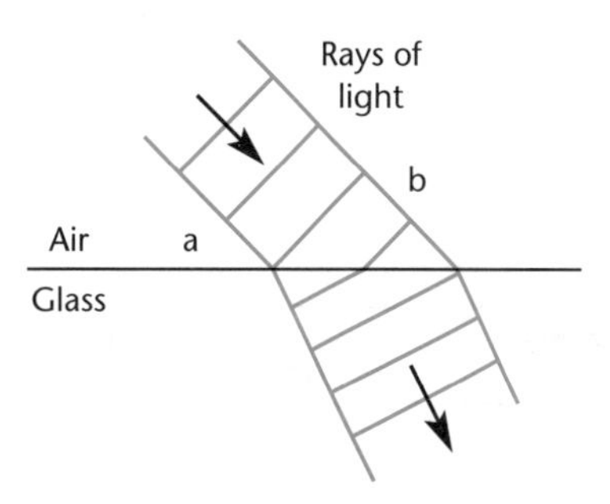

Refracting waves

In the diagram side *a* of the ray goes into the glass first and is slowed down before side *b*. This bends the ray towards the normal. Notice that the ***wavelengths*** of the waves inside the glass are shorter than outside. This is because there are still the same number of waves each second (the same ***frequency***) but they are going more slowly so they have to be shorter to fit into the smaller space.

If the ray is travelling along the normal then both edges of the ray are slowed down at the same time and the ray goes straight on in the same direction. The waves will still be slower and get shorter.

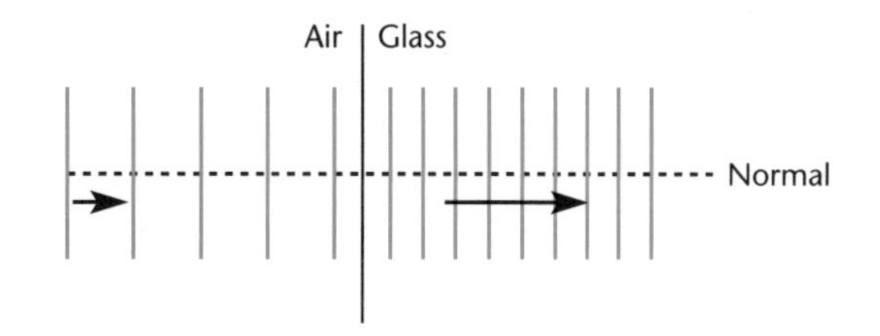

Waves along a normal

All waves are refracted. Sometimes it is less obvious than with light and glass blocks. Lenses work by refracting the light as it goes in and out so that it is going in the direction that you need. Sound waves can be refracted by sending them through gases of different density, such as air and carbon dioxide.

You can even focus sound a little by sending it through a balloon of carbon dioxide, which behaves a bit like a lens does with light waves.

> *CHECKPOINT*
>
> When light waves go from a more dense to a ______ dense materials they are bent ______ the ________ .

Apparent depth, Dispersion, Light, Reflection

RELAY

A relay is used so that one electric ***circuit*** can switch another circuit on and off. This can be very useful as you can use a small switch with thin wires to switch big currents or voltages in a separate circuit.

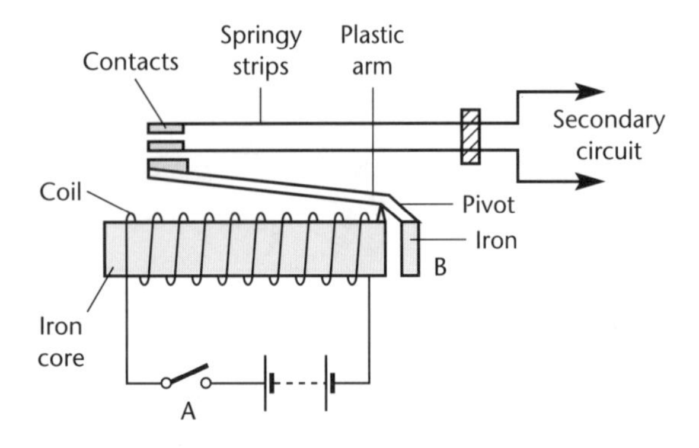

The relay

When switch A is pressed, ***current*** flows through the coil and the iron core is magnetized. This first circuit is often called the primary circuit. The iron core now attracts the piece of iron (B) in the end of the plastic lever and the plastic arm pushes together the contacts of the other circuit. The second (secondary) circuit has now been turned on. If the primary circuit is turned off, the ***electromagnet*** no longer attracts the iron in the lever and the springy metal strips holding the contacts push them apart. The secondary circuit is also turned off.

Uses

You may have an light outside at home that comes on automatically when it gets dark. The light sensor will be in a low voltage circuit that turns the mains lamp on through a relay.

The small button inside a lift will switch the large current for the lift motor through a relay.

There are several uses in a car including turning the headlights on and off by a small switch on the steering column. The thin wires to this switch cannot carry the current for the headlight bulbs so there is a relay in the engine compartment.

In a similar way there is a relay to control the larger current for the heated rear windscreen.

> *CHECKPOINT*
>
> Show someone the diagram for the relay and explain to them how it works.
>
> Tell them two uses for the relay.

Electromagnet

REPRODUCTION

This is an important ***life process***. It means making new individuals (offspring) that are like the parents. There are two types of reproduction, ***asexual*** and ***sexual*** reproduction.

Asexual reproduction

This occurs in many plants, in microbes and in some simple animals. Only one parent is involved, and the offspring are *identical* to the parent and to each other. They are sometimes called ***clones***.

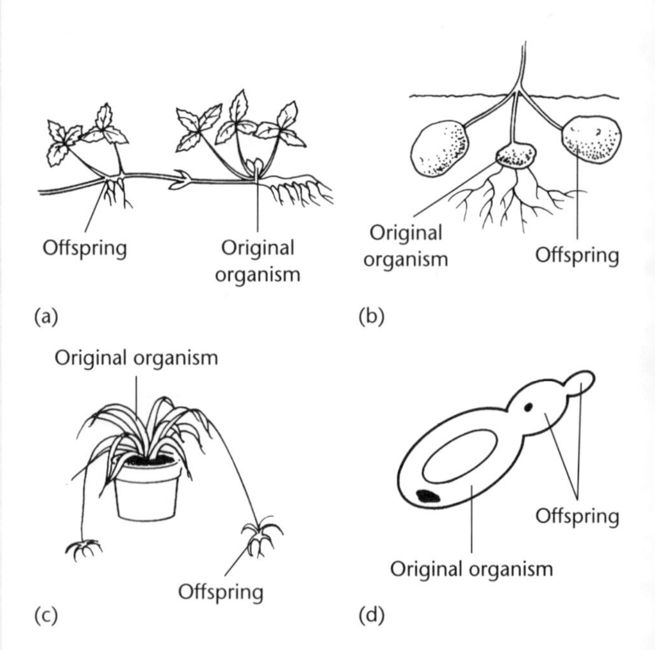

Asexual reproduction: (a) in strawberry plants (runners), (b) in potato plants (tubers), (c) in spider plants, (d) in yeast (budding)

Sexual reproduction

This occurs in most living things (plants and animals). Usually two parents are involved, and the offspring are *similar*, but not identical, to the parents and each other.

Sexual reproduction always involves the joining of two sex cells (***gametes***) in a process called ***fertilization***.

In *humans*, the gametes are **ova** and **sperm**.
In *plants*, the gametes are **ovules** and **pollen** grains.

Reproduction in humans

In humans, the male and female reproductive systems are completely different because they have different functions:

male
- to make **sperm** (gametes),
- to get them as close as possible to the ovum,

female
- to make **ova** (gametes),
- to provide a safe place for the baby to grow during **pregnancy**.

The male and female reproductive systems do not develop fully until the person reaches **puberty**. This occurs around ages 9 to 16, and is usually earlier in girls than in boys. After this, a girl produces ova and boys make sperm, so girls could become pregnant if they have **sexual intercourse**.

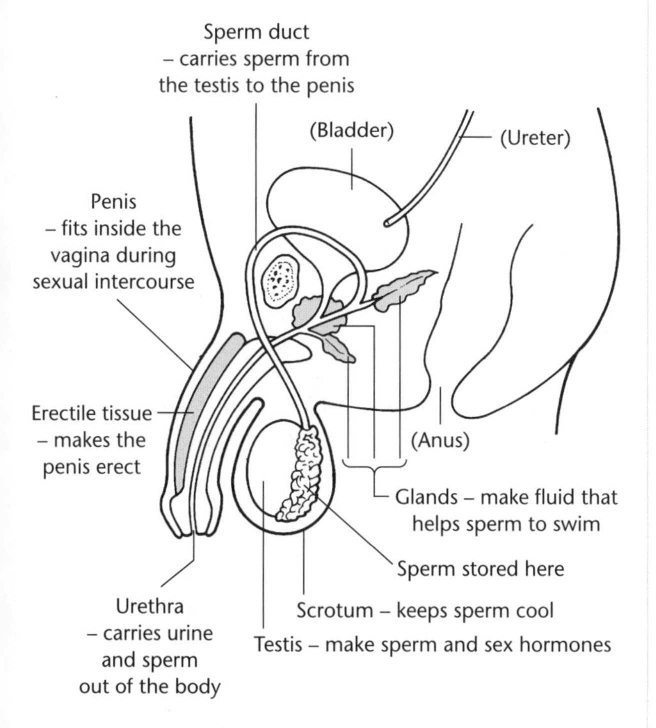

Male reproductive system

Once each month an ovum (egg cell) develops inside one of the ovaries and is released into the fallopian tube – this process is called **ovulation**. The ovum moves through the fallopian tube towards the uterus, and if it meets sperm in the fallopian tube (after sexual intercourse), it can be **fertilized** to form a **zygote**.

If it is fertilized, the zygote will continue to move towards the uterus, dividing to make more and more cells. Once it reaches the uterus it will sink into the soft, blood-filled lining – this is called *implantation*, and the woman is now pregnant.

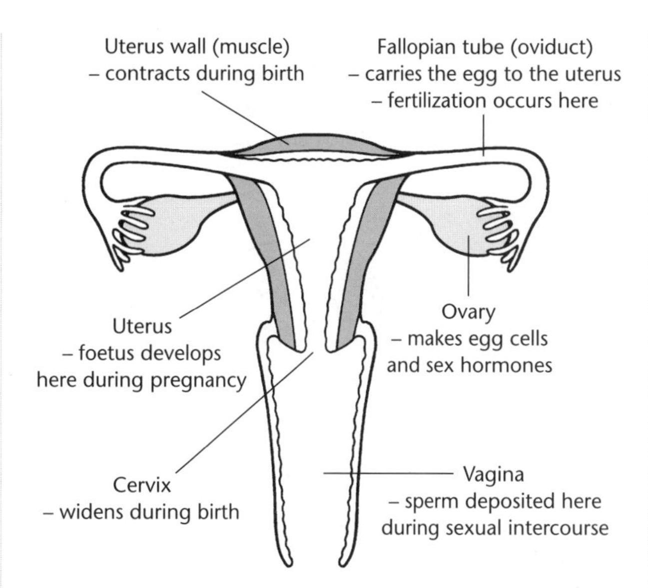

Female reproductive system

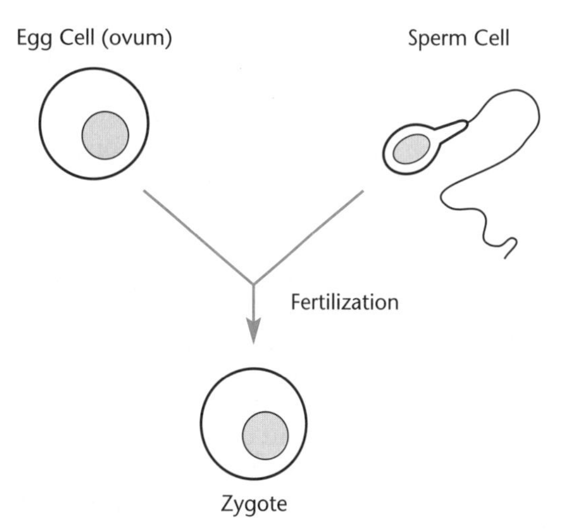

Fertilization

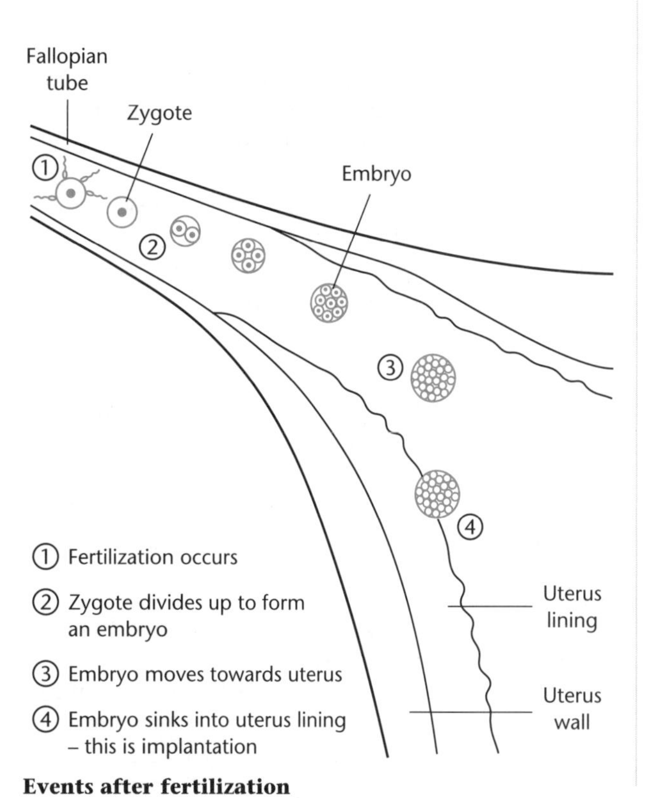

Events after fertilization

The ball of cells will grow and develop, first into an ***embryo***, then into a ***foetus***. The ***placenta*** will develop, and this helps to keep the foetus alive by exchanging substances between the mother and the foetus.

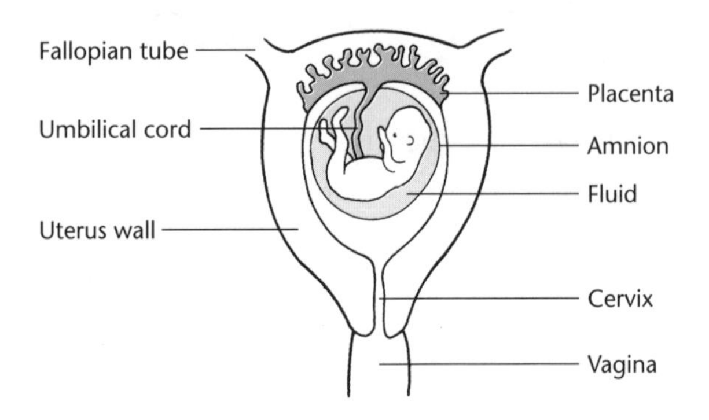

Foetus inside the uterus

The foetus gets all of its food and oxygen from the mother through the placenta and ***umbilical cord***. It floats in a bag of fluid called the ***amnion***, which helps to cushion it from bumps. For nine months it grows and develops inside the mother's uterus, then it is time to be born.

The muscles in the wall of the uterus start to contract to push the foetus out, and the cervix starts to widen: this is called *labour*. After a while, the cervix is fully open so the baby can be pushed out, usually head first, through the vagina. Once the baby is outside the mother's body, it will start to breathe by itself and the umbilical cord can be clamped and cut. The placenta and the rest of the umbilical cord is still inside the uterus, so the uterus wall contracts again to push it out – this is called the *afterbirth*.

Reproduction in plants

The male and female reproductive organs are found inside the ***flower***. Many flowers contain both male and female reproductive organs, so we can say they are hermaphrodite.

Pollen grains (male ***gametes***) develop inside the anther, and when they are ready the anther bursts open to release them. ***Pollination*** can now occur – this is the transfer of pollen from the anthers to the stigma. Pollen cannot move on its own, so there are two main methods of pollination:

- insect pollination — insects visiting the flower will accidentally pick up pollen and transfer it to another flower,
- wind pollination — pollen is blown from one flower to another.

Once the pollen has been transferred to the stigma, a pollen tube will start to grow.

It grows down through the style and ovary until it reaches the ***ovule***. The pollen grain nucleus moves through the pollen tube until it, too, reaches the ovule, then it fuses with the ovule nucleus. This is ***fertilization***

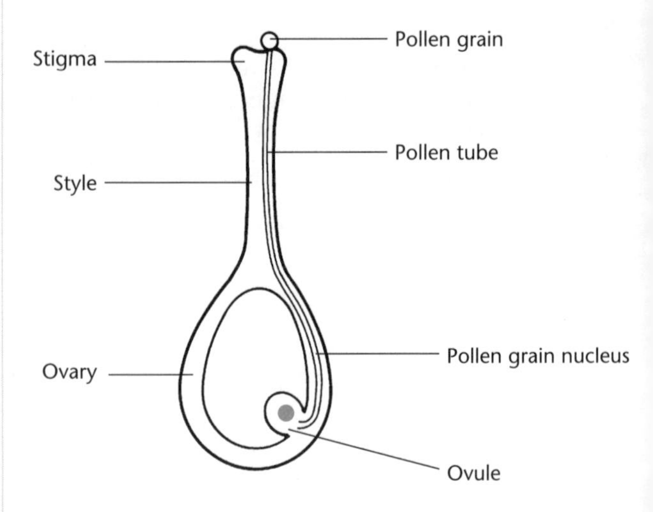

Growth of a pollen tube, leading to fertilization

Once fertilization has occurred, the following things happen:

- the petals, sepals and stamens shrivel up and die, because they are no longer needed,
- the ovary gets bigger and develops into a ***fruit***,
- the fertilized ovule develops into a ***seed***.

Dispersal, Germination

RESISTANCE

Resistance is a measure of how hard it is for ***current*** to get through that part of the ***circuit***.

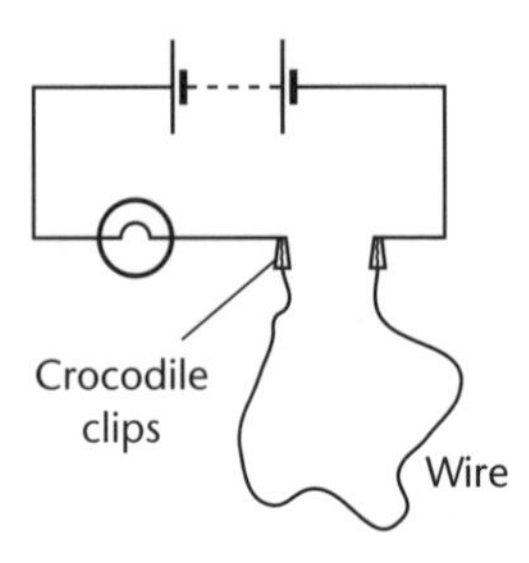

Resistance of a wire

If you make the resistance bigger in a circuit then less current will get through. When you put two bulbs in ***series*** with a ***battery*** there is twice as much resistance as when you only use one bulb. Less current can get through and so the two bulbs are dimmer than one on its own. This means that when parts of a circuit are put in series their resistances add.

You can show how the resistance of a wire changes by using the circuit in the figure. When resistance gets larger less current flows and the bulb gets dimmer. You would find that the resistance gets larger if the wire is thinner or longer. Different

metals also have different resistances for the same size piece of wire. Copper has a low resistance, which is why it is often used in electricity cables.

To make a larger current go through a resistance you would have to push the current harder by using a bigger voltage.

> *CHECKPOINT*
>
> An electric motor is connected in series with a battery and a variable ***resistor***. When the resistance is made smaller, the current in the circuit becomes ________ and the motor goes ________ .

Resistor

RESISTOR

Sometimes you need to control the ***current*** through part of a ***circuit***. This can be done by including a resistor that has the amount of ***resistance*** that you need. These are usually little cylinders with a connecting wire sticking out of each end. The current has to go through a thin layer of ***carbon*** on the cylinder. Coloured rings on the resistor tell you its resistance using a colour code.

Big resistors that are made to carry quite a lot of current will be made from coils of wire so that they can stand the heat.

Circuit, Resistance, Variable resistor

RESPIRATION

This is a chemical reaction occurring in all cells of all living things to make energy.

There are two types of respiration, aerobic and anaerobic.

Aerobic respiration

If oxygen is available, cells use oxygen and food to make ***energy***. The waste products are carbon dioxide and water.

Food + Oxygen ⟶ Energy + Carbon dioxide + Water

The food is normally sugar (***glucose***), and it is used as a fuel to provide energy.

Animals and plants respire like this.

Anaerobic respiration

If oxygen is not available, some cells can make ***energy*** without it for a while.

Yeast cells growing in liquid without much oxygen can do this.

Food ⟶ Energy + Alcohol + Carbon dioxide

This is useful to humans who use yeast in two ways:

1. making bread – the bubbles of carbon dioxide make the bread rise,
2. making alcohol – yeast is used to produce the ***alcohol*** in alcoholic drinks, e.g. beer, wine, lager. This is called ***fermentation***.

Muscle cells in animals can do this for a short time.

Food ⟶ Energy + Lactic acid

This is useful because it means that we can carry on exercising, even if the muscles are short of oxygen. However, this cannot go on for too long because the lactic acid builds up in the muscles and causes pain (we call this a stitch!).

Remember: Respiration is not the same *as breathing.*
Respiration *is a chemical reaction happening inside all cells to make energy.*
Breathing *only occurs in animals, and it means getting gases in and out of the body.*

RESULTS

Always put the results of an experiment or an ***investigation*** into a clear table.

Do not mix up the results with your description of how you did the experiment (the method) and include *all* your results. If you did the tests more than once, or if you did them several times and found the average, make sure that all the measurements are in a table and not just your final or average measurements. This shows the person marking your work that you have been careful and thorough and will improve your marks.

Do plot a ***graph*** or chart of your results.

If both ***variables*** can be continuous, plot a *line graph* (e.g. temperature, time or mass can have any value and are continuous).

If one of the variables is not continuous and can only change in steps then draw a *bar chart* (e.g. changing the colour of a container or using a different metal is changing in steps).

Results that do not fit the pattern of the others are often caused by you making a mistake and are called *rogue results*. These often show up more clearly when you plot a graph of the results.

Graphs, Investigation

Ribs

These are twelve pairs of long thin ***bones*** making up the rib-cage. They have two main functions:

1. to protect the lungs and the heart,
2. to move during the process of ***breathing*** so that the ***lung*** volume increases or decreases. They move when the ***muscles*** between them contract or relax.

Rock cycle and rocks

There are three types of rock, ***igneous***, ***sedimentary*** and ***metamorphic***. Various processes are involved in changing one rock type to another, as shown in the rock cycle.

- Igneous rocks are formed by cooling magma. The rocks have crystals. If the rock has cooled down slowly, the crystals are large. These rocks do not have fossils or bands. Basalt and ***granite*** are examples of igneous rocks.
- Sedimentary rocks are formed by deposition of rock fragments and fossils. These rocks have beds or layers and often contain fossils. ***Limestone*** and ***sandstone*** are examples of sedimentary rocks.
- Metamorphic rocks are formed by increases in temperature and/or pressure changing a rock. They have crystals but no fossils. ***Marble*** and slate are examples of metamorphic rock.

Root

This is the part of the plant that is underground. The root has three main functions:

1. to collect water from the soil,
2. to collect ***minerals***, e.g. nitrate, from the soil,
3. to anchor the plant in the soil.

Just behind the tip of the root is a region where there are ***root hair cells***. These increase the surface area so that the absorption of water and minerals is more efficient.

Roots never contain chlorophyll, so they are normally white or brown.

Root hair cell

These cells are found close to the root tip in plants.

They each have a long root hair to increase the surface area, so the plant can absorb more water and ***minerals*** from the soil.

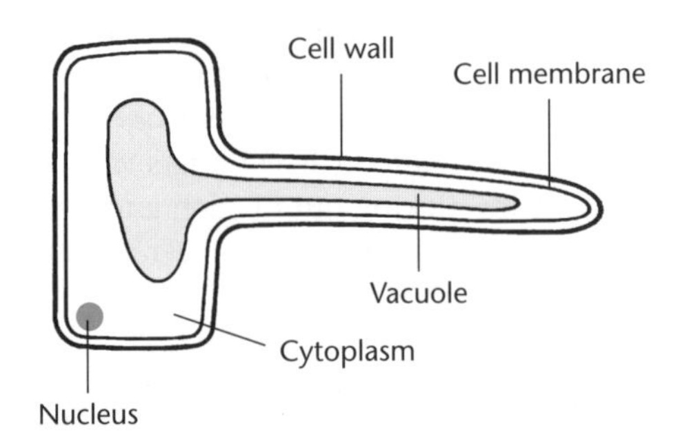

Root hair cell

Roots

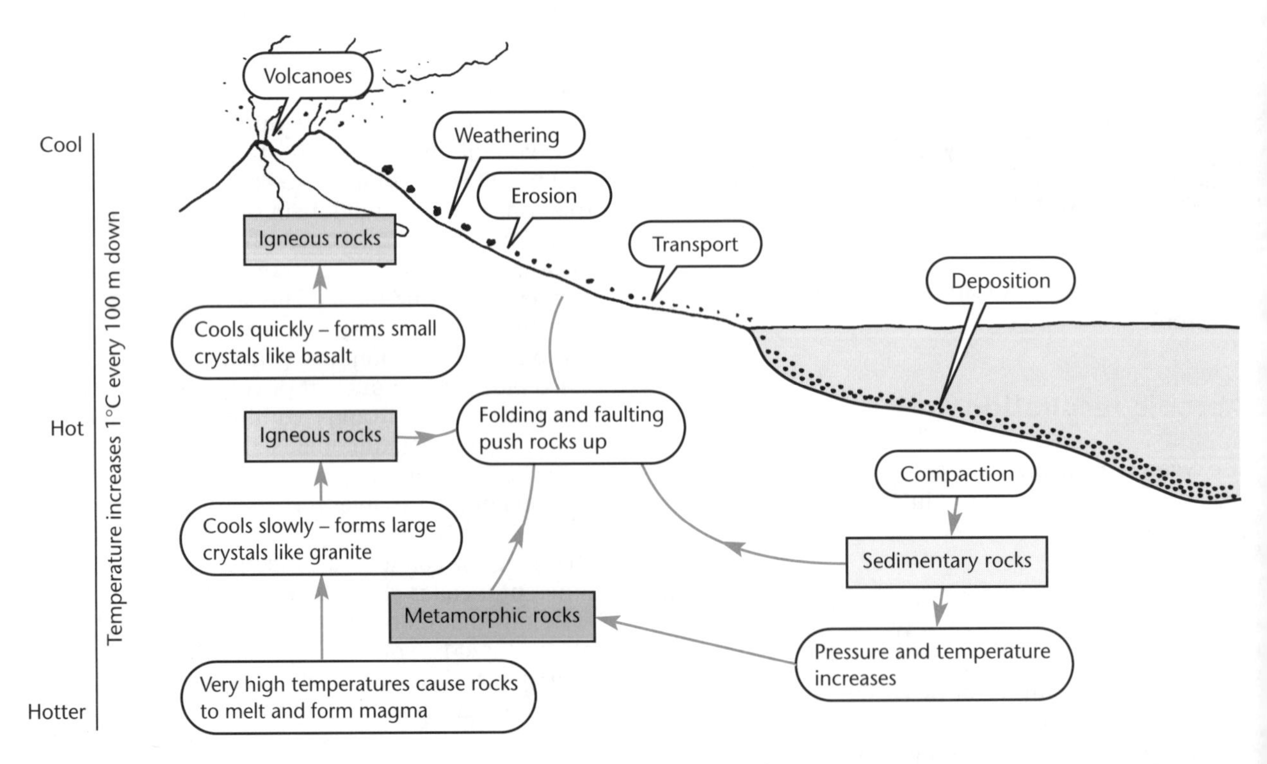

The rock cycle

Salt

This is the common name for sodium chloride. When salt dissolves in water, it is called ***brine***.

Salts

Acids all contain hydrogen. This hydrogen can be replaced by a metal ion. The substance formed when the hydrogen is replaced is called a salt. For example:

Hydrocholoric acid + Zinc ⟶ Zinc chloride + Hydrogen gas

$$2HCl + Zn \longrightarrow ZnCl_2 + H_2$$

Zinc chloride = A salt

Salts are formed when acids react with each of the following:

- Metals: Metal + Acid ⟶ Salt + Hydrogen gas
  e.g. Magnesium + Hydrochloric acid ⟶ Magnesium chloride + Hydrogen
- Alkalis: Alkalis + Acid ⟶ Salt + Water
  e.g. Sodium hydroxide + Sulphuric acid ⟶ Sodium sulphate + Water
- Metal carbonates: Metal carbonate + Acid ⟶ Salt + Water + Carbon dioxide
  e.g. Calcium carbonate + Nitric acid ⟶ Calcium nitrate + Water + Carbon dioxide

The type of salt produced depends on the acid used.

Hydrochloric acid produces	Chlorides
Sulphuric acid produces	Sulphates
Nitric acid produces	Nitrates

CHECKPOINT

Complete the following word equations:

1. Zinc + Nitric acid ⟶ + Hydrogen gas
2. Potassium hydroxide + Sulphuric acid ⟶ Water +
3. Sodium carbonate + Hydrochloric acid ⟶ Carbon dioxide + +

Sandstone

This is an example of a ***sedimentary*** rock. It is formed from sand grains that have been cemented together deep under the sea. They sometimes contain fossil remains of the animals that were living in the sand before it was buried.

Satellite

A satellite is an object that spins in an orbit around a bigger object. It stays in its orbit because it is attracted to the larger object by ***gravity***. This ***force***, called a centripetal force, keeps the satellite in orbit and stops it from moving away into space. There are natural satellites such as the moon orbiting the Earth, and man-made ones that we put into orbit from rockets or from the space shuttle.

There are two main types of man-made satellites.

Polar orbital satellites

This orbit goes round the Earth passing over both poles. As the Earth is also rotating on its axis, the satellite will be over a different part of the Earth on each orbit. After a few orbits it will have passed above all of the Earth's surface. It can be used to watch clouds and weather and track hurricanes. Other uses include watching military movements and checking on crops and climate.

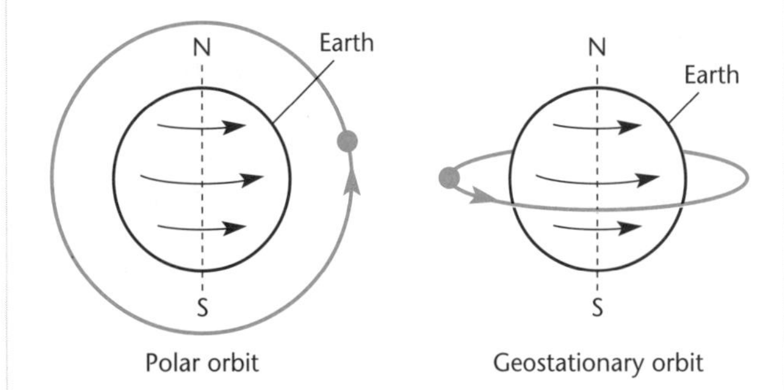

Orbits for satellites (not to scale)

Geostationary satellites

This orbit is directly above the equator (but very high). It is specially chosen because the satellite goes round its orbit once each day. If the Earth below it is also spinning round once each day the satellite appears to stay in the same position above the surface. This makes it very useful for relaying telephone calls or beaming down TV programmes.

Satellites are also used to explore the ***solar system*** and look at the ***stars***. Pictures from Earth are always made poorer by the atmosphere and the dust in it, which scatters the light. Pictures from space do not have this problem and are much sharper and clearer.

Some other ***radiation*** from space is absorbed by the atmosphere and can only be observed properly from satellites.

Gravity, Moon

Saturated solution

If you keep dissolving a ***solute*** in water at a particular temperature, you will reach a point where no more will dissolve. The ***solution*** is said to be saturated.

Scavengers

These are carnivores that feed on dead animals, e.g. raven, fox, crab.

Scientific name

All organisms are given a scientific name that tells us about its genus and ***species***. This name is always made up of two parts, and it is in Latin, for example:

Homo sapiens – humans
Bellis perennis – daisy
Patella vulgata – limpet

A scientific name is useful because:

- it tells scientists which organisms are classified into the same group,

  e.g. *Panthera leo* (lion), *Panthera tigris* (tiger), *Panthera pardus* (leopard) } are all part of the same group,

- all scientists use the same names, no matter which country they come from, so there are no misunderstandings.

Classification

Sea water

Sea water is an example of a ***mixture***. It contains large quantities of sodium chloride and other ***salts***. Sea water is the main raw material from which bromine, magnesium and iodine, as well as sodium chloride, are extracted.

Brine

Sedimentary rocks

These rocks are formed from the cementing together of broken down fragments of previously existing rocks. ***Sandstones*** are formed by the cementing together of sand grains. Sand is simply weathered fragments of rock. ***Limestone*** is also a sedimentary rock, which is made up of the bodies of dead sea animals that have been cemented together after their burial under the sea.

Seed

This develops from the fertilized ***ovule***. Although the structure of seeds varies between species, there are always three main parts.

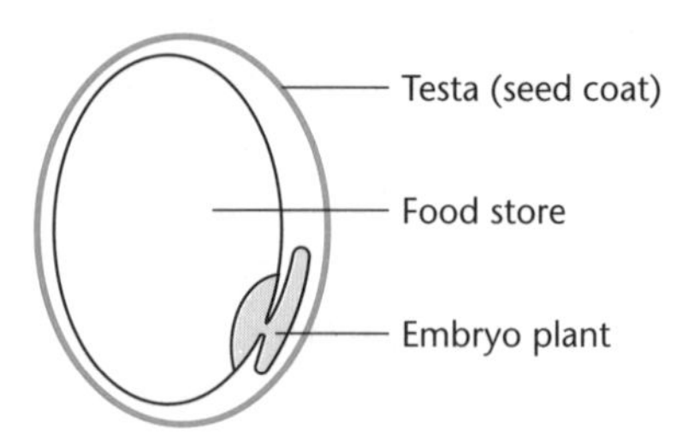

Inside a seed

Once it has been spread away from the parent plant (this process is called ***dispersal***), the seed can remain dormant until conditions are right for it to ***germinate***. Seeds can remain dormant for many years.

Most plants produce large numbers of seeds, because not all of them will germinate successfully, e.g. they may be dispersed to an unsuitable place, they may be eaten by animals, they may start to grow and then be killed.

Seeds form an important part of the human diet, e.g. peas, beans, corn, wheat (flour is made from this). They are very nutritious due to the food stores they contain.

Selective advantage

If one organism is more likely to survive in particular conditions than another, we say it has a selective advantage. For example,

- a bacterium resistant to antibiotics has a selective advantage over bacteria that are not resistant,
- a moth that is well camouflaged has a selective advantage over a moth which is easily seen.

Natural selection

Selective breeding

This means that humans decide which parents to breed together to get offspring of a particular type. It is sometimes called ***artificial selection***.

Humans have been carrying out selective breeding for thousands of years to develop ***varieties*** or ***breeds*** of organisms that are more suitable for human needs. All of the crop plants (e.g. wheat, potatoes, apples) and domesticated animals (e.g. farm animals, pets) that we have today have been developed by selective breeding.

How does selective breeding work?

Take the following steps:

- choose parents with the characteristics you want to pass on,
- breed them together,
- look at the offspring produced, and decide which ones have inherited the characteristics you want,
- use these offspring to continue your breeding programme,
- reject all the other offspring (i.e., do not breed from them).

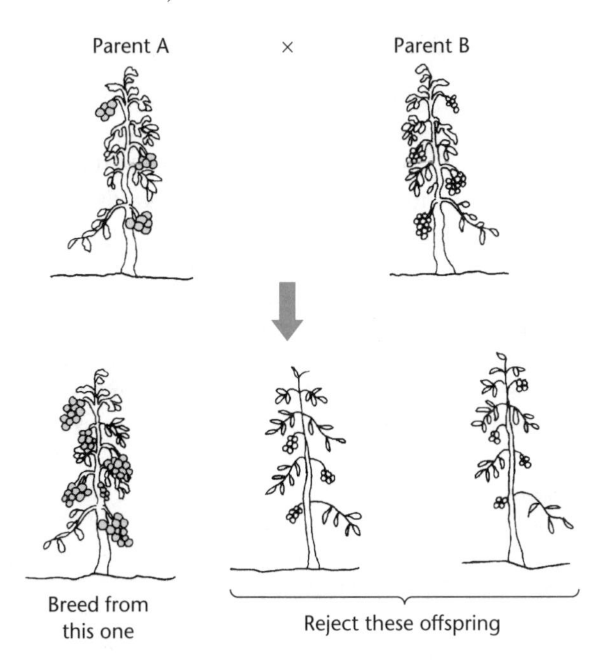

Selective breeding

Examples of successful selective breeding

The following have come about through selective breeding:

- development of different breeds of dog from wild dogs, e.g. alsatian, poodle, sheepdog, etc.,
- development of different breeds of apple from wild apples, e.g. Golden delicious, Cox's, Granny Smiths, etc.,
- development of wheat with large, strong ears from wild wheat (small, brittle ears with less protein),
- development of different breeds of cattle from wild cattle, e.g. Friesian, Lincoln red, Aberdeen angus, Welsh black.

Remember: Humans decide which parents to breed together to get the sort of offspring they want. Selective breeding always benefits humans.

✦ ***Genes, Species, Variation, Varieties***

SEMEN

This is the name for the mixture of ***sperm*** and fluid that comes out of the ***penis*** during ***sexual intercourse*** (normally about 5ml). The fluid helps the sperm to swim through the vagina and into the uterus.

✦ ***Reproduction***

SENSE ORGANS

Humans have five important sense organs to help them to find out about their surroundings.

Table to show human sense organs

Sense organ	*Sense*	*Stimulus it can detect*
Eye	Sight	Light
Nose	Smell	Chemicals in air
Ear	Hearing	Sound
Tongue (taste buds)	Taste	Chemicals in food
Skin	Touch	Pressure, temperature, pain

✦ ***Eye, Sensitivity***

SENSITIVITY

This is an important ***life process***. It means that living things can detect changes in their surroundings, and can respond to them,

e.g. if you feel cold, you can put a jumper on,
if you hear your alarm clock, you can choose to get out of bed (or not!).

Most animals have ***sense organs*** to detect changes in their surroundings.

Plants do not have obvious sense organs, but they still show sensitivity. For example:

- plants will grow towards the light,
- some flowers close their petals at night,
- some plants, e.g. peas, have tendrils that will wind around supporting canes.

Animals usually react to things more quickly than plants. The factor that causes a reaction is called a stimulus.

✦ ***Ear, Eye***

SEPARATING MIXTURES

Mixtures contain two or more ***elements*** or ***compounds*** that are not bonded together. They can be separated because they have different physical properties. For example, some substances may be insoluble in water while others are soluble. Substances may have different boiling points. These different physical properties often allow mixtures to be separated into their component parts.

Chromatography, Distillation, Evaporation, Filtration,

SERIES

Parts of a ***circuit*** are in series when they are placed one after the other so that the ***current*** must flow through each of them in turn. This means that the current does not divide along different routes in that part of the circuit.

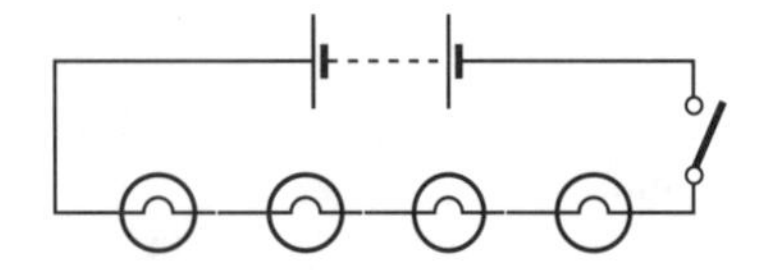

Bulbs, batteries and a switch, all in series

The figure shows several bulbs, a battery and a switch all connected in series. The same current will flow through all of the bulbs. If one of the bulbs fails then all the bulbs go out because the circuit is not complete and no current can flow round it. If you want all the bulbs to be at their normal brightness, the supply voltage will need to be the sum of all the voltages needed for the individual bulbs. An example of this sort of circuit is in Christmas tree lights where twenty 12 V bulbs are connected in series across the 240 V 'mains' supply.

Two identical bulbs in series across a battery will both be the *same* brightness but dimmer than when one of them is connected across the same battery. To get back to 'normal' brightness will need twice the voltage that one bulb needs.

Cells can be connected in series to form a ***battery*** and their ***voltages*** will add. A 9 V battery for your transistor radio will contain six 1.5V cells connected in series.

The size of the current that flows round a series circuit will depend on the number of cells in the battery and on the number and type of the other components. (See ***resistance***.)

> CHECKPOINT
>
> A circuit has a battery, bulb and a switch in series.
>
> What will you see happen to the bulb if another bulb is placed in series with it?
>
> What will have happened to the current in the circuit?
>
> What would you do to make the two bulbs have the same brightness as the original one?

Current, Parallel, Resistor

SEXUAL INTERCOURSE

Before intercourse can occur, the ***penis*** must be erect, and this happens when spaces in the erectile tissue fill with blood. The penis can now fit inside the vagina, and is moved backwards and forwards. After a while, ejaculation occurs: ***sperm*** from the testes, mixed with fluid from the glands, is pumped out of the penis into the woman's vagina. This liquid is called ***semen***, and normally about 5ml is released, but this contains millions of sperm cells. The liquid from the glands helps the sperm to swim through the ***uterus*** and fallopian tubes to ***fertilize*** the ***ovum***.

Reproduction

SEXUAL REPRODUCTION

This type of reproduction usually involves two parents, and produces *similar* offspring.

Reproduction

SHADOWS

Light waves travel in straight lines. This means that they cannot bend round behind objects that are put in their path. This makes an area of darkness called a shadow behind such objects.

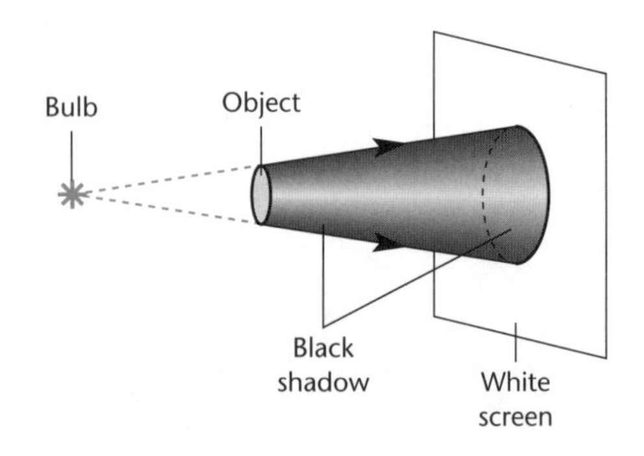

Shadow from a small source

A small light source such as a bulb will make a black shadow with sharp edges and the same outline as the object. The two light rays on the diagram are rays that just pass by the object. Lots of rays doing this in straight lines will make the edge of the shadow.

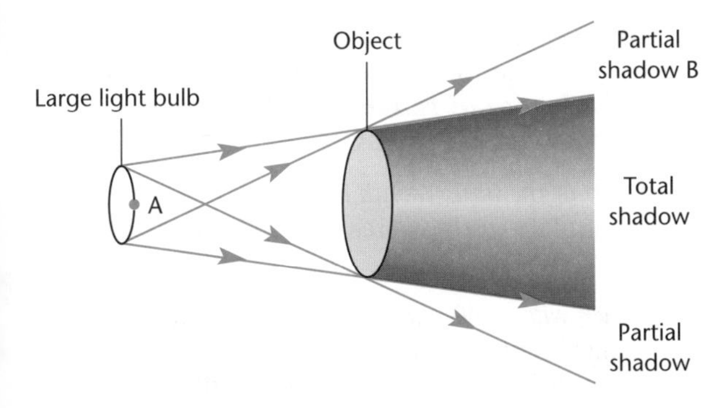

Shadow from a large source

A bigger bulb, or a large hot object, will make shadows that do not have such clear edges. There is still a perfectly black area in the centre but around it is a shadow area that can be reached by *some* of the light from the source. This outer shadow gets lighter as you move outwards because it receives more and more light until it becomes the fully lit area outside the shadow. The edges of the different types of shadow can again be found by drawing in rays as shown in the diagram. Try drawing a straight ray from point A past the edge of the object. Light from this point can reach the areas of partial shadow. A point in partial shadow B would get light from the top of the large bulb but not from the bottom.

Some Physics text books will call the total shadow *umbra* and the partial shadow *penumbra*. This is the sort of shadow that the moon makes in sunlight. We see an eclipse when the shadow passes over the Earth as the moon goes round in its orbit.

 *Light*

SIMPLE ORGANISMS

This is the general name for ***Protoctists***. They are microscopic, single-celled organisms, and most live in water. They are important links in aquatic ***food chains***.

SKELETON

Animals that have an internal skeleton are called ***vertebrates***. The skeleton is made up of ***bones***, and is important for four reasons:

1. it helps to support the body,
2. it allows the body to move,
3. it protects the internal organs of the body, e.g. skull protects the brain,
4. blood cells are made inside bones.

Human skeleton

This is made up of 206 bones. The largest is the femur (thigh bone) and the smallest is the stirrup bone inside the ear (involved in hearing). The skeleton is symmetrical and contains several different types of ***joints***.

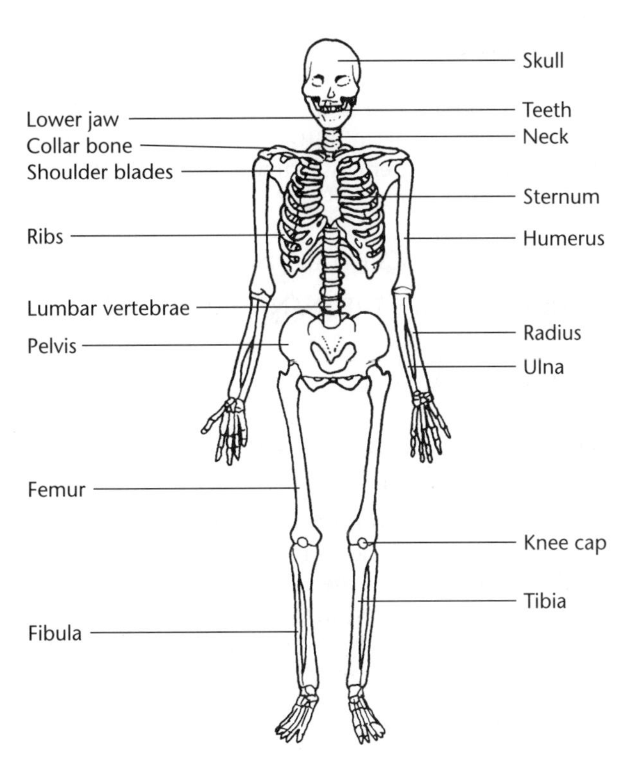

Human skeleton

SKIN

This is the largest organ of the body. The skin is made up of several layers of living and dead cells covering the whole of the outside of the body.

In some places (e.g. soles of feet, palms of hands) the skin is very thick to protect the delicate structures underneath. In some places the skin is covered with hair.

The skin has four main functions:

1. it is a waterproof covering and prevents the entry of germs (bacteria, viruses, fungi) except at the points where there are openings, e.g. mouth, eyes,
2. it protects the structures underneath it, e.g. nerves, and blood vessels from physical damage, e.g. bumps, and from sunlight,
3. it helps to control body temperature, e.g. by regulating sweating and by regulating the amount of blood flowing near to the body surface,
4. it is a sense organ, containing receptors sensitive to touch, pain, pressure and temperature.

SMELTING

This is the process by which iron and zinc are extracted from their ***ores***.

✦ ***Blast furnace***

SMOKING

Cigarettes contain lots of different chemicals, and many of these are harmful to the body, so cigarette packets and advertisements carry a government health warning, e.g.

SMOKING CAUSES FATAL DISEASES

SMOKING WHEN PREGNANT HARMS YOUR BABY

SMOKING CAUSES CANCER

When you smoke a cigarette, smoke is inhaled into the ***lungs***. What happens next?

- Smoke particles and tar are trapped on the walls of the air passages leading into your lungs. The tiny hairs (cilia) on the ***ciliated cells*** are damaged and stop working properly. This means that the lungs are more likely to get clogged up with dirt and mucus – this is why smokers cough so much.
- Tar coats the surface of the ***alveoli*** and makes ***gas exchange*** less efficient. Tar is also known to increase the risk of lung ***cancer*** – every year thousands of people die from lung cancer in Britain, and 90 per cent of these are smokers.
- Carbon monoxide gas diffuses into the blood. This stops the ***red blood cells*** from carrying oxygen efficiently.
- Nicotine diffuses into the blood. This travels round the body in the blood, and has two main effects:
  1. It damages the walls of the blood vessels (it is called hardening of the ***arteries***). This means that they are less stretchy and elastic, so the person is more likely to have heart attacks and other circulatory problems. People who smoke twenty cigarettes a day are twice as likely to have heart attacks as those who do not smoke.
  2. It is addictive, so people who smoke depend on the nicotine in their bodies, and find it very hard to give up.

Health problems

As well as lung cancer and heart disease, smokers are also more likely to suffer from the following health problems:

- *bronchitis* – the tubes in the lungs (***bronchi and bronchioles***) are damaged by the chemicals in smoke and become clogged up with mucus. They are then much more likely to get infected by bacteria or viruses, so the person gets bronchitis.
- *emphysema* – the thin walls of the alveoli are damaged and break so there are larger air pockets inside the lungs. This reduces the surface area available for ***gas exchange***, so the person becomes very breathless.
- *cancer of the nose, mouth and throat* – tar can accumulate in these areas and will increase the risk of cancer.
- *women who smoke during pregnancy* are likely to have smaller, lighter babies, and there is an increased risk of their baby being born dead (stillborn). This is because carbon monoxide in cigarette smoke prevents enough oxygen being passed on to the developing baby during pregnancy.

What is passive smoking?

When a person is smoking a cigarette they spend a lot of time simply holding it, and letting the smoke escape into the air around them. When they inhale the smoke, they breathe it into their lungs, then breathe it out again. Both of these things mean that the air around a smoker is polluted with cigarette smoke.

Other people nearby will breathe it in, and this is *passive smoking*. Non-smokers who breathe in cigarette smoke have an increased risk of smoking related diseases, e.g. lung cancer, bronchitis, etc., especially if they spend a long time in smoky places, e.g. children at home with parents who smoke, workers in an office/factory with colleagues who smoke.

People who suffer from ***asthma*** may have breathing difficulties if they are in a smoky atmosphere, and many non-smokers simply find it unpleasant to breathe in smoke. For all of these reasons, smoking is banned in many public places, e.g.

in cinemas and some restaurants,
in parts of public transport, e.g. buses, trains, planes,
in many workplaces.

> CHECKPOINT
>
> Which parts of cigarette smoke do the following:
>
> - cause cancer?
> - make you depend on cigarettes?
> - decrease the weight of babies born to women who smoke?
> - cause heart attacks?
> - damage cilia?

✦ ***Addiction, Breathing***

SOIL

Soil is important to living things because most plants grow in it. If you take a sample of soil and look at it closely you will see that it contains several different things.

- rock particles,
- water with dissolved minerals in it,
- air spaces,
- humus (rotted plant or animal material).

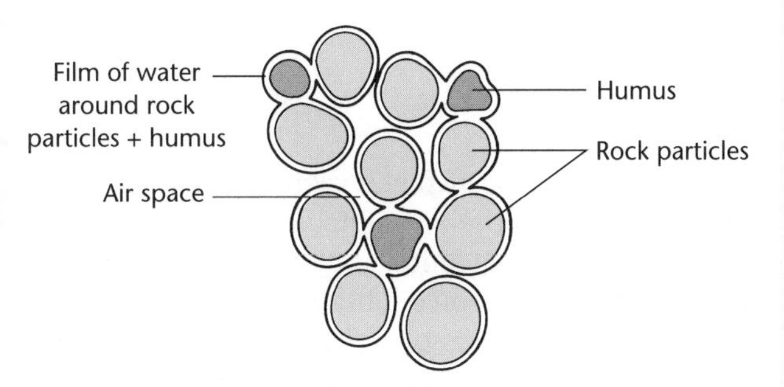

Looking closely at soil

Not all soil is the same:

- some has very small rock particles and is easily waterlogged (clay soil),
- some has very large particles, so water and minerals drain away from it quickly (sandy soil),
- some soils are acidic,
- some soils are alkaline,
- some soils lack ***minerals***.

A fertile soil will have lots of minerals and humus, with the right amount of air and water in it. Most plants grow best in neutral soil with medium sized particles. Some plants thrive in extreme conditions, e.g. marram grass on sand dunes, sundew grows in waterlogged soil, because they are ***adapted to their environment***.

SOLAR ENERGY

Solar ***energy*** can be used to heat water in solar panels. In some 'hot' countries, mirrors have been used to focus enough energy in one place to create a solar furnace. The energy can also be used to produce a small electric current from a *solar cell*. You may see this demonstrated to run a small electric motor from a solar cell about 10 cm by 5 cm but the current produced is small. It is big enough to drive things like solar powered calculators. The energy per m^2 in this country is not sufficient to make large-scale use practical and our weather makes it unreliable, but it does have some small-scale applications in electronics where the energy required is small or can be stored in batteries.

Sources of energy

SOLAR SYSTEM

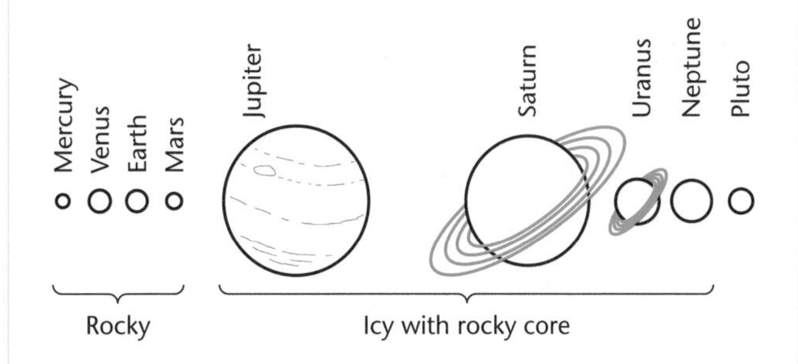

The solar system

The solar system consists of a ***star*** (the ***Sun***) and the nine ***planets*** that are in orbit around it. Some of the planets have captured other objects, which orbit them as moons. The ***Earth*** has one ***moon*** but Jupiter has sixteen, some of them larger than our moon. The table will give you a lot of the facts about the planets. Try to remember their names and order. You will not be tested on the other numbers but they might help you to compare them.

	Mercury	Venus	Earth	Mars	Jupiter	Saturn	Uranus	Neptune	Pluto
Mass	0.06	0.81	1	0.11	318	95	14.5	17.2	0.1
Diameter	0.38	0.95	1	0.53	11	9	4	4	0.2
Gravity	0.38	0.9	1	0.38	2.6	1.2	0.9	1.2	0.1
Density	5.4	5.2	5.5	3.9	1.3	0.69	1.2	1.7	1.8
Rocky/icy	rocky	rocky	rocky	rocky	icy	icy	icy	icy	icy
Moons	0	0	1	2	16	17	10	8	1
Orbit time	88d	225d	1y	1.9y	11.9y	29.5y	84y	165y	248y
Average distance to Sun in million km	58	108	150	228	778	1427	2870	4500	5900

In the table mass, diameter and gravity are compared to that of Earth, which is taken as 1. Density is relative density (i.e., number of times the density of water). Average distance to Sun is in millions of km.

Planets closer to the Sun will receive more heat radiation and will be warmer. We think that the planet Neptune is so far away that its temperature is about –230°C. Rocky planets are small and dense with a rocky surface. Icy planets are large and cold with a thick atmosphere. Simple chemical and gases such as water or ammonia would be solids or liquids on an icy planet.

Galaxy, Plane, Sun

SOLID

Solids have a fixed shape and a definite volume. The particles fit together in a regular arrangement. Ice is solid water.

Changes of state

SOLUBILITY

The solubility of a solution is the number of grams of the ***solute*** that will dissolve in 100g of water at a particular temperature. The solubility changes as the temperature changes. Graphs, such as those below, are called solubility curves.

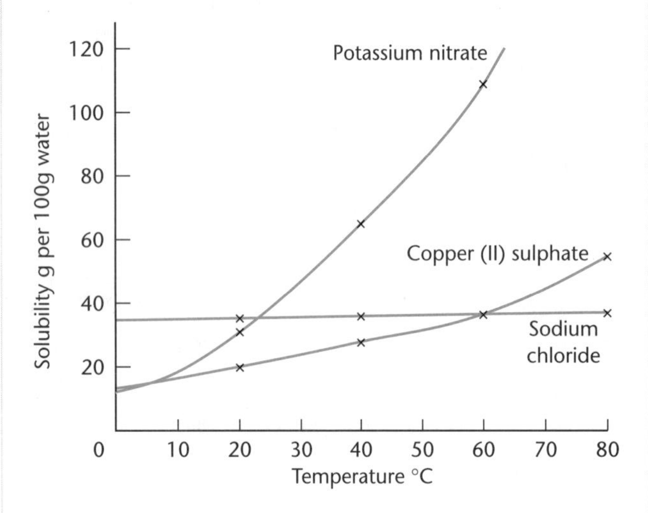

Solubility curves

SOLUTE

This is a soluble substance that dissolves in a ***solvent*** to give a ***solution***. For example, sugar dissolves in tea to form a solution. Sugar is the solute.

SOLUTION

A solution contains very tiny dissolved particles. For example, when copper sulphate is added to water it dissolves. The particles are so small that it is not possible to see them. It is very obvious that they are still in the beaker or test tube because it has a very distinctive blue colour.

Solute + Solvent ⟶ Solution

Copper sulphate + Water ⟶ Copper sulphate solution

SOLUTION MINING

Most of the ***salt*** used in this country has come from the salt mines of Cheshire. These salt deposits are millions of years old and buried under the Cheshire countryside. The salt is mined by solution mining. Hot water is pumped down a large pipe. When it reaches the salt deposits, it dissolves the very soluble salt. This is then pumped onto the surface for further processing.

Brine

SOLVENT

This is a liquid that dissolves ***solutes*** to make a ***solution***. Water is the most important solvent. However, organic chemicals from ***crude oil*** are also useful. They can dissolve substances like ink that water finds hard to dissolve. These solvents are used for dry cleaning. Glue molecules are dissolved in harmful solvents that have a very low boiling point. They are designed to evaporate as soon as the glue is spread. These solvents often smell very strongly and are very toxic.

SOLVENTS

These are found in products such as aerosols, e.g. deodorant, furniture polish, glue, lighter fluid and petrol. They are EXTREMELY DANGEROUS – they can kill a person the first time they are used.

Solvents are inhaled (breathed in) and the effects start immediately, lasting about half an hour. They include feeling 'drunk', but repeated inhaling can cause dizziness, loss of control and unconsciousness.

Why are solvents so dangerous?

Here are a few of the reasons:

- if they are squirted straight into the mouth, e.g. deodorant, they can cause immediate death because the air passages (bronchi and bronchioles) in the lungs close up,
- if the person is sniffing solvents in a plastic bag, they may suffocate,
- some solvents (e.g. butane gas, aerosols) cause heart failure,
- if the person becomes unconscious and then is sick, they can choke on their own vomit,
- the person may become confused and have an accident, particularly if they are on their own, e.g. on a riverbank, near a railway line.

Drugs

SOUND

Sound is a longitudinal ***wave*** and therefore travels through a material as a series of compressions. It cannot travel through a vacuum as there are no particles in a vacuum that could vibrate and carry the energy.

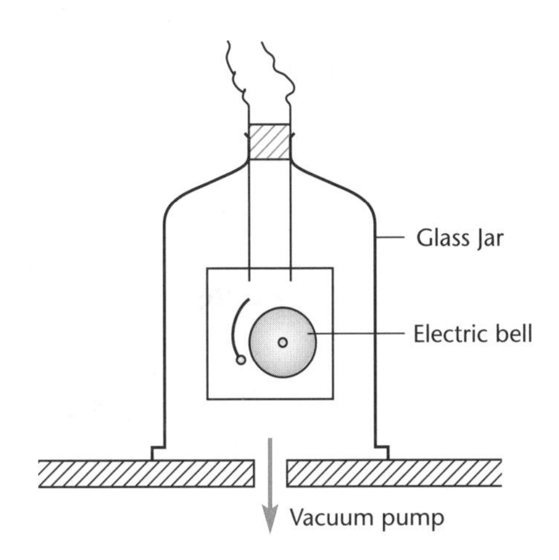

No sound in a vacuum

When the air is pumped out of the jar you can see the bell working but you do not hear it. Men on the moon needed radios unless their helmets touched!

As sound is a vibration of the layers of air, its source is always a vibration at the same ***frequency***. Sometimes the vibrations are too fast to see easily, especially if the ***amplitude*** is small (and therefore produces a quiet sound). In other cases you may be able to see the vibrations if you look closely – e.g. a loudspeaker making a loud low frequency sound, or the string of a guitar. Your vocal chords in your throat vibrate to produce the sounds for speech. We can hear sounds in an approximate range of frequencies from 20 Hz to 18 kHz, but this varies a lot from one person to another. Most people hear best at about 2,000 Hz.

The ***speed*** of a sound wave will depend on the material that it travels in and the temperature of that material. The table gives an approximate idea of the speed in some different materials.

Material	*Speed in m/s*	*Material*	*Speed in m/s*
Air	330	Water	1500
Glass	5000	Brass	3500
Aluminium	5100	Wood	3850

You can see that sound will travel though liquids and solids as well as gases. You will already know this if you swim under water or have noisy neighbours!

To measure the speed of sound in air we use the fact that we can see things happen almost instantly because the speed of light is so fast that the time taken for it to reach you is *very* short. If a pupil stands at one end of a sports pitch and bangs two pieces of wood together you can measure the time between seeing it happen and hearing it at the other end of the pitch. Measure the length of the pitch and you can find the speed of the sound. This is not a very accurate experiment because the times are so short and difficult to measure. It can be improved by doing it in both directions to allow for any wind.

If you have a tall building or a cliff and a lot of space in front of it then you can get a much better answer by making a sound and finding the time taken for the echo to return. Remember that the distance travelled is there and back. You might be able to do this from your school playing field if you have a large flat side of a building to reflect the sound.

> *Remember: The speed of sound is much less than the speed of light.*

To accurately determine the speed of sound you can use a short sound from a small loudspeaker. The loudspeaker is in one side of a container of the material that you are testing and the sound reflects back from the other side and is picked up by a microphone. The time taken can be measured electronically.

- An ***echo*** is sound that is reflected back to you. Echoes are often used to determine the depth of the sea or to find shoals of fish. These often use *ultrasonic sound* (beyond the range that we can hear) as it is easier to keep in narrow beams and does not become confused with engine noises, etc.

For example: a foghorn on a ship sends out a sound and the echo from a cliff is heard 4 s later. How far away is the cliff? (Speed sound in air = 330 m/s.)

$$\begin{aligned}\text{Distance} &= \text{speed} \times \text{time}\\ &= 330 \times 4\\ &= 1320 \text{ m}\end{aligned}$$

This is the distance to the cliff and back so the distance to the cliff = 660 m

Low pitch sound, often called *bass*, has low frequencies. High pitch sound, often called *treble*, has high frequencies. You may hear these notes and find your range of hearing at school by using a sound generator and a loudspeaker. If the output is also connected to an oscilloscope you will be able to see the waves on its screen. As the frequency is increased you see more waves on the screen, their ***wavelength*** is shorter and you hear a higher note.

Ultrasonic sound (above the frequencies that we can hear) is often used in medical 'scans' as it reflects from bone and tissue without causing the damage that can happen with X-rays. Because it causes no damage, ultrasound is often used to examine unborn babies. The reflected sounds are picked up by a microphone and processed by a computer to make an image on a screen.

Large halls used for music concerts have to be designed carefully to control the echoes that could spoil the sound. Materials like carpets and seat coverings, even the audience, all help to absorb sound.

CHECKPOINT

What type of wave is sound?

What is an echo?

Describe one way to find the speed of sound. Which measurement will be the hardest to make accurately?

Why can't sound travel through a vacuum?

Amplitude, Frequency, Speed, Wave

SOURCES OF ENERGY

There are a number of major sources of ***energy***. Some, mainly those that are rich in ***chemical energy***, have been used as ***fuels*** for a long time. Others are now being investigated as the original fuels run out and become more expensive. Some may have the advantage of being cleaner to produce or create less pollution when they are used.

Most of the sources of energy can be used to make electricity. This is convenient and clean to use and can be moved quickly to where it is needed. Electricity is called a *secondary source* because another, *primary source*, must be used to make it.

Non-renewable resources

These are the resources that we use and then cannot replace.

Coal, oil, gas and nuclear fuels are all non-renewable resources. They are becoming more difficult to obtain as we use up the existing stocks and have to find new supplies. Coal, gas and oil are known as ***fossil fuels*** because of the way in which they were originally formed millions of years ago and they are burned to release some of their chemical energy as heat. Their main disadvantage is the production of air ***pollution*** including ***carbon dioxide***, which increases the ***greenhouse effect***. Nuclear power is much cleaner to use and causes less problems with air pollution. Some of the waste products, however, will be radioactive for thousands of years and accidents can release dangerous radioactivity into the air.

Renewable resources

These are resources that we can replace or which do not run out.

The main ones are: ***solar energy***, ***wind power***, ***wave power***, ***hydroelectric power (HEP)***, ***biomass***, ***tidal energy*** and ***geothermal energy***.

Energy from the Sun

Solar energy, wind power, wave power, hydroelectric power (HEP) and biomass together with the fossil fuels coal, oil and gas all originally got their energy from the ***Sun***. Nuclear fuels, tidal energy and geothermal energy did not.

The summary table may help you to learn which is which.

Energy resources

Energy Source	Renewable	Non-renewable	Energy from Sun originally	Fossil fuel
Gas	✘	✔	✔	✔
Coal	✘	✔	✔	✔
Oil	✘	✔	✔	✔
Electricity*	✔	✘	*	✘
Wind	✔	✘	✔	✘
Wave	✔	✘	✔	✘
Tide	✔	✘	✘	✘
Geothermal	✔	✘	✘	✘
Biomass	✔	✘	✔	✘
Hydroelectric	✔	✘	✔	✘
Solar	✔	✘	✔	✘
Nuclear	✘	✔	✘	✘

* Electricity may have energy that originally came from the Sun but it depends on fuel, which is used to drive the generator.

CHECKPOINT

Write down the names of the main fossil fuels.

Write down as many renewable sources of energy as you can.

Write down the names of two sources of energy that did not originally get their energy from the Sun. Where does the energy come from in these cases?

Biomass, Energy, Geothermal energy, Hydroelectric power, Pumped storage, Solar energy, Tidal energy, Wave power, Wind power

SPECIES

This is the name given to a group of the same type of organisms that can breed together successfully, e.g.

- all humans are the same species,
- all dogs are the same species,

- cod and haddock are both types of fish, but they are different species because they do not breed together,
- lions and tigers are both types of mammal, but they are different species because they do not breed together.

All organisms are given a ***scientific name*** that tells us about its species and genus. This name is in Latin, e.g.

Homo sapiens humans
Bellis perennis daisy

This is very useful for ***classification***.

✣ ***Breeds, Variation, Varieties***

SPECTRUM

Electromagnetic

This is a whole range of ***waves*** that travel at the same speed in a vacuum and are different only because of their ***wavelength*** and ***energy***. They are all transverse waves and the vibration is in a ***magnetic field*** and an electric field.

Starting with the shortest waves that have most energy and are most penetrating you might hear about the following: gamma, X-rays, ultraviolet, visible light, infra-red, microwaves, radio and TV waves.

Visible

This is the part of the electromagnetic spectrum that our eyes can see. We think that our eyes have evolved to detect these waves because they are the strongest ones given out by the Sun.

White light or sunlight is a mixture of these ***waves***. If we send a beam of white light through a glass prism we can see that the different ***wavelengths*** affect our eyes in a slightly different way so that we see them as different colours. The set of colours from white light is often called a spectrum and the splitting up process is called dispersion.

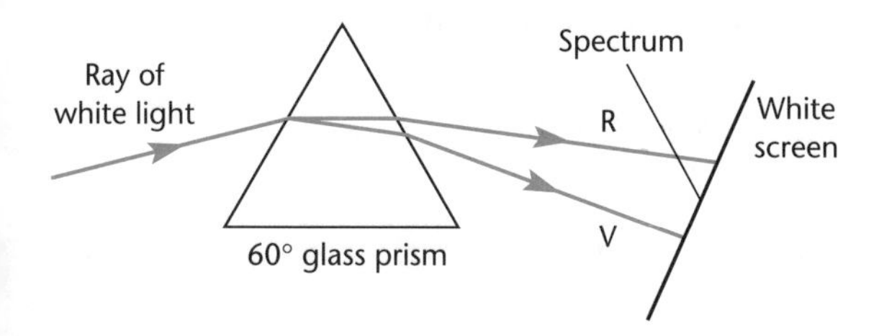

Dispersion of white light

As each wave goes through the prism it is bent twice, once going in and once coming out again. This is called ***refraction***. The longer waves are refracted less than the shorter ones and you can see all the separate colours.

The colours steadily blend from one to the next as you go across the spectrum but we name the main colours as Red, Orange, Yellow, Green, Blue, Indigo, and Violet. This list has the longest waves first and shortest waves last. Notice that many colours that we can see are not pure colours and are mixtures of these spectrum colours. The spectrum does *not* have pink or brown or purple!

The initial letters of the following bit of history helps you to remember the colours: Richard Of York Gained Battles In Vain.

✣ ***Colour, Filter, Frequency, Light, Refraction, Wave, Wavelength***

SPEED

The speed of an object is the distance that it travels in each second. It will be in m/s. To find the speed of an object you will need to measure how far it can travel in a certain time and the use the equation:

$$\text{Speed} = \frac{\text{Distance moved}}{\text{Time taken}}$$

For example, a car moves 100 m in 5 s. What is its speed?

$$\text{Speed} = \frac{\text{Distance moved}}{\text{Time taken}} = \frac{100}{5} = 20 \text{ m/s}.$$

A loud noise travels 160 m across the playground in 0.5 s. What is the speed of sound?

$$\text{Speed} = \frac{\text{Distance moved}}{\text{Time taken}} = \frac{160}{0.5} = 320 \text{ m/s}.$$

CHECKPOINT

Write down the equation for speed.

Sam cycles 3 km to school in 20 minutes. What is her average speed? Hint: speed should really be in m/s so convert to m and s first!

✣ ***Velocity***

SPEED OF REACTION

Rate of reaction

SPERM CELL

The function of the sperm cell is to ***fertilize*** the ***ovum***. It has a long tail to help it to swim and the ***nucleus*** contains 23 ***chromosomes*** (half the normal number).

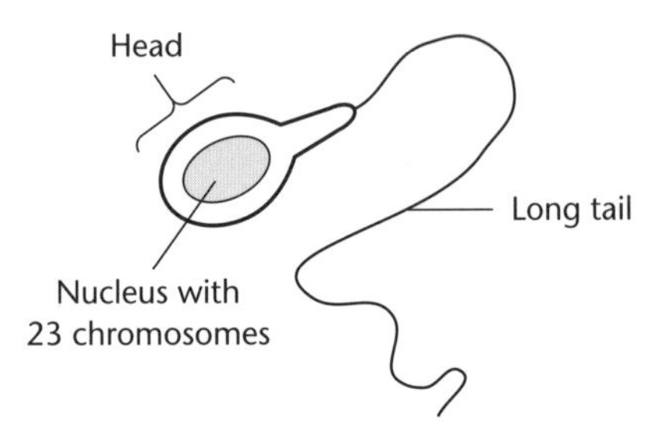

Sperm cell

Fertilization, Gamete, Reproduction

STAMEN

This is the male reproductive organ in plants. ***Flowers*** contain several stamens.

The stamen is made up of two parts:

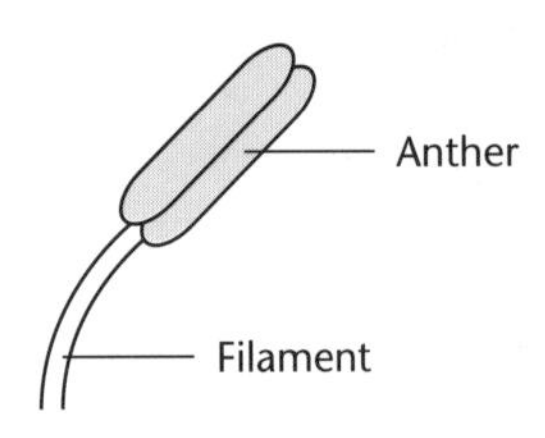

Stamen

1. anther: this contains four pollen sacs where ***pollen*** grains are made and stored,
2. filament: this is a stalk that supports the anther.

Pollination, Reproduction

STAR

A star is a bright hot object out in space, which is sending out the radiation that we can see. (Other objects such as planets only reflect the light to us).

There are huge numbers of stars and they are collected together into ***galaxies***. The ***Sun*** is our nearest star. The next nearest one, Proxima Centauri, is about 270,000 times farther away. The distances between stars are very large. We usually measure them in light years where one light year is the distance travelled by light in one year at a speed of 300,000,000m/s.

Stars are mostly made from hydrogen and helium and they use these as a fuel to release lots of energy.

Some of the stars in the sky seem to make patterns, even though the stars are often enormous distances apart. Many of these patterns have names and the stars in them are called ***constellations***. Finding these patterns can help to identify individual stars. If you look towards the north you might be able to see the constellation called the Plough (the Americans call it the Big Dipper and its correct name is Ursa Major). You can find the pole star by looking along a line through the last two stars of the blade of the plough.

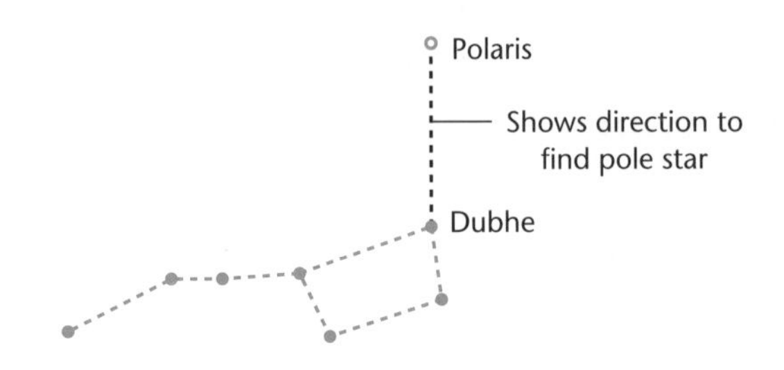

The Plough

Stars seem to move rather than being fixed in the sky. There are two reasons for this.

The Earth's rotation

As the ***Earth*** spins on its axis the stars will appear to revolve round the axis once each 24 hours. The pole star, *Polaris*, appears to be stationary because it is along the line of the axis. If you look towards the north in the night sky and then do it again a few hours later you will be able to see that the stars have moved around quite a lot (the full rotation would take 24 hours, so three hours will see the star pattern rotate by 45° round the pole star).

The Earth's orbit

The stars will also change position during the year as we are looking at them from different places on the Earth's orbit around the Sun.

Galaxy, Milky way, Sun

STARCH TEST

This test is often used to show that ***photosynthesis*** has occurred. It is made up of five simple steps:

1. Boil the leaf in water to kill it.
2. Boil the leaf in ethanol to remove the chlorophyll (decolourize it).

3. Wash the leaf to soften it.
4. Lay it flat on a tile.
5. Cover it in iodine solution. If starch is present, that part of the leaf will turn black. This shows that photosynthesis has occurred there. If starch is not present, the leaf will appear brownish-orange.

STATE

Materials will be in one of three states depending on their temperature. The states are ***solid***, ***liquid*** and ***gas***.

✦ *Changes of state, Kinetic theory*

STATE SYMBOLS

State symbols are used in ***chemical equations*** to identify the ***state of matter*** of the substance.

The symbols are:

(s) solid state
(l) liquid state
(g) gas state
(aq) aqueous state, i.e., dissolved in water

e.g. ice = H_2O (s)
water = H_2O (l)
steam = H_2O (g)
salt dissolved in water = NaCl (aq)

STATES OF MATTER

✦ *Changes of state, Gas, Liquid, Solid*

STATIC ELECTRIC CHARGE

Insulators can be given a charge of static electricity by rubbing them with another material such as fur or cloth. This is called *charging by friction*. You can see this if you rub a plastic pen or ruler on your sleeve – it can then pick up small pieces of paper. Charged objects will attract uncharged objects.

Bringing charged objects close to each other shows that charges sometimes attract and sometimes repel. The ones that attract can cancel each other so that the objects have no charge – we say that objects with no charge have become *neutral*.

Doing this more carefully as in the diagram shows that:

Charges that are the same repel.
Charges that are opposite attract.

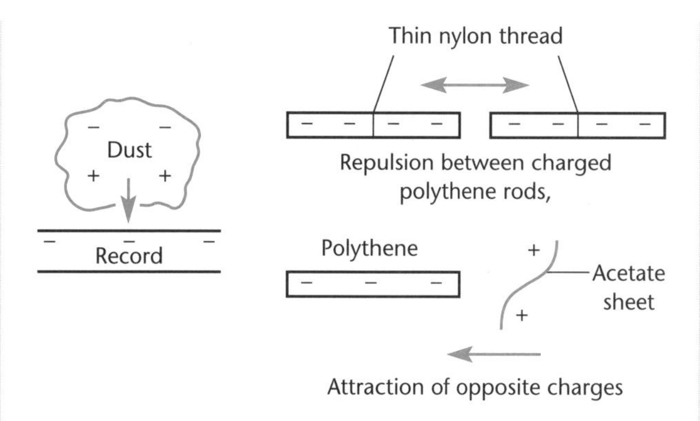

Forces between charges

The two sorts of charges are called *positive* and *negative* because they can cancel out to make neutral. Rubbing polythene or a pen with cloth gives a negative charge. Rubbing acetate with cloth gives a positive charge.

Electrons carry a tiny negative charge and are easily moved around. If a neutral object gains some electrons it becomes negative. If it loses some electrons it becomes positive. Note that the negative electrons from the outside of atoms move but the positive ***protons*** always stay where they are.

Negative = gained some electrons.
Positive = lost some electrons.
Neutral = has equal numbers of protons and electrons.

On an insulator the charge remains trapped because the electrons cannot move around. On a ***conductor***, or an insulator with a layer of damp, the charge will rapidly leak away. This is because all the charges repel each other and will try to get to earth so that they are as far apart as possible.

You may also feel small electric shocks as electric charges try to get to earth through you, leaving the originally charged object neutral. Sometimes the effect is big enough to make a small spark as the electrons jump across a gap to get to earth. You can hear and feel this when you pull your jumper over your shirt!

Small pieces of dust will be attracted to a charged object such as a record by the same forces that attracted the small piece of paper to your pen. The electrons are repelled to the far side of the dust particle, which is left with a positive charge closer to the negative record. The opposite charges attract and the dust 'sticks' to the record. This effect has uses in electrostatic precipitation, which removes the dust from factory chimneys. It has a less useful effect in collecting dust whenever you clean plastic materials by rubbing them!

Sprays for paint and insecticides often charge the droplets of liquid that are sprayed out so that they are attracted to their target and cover it better.

CHECKPOINT

Write down two problems caused by static electricity and two uses of static electricity.

Give a brief explanation of one of the problems and one of the uses. Make sure that your explanation is clear about what is happening to the *charges*.

Charge, Current

Steam

Steam is water vapour. It is water that has turned into a gas.

Changes of state

Steel

Steel is an ***alloy*** of iron. Mild steel contains 99.7 per cent iron and 0.3 per cent carbon. Stainless steel contains 70 per cent iron, 20 per cent chromium and 10 per cent nickel.

Stem

This is part of the shoot system of a plant. It has three main functions:

1. it holds the ***leaves*** above the ground so that they get more light for ***photosynthesis***,
2. it holds the ***flowers*** above the ground so that ***pollination*** is more likely to occur,
3. it contains tubes called ***xylem vessels*** to carry water around the plant, and ***phloem tubes*** to carry sugar around the plant.

Stigma

This is part of the ***carpel*** inside a ***flower***. Pollen grains are transferred here from the anther in the process of ***pollination***. In wind-pollinated flowers, the stigma is feathery, like a net to trap pollen.

Stomach

This is part of the ***digestive system***. Food stays here for up to five hours, and it is mixed with ***enzymes*** and ***acid*** made by glands in the stomach wall. The enzymes start to digest any protein in the food. The acid helps the enzymes to work properly, and also kills ***bacteria***, which may have been eaten with the food.

Strong muscles in the stomach wall contract to churn and mix the food with the enzymes and acid until it is like porridge. It then passes into the small intestine and digestion continues there.

Stomata

These are tiny holes (pores) found on the underside of leaves in all plants. They are surrounded by two guard cells, which can change shape so that the stomata are open or closed.

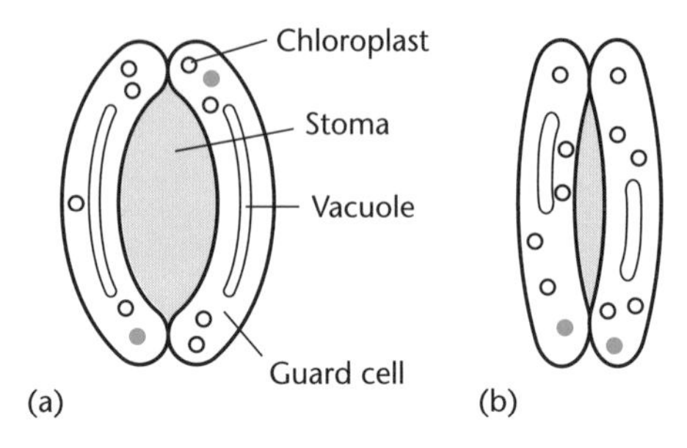

Stomata: (a) open, (b) closed.

Their main function is to allow gases to enter or leave the leaf during ***gas exchange***. They also allow water vapour to escape from the leaf in a process called ***transpiration***.

Strong acid

These have pH values of 1–3. Sulphuric acid and hydrochloric acid are examples of strong acids.

pH scale

Strong alkalis

These have pH values of 8–14. Sodium hydroxide and ammonia gas are examples of strong alkalis.

pH scale

Sublimation

When a substance changes directly from a ***solid*** into a ***gas*** without becoming a ***liquid*** it is said to sublime. Solid carbon dioxide, commonly called dry ice, changes directly into a gas. It is often used for special effects in the cinema. It is called *dry ice* because it does not leave a puddle!

Changes of state

Sulphur dioxide

This gas is one of the major causes of ***acid rain***. It is produced when sulphur burns in oxygen.

Sun

The sun is the centre ***star*** of the ***solar system***. The ***Earth*** orbits round it at an average distance of 150 million km, and light from the Sun takes a little over eight minutes to reach us. The Sun is about 1.3 million km across and it has a temperature of about 13 million °C at its core. The surface of the Sun will be 'only' about 6,000°C. It is powered by a type of nuclear reaction called a *fusion reaction*. This joins together some of the smaller atoms of hydrogen and helium, from which the Sun is mostly made, and makes bigger atoms. The energy that is left over is released as huge amounts of ***heat energy***. We think that the Sun is about 5 billion years old.

✢ *Solar system, Star*

Survival of the fittest

In most ***habitats***, there are not enough resources to support all the organisms that live there, so there is ***competition for resources***, e.g.

- plants may produce hundreds of seeds, but there is not enough space for them all to grow,
- frogs may lay hundreds of eggs, but there is not enough food for them all to grow, and some will be eaten by predators.

Individual organisms are not all identical to each other, and some will have a ***selective advantage*** – they have characteristics that will help them to survive. For example,

- one plant may grow faster than others, so it can obtain more light for photosynthesis,
- one tadpole may swim faster than others, so it is less likely to be eaten by predators.

The organisms that have a selective advantage are most likely to survive and breed, and they will produce offspring like themselves, i.e., which have inherited their useful characteristics. This is sometimes summed up as 'survival of the fittest'.

✢ *Natural selection*

Suspension

When an insoluble substance is added to water, it forms a suspension. Muddy water is an example, when, after a while, the mud settles to the bottom. Suspensions are frequently cloudy to look at. Milk of magnesia is also an example of a suspension. Most suspensions can be ***filtered***.

Symbol

Each element in the ***periodic table*** has its own individual symbol. Some of these seem logical. For example, the symbol for oxygen is O and nitrogen is N. However, sodium (Na) and iron (Fe) are not quite so straightforward. Their symbols come from the Latin names for the substance; sodium is *natrium* and iron is *ferrum*.

Synovial fluid

This is a lubricating fluid found inside ***joints***. It allows the ***bones*** to move smoothly, acting like the oil in a machine. It is made by cells in the synovial membrane.

Systems

A system is a group of ***organs*** that work together to carry out a particular function.

Systems in humans

There are seven main systems in humans:

Systems of the human body

System	*Functions*	*Organs/parts*
Circulatory	• To transport substances around the body, in blood	Heart Blood vessels
Respiratory	• To transfer oxygen into the body and remove carbon dioxide	Lungs Trachea Diaphragm
Urinary	• To remove urea, salts and water from the body, in urine	Kidneys Bladder

Systems of the human body cont...

System	*Functions*	*Organs/parts*
Nervous	• To control all the activities of the body • To link all parts of the body to the brain, and pass impulses (messages) between them • To find out about our surroundings	Brain Sense organs, e.g. eyes Nerves
Digestive	• To digest the food we eat • To absorb digested food into the blood	Stomach Intestines Liver
Reproductive	• To make sperm and egg cells • To provide a safe place for the foetus to develop	Testes, Penis } male Ovaries, Uterus } female
Skeletal	• To move parts of the body • To protect soft organs, e.g., skull protects brain	Bones Muscles

Systems in plants

Plants have two main systems:

- shoot system (all parts above ground),
- root system (all parts below ground).

Organs

TEETH

Adult humans have 32 teeth for biting and chewing their food. There are four types of teeth:

- Incisors (eight) – biting and slicing
- Canines (four) – biting and gripping
- Premolars (eight) – chewing and grinding
- Molars (twelve) – chewing and grinding

Teeth are held in sockets in the jawbone and their roots are protected by a layer of gum.

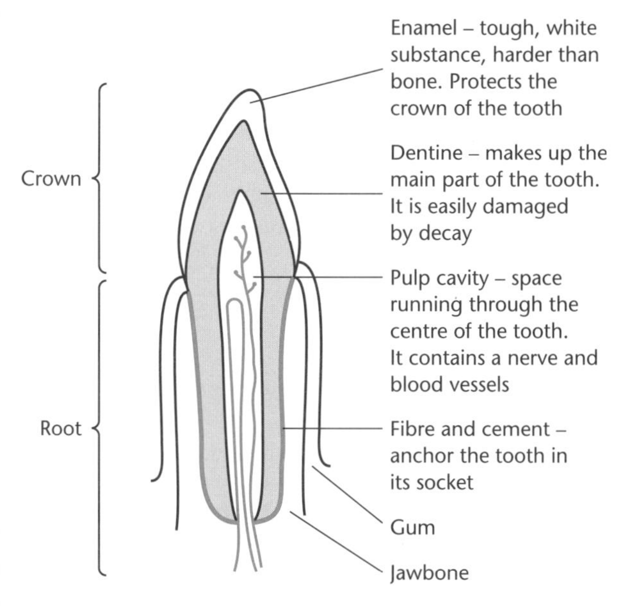

Inside a canine tooth

✣ ***Tooth decay***

TEMPERATURE

Temperature is usually thought of as a measure of how hot or cold something is. ***Kinetic theory*** tells us that it is really a measure of how fast the ***particles*** of the material are moving. (See ***heat energy***.)

It is important to realise that heat and temperature are connected but that temperature is *not* a measure of heat. Imagine using an electric heater to put heat energy into 200 ml of water in a beaker and then measuring the rise in temperature. You could then repeat the experiment with 1,000 ml of water in a larger beaker, switching the same heater on for the same length of time. The water has gained exactly the same amount of heat energy but will have a smaller rise in temperature. The same sort of thing will happen if you use the same mass of a different liquid. When you put heat into something you increase the internal energy in it by that amount. Depending on which material it is and how much there is of it, the particles that it is made from will go faster and we notice that it is 'hotter' – its temperature has gone up.

We usually measure temperature in °C but heat energy is measured in ***joules***.

Remember: Do not confuse heat and temperature!

✣ ***Heat energy, Kinetic theory, Temperature scale***

TEMPERATURE SCALE

To fix a temperature scale you need two temperatures called *fixed points*. The lower fixed point is the ***temperature*** at which pure ice melts (impurities would lower this temperature). This is called 0°C on the Celsius scale. The upper fixed point is the temperature at which pure water boils under a pressure of one atmosphere. This is called 100°C on the Celsius scale. The range between the two fixed points is divided into 100 equal degrees. You can make a thermometer and mark it with a scale using the apparatus shown in the diagram. You could also check that a thermometer was reading correctly in the same way.

Here are some temperatures that may help you understand the Celsius scale:

Hot summer day	30°C
Body temperature	37°C
Water freezes	0°C
Water boils	100°C
Room temperature	20°C
Iron melts	1500°C
The Sun (centre)	15 million °C
Oxygen boils	–183°C
Gold melts	1063°C
Temperature in a freezer	–20°C

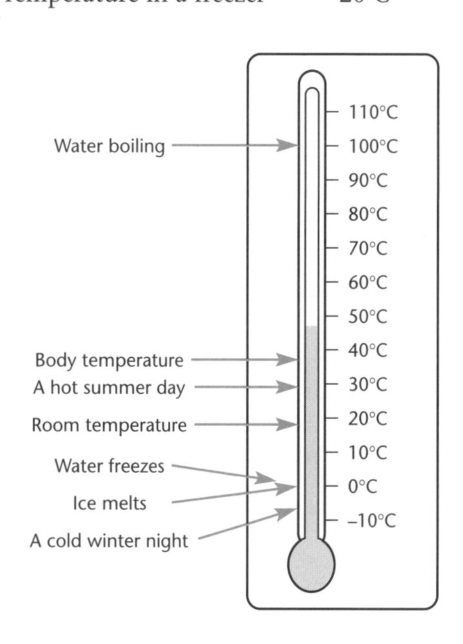

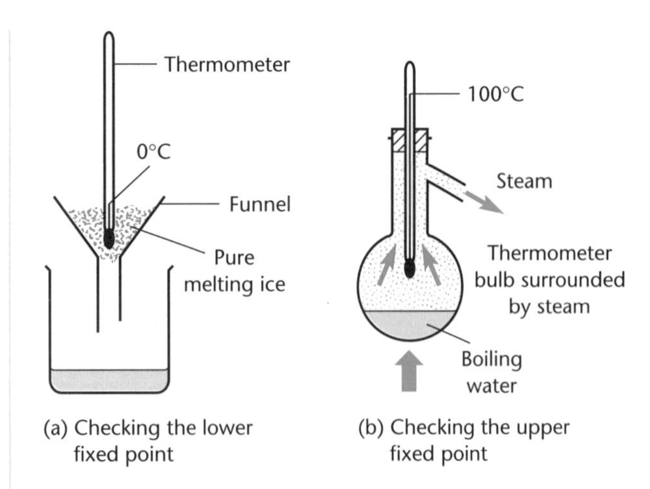

Calibrating a thermometer

A ***thermometer*** does not have to be a mercury-in-glass type that works by expansion of the liquid. Any property that changes reasonably steadily with temperature will do. The thermometer can still be calibrated in the same sort of way.

> *CHECKPOINT*
>
> To make a temperature scale you need ________ temperatures called ________ points. For the C scale they are the freezing point of water at ____°C and the boiling point of water at 100____.
>
> What are the hottest and coldest temperatures in the table of temperatures?

Heat temperature, Temperature, Thermometer

Tendon

These are strong fibres that attach ***muscles*** to ***bones***. Each muscle has at least one tendon at each end. You can see or feel your own tendons on the back of your hand and the front of your wrist, at the back of your knee and your ankle (Achilles tendon) and in your neck. It is easier to see tendons when the muscle is contracted, so they stand out. Tendons are very tough and will not stretch.

Terminal velocity

This is the constant velocity reached by an object when the forces on it are balanced, e.g. a skydiver reaches terminal velocity when the drag of the air is equal and opposite to his or her weight.

Counter forces

Test-tube babies

This is the everyday name for a process called *in vitro fertilization*. It is sometimes used to help infertile couples to have a baby. The process involves six main steps:

1. the woman is given fertility drugs so that several ova will develop in her ***ovary***,
2. she has an operation to remove these ova, and they are placed in a sterile glass dish,
3. they are mixed with ***sperm*** collected from the man, and ***fertilization*** will occur in the dish to form ***zygotes***,
4. the zygotes will be monitored carefully, until they have started to divide to form ***embryos***,
5. two or three of the embryos will be put inside the woman's ***uterus*** so they can implant and the rest will be frozen (in storage),
6. if an embryo does implant the woman is ***pregnant***, and the pregnancy will develop as normal. If the embryos do not implant, the couple will be able to try again with the embryos they have in storage.

In vitro fertilization now has a reasonably high success rate. Thousands of babies have been conceived like this since 1978, when the process was first carried out.

Reproduction

Testes

Men have two of these small organs (each one is called a testis). From the time a boy reaches ***puberty*** until he dies the testes will make ***sperm cells***, at the rate of millions per day. The testes are outside the abdomen in the scrotum where it is cooler – this is better for producing healthy sperm. Sperm are stored in the testis until they pass along the sperm duct and out through the penis.

The testes also make the male sex ***hormone*** testosterone.

Thermal decomposition

When a ***compound*** is broken down into smaller ***molecules*** by heat, the reaction is called thermal decomposition. When ***limestone*** is heated strongly, it breaks down into calcium oxide and carbon dioxide. Calcium oxide is sometimes called lime. This reaction also gives out light, so that, in Victorian theatres, the name 'limelight' was often used.

Thermometer

A thermometer is an instrument that is used to measure ***temperature***. There are a number of

different types of thermometer, which work in different ways and are suitable for different purposes. All depend on some property that changes as the temperature changes.

The liquid in glass thermometer

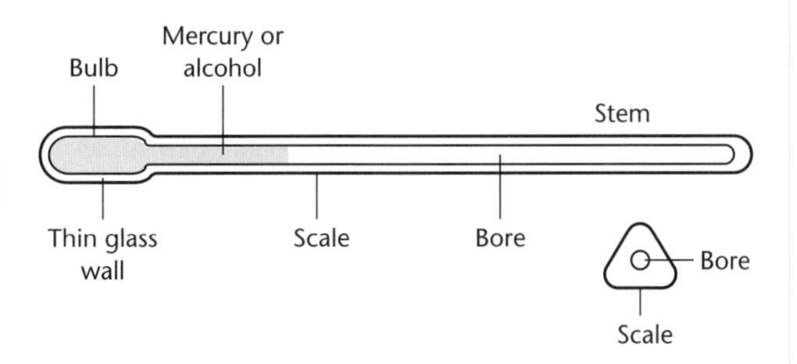

Liquid in glass thermometer

As the liquid gets warmer it expands along the bore of the stem and the scale is read at the end of the 'thread' of liquid. The bulb of the thermometer contains most of the liquid and has thin walls so that the heat is conducted to the liquid quickly. The bore must be the same width all the way along the stem so that the liquid expands the same distance along the bore for each degree of temperature rise. Making a thermometer that which a narrower bore makes the liquid move more for each degree and produces a more sensitive thermometer, which may be marked in fractions of a degree. The glass of the stem is often thicker on one side and this acts as a magnifying glass to enable the scale and liquid thread to be seen clearly. Two different liquids are commonly used depending on the intended use; mercury and alcohol.

Alcohol has a lower freezing point (78°C) and can be used at lower temperatures. Mercury has a higher boiling point (357°C) and can be used at higher temperatures. An alcohol thermometer would be broken as the alcohol boiled if you tried to measure the boiling point of water, so mercury thermometers are usually used in school/college labs. Alcohol thermometers are cheaper to make and are used in greenhouses and tropical fish tanks where the temperature range is more suitable.

Both liquids are dangerous but the mercury is more poisonous, especially the vapour.

The clinical thermometer

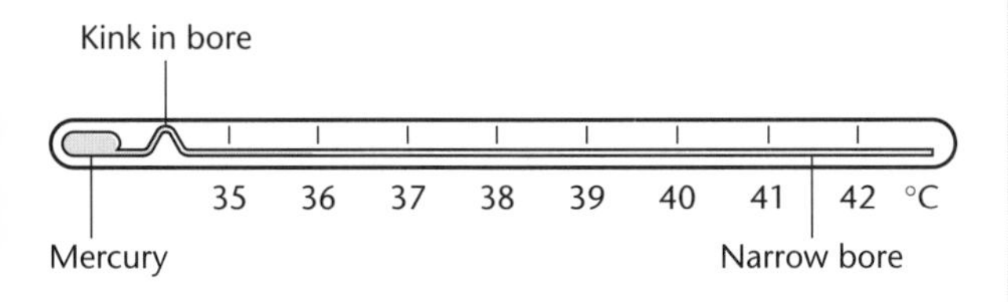

Clinical thermometer

This is a mercury in glass thermometer with a kink in the bore that prevents the mercury returning to the bulb as it cools. After reading the thermometer it is shaken to return the mercury past the kink. The bore will be narrow enough to allow temperatures to be read to 0.2°C but can be short as the temperature scale need only read between about 35°C and 42°C (body temperature is 37°C). There are also some digital versions. One type is electronic with a thermistor as the sensor and has an LCD readout. (LCD = Liquid Crystal Display as on some watches.)

Another type has a strip that goes transparent at different places along its length to show the different temperatures on the scale underneath it. The idea is that you put the strip on your forehead to get the reading. There have been experiments using a version of this that keeps the final temperature permanently for hospital records.

The thermocouple

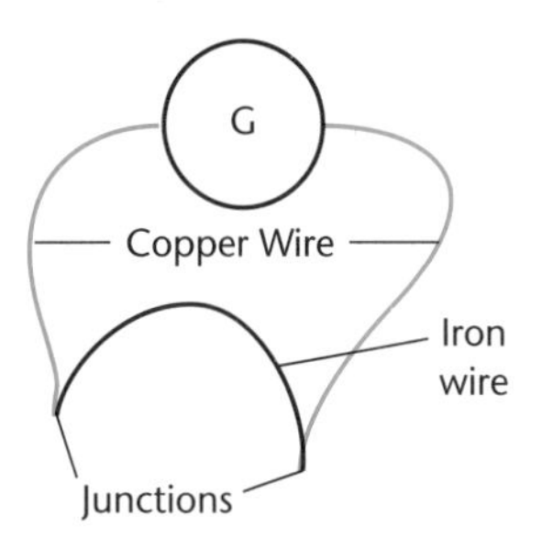

Thermocouple

The thermocouple has two wires of different metals joined as shown in the diagram. If the two junctions are at different temperatures, a voltage is produced and a reading is obtained on the galvanometer. (A galvanometer is a meter that can show very small electric currents.) A larger temperature difference produces a larger reading. The scale of the meter is usually marked in degrees so that the temperature can be read directly. The junctions can be made very small and strong and take in very little heat, which is often useful. The thermocouple can be used at much higher temperatures than a liquid in glass thermometer.

The thermistor

A thermistor has an electrical ***resistance*** that gets smaller as the temperature increases. As the temperature changes, the current through the thermistor will also change and the effect of this can be shown as the temperature on a meter or digital display.

The device can be made very small and sensitive but will be damaged by temperatures above about 50°C.

The pyrometer

In the case of very hot materials (furnaces, etc.) an ordinary thermometer would melt. A pyrometer works by looking at the colour of the light that is given out by the hot object. As the temperature of a hot object increases it gives out light that is dull red then orange, white and finally a bright bluish white. As the colour changes it is also getting brighter.

✧ *Temperature scale*

THORAX

In humans, this is the part of the body above the ***diaphragm***, containing the ***lungs*** and ***heart***. In insects, this is the middle section of the body: the legs and wings are attached to it.

TIDAL ENERGY

Tidal ***energy*** is caused by the moon orbiting the Earth. The moon attracts the water in the ocean towards it and this causes two slight bulges in the water on the surface of the Earth. As the Earth spins once each day, places on its surface go through these two higher water levels and we have two tides each day. At each tide the water level rises and then falls again. We can use this by making the water flow through barriers driving turbines as it does so. The main problem is in providing suitable sites and the large building costs. There are also worries about the ecological effects of the changed water level after the barrier and the visual impact of the barrier on coastal sites.

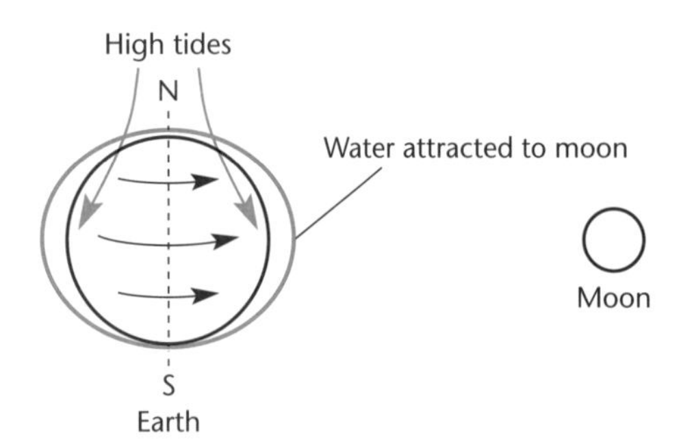

The tides

✧ *Sources of energy*

TISSUES

This is a collection of the same type of cells that work together to carry out a particular function, e.g.

muscle tissue (muscle cells),
bone tissue (bone cells),
nervous tissue (nerve cells).

Tissues are grouped to form ***organs***.

TOOTH DECAY

When we eat sugary foods, some of the sugar is left behind as a coating on our teeth. Bacteria living in our mouths start to feed on this sugar and change it into acid.

The sticky mixture of sugar and bacteria is called ***plaque***. The acid damages tooth enamel and can make a hole in it. This takes a long time because enamel is extremely strong. Once the decay reaches the dentine, damage is much faster because the dentine is softer. The tooth may become painful as the decay gets nearer to the pulp cavity, which contains a nerve.

Avoiding decay

You can do this by doing the following:

- avoid eating sugary food or drinks, particularly between meals,
- brush your teeth thoroughly at least twice a day to remove plaque,
- use a fluoride toothpaste because it strengthens the tooth enamel,
- use dental floss to remove food particles stuck between your teeth,
- make sure your toothbrush is in good condition,
- visit the dentist every six months so that your teeth can be checked, and any minor problems can be treated.

✧ *Teeth*

TRACHEA

This is a tube leading from the throat to the ***lungs***. It is also known as the windpipe. It is lined with ***ciliated cells*** to trap dust and dirt, so that they cannot clog up the tiny tubes and airsacs inside the lungs.

TRANSDUCER

A transducer is a device that changes ***energy*** from one form into another.

A microphone is a transducer that changes sound energy into electrical energy. A loudspeaker is a transducer that will reverse that process.

✧ *Energy*

TRANSPIRATION

This is the way that water vapour is lost from plant leaves. On the underside of every leaf are thousands of tiny holes called ***stomata***. When the stomata are open, water vapour can escape from the leaf into the atmosphere, and this process is called transpiration.

Transpiration is important because it helps to move water *upwards* from the roots to the leaves – it acts like a pump. The transpiration force is very powerful, because it can move water many metres, to the highest leaves at the top of a tree.

The *rate* of transpiration depends on environmental factors. It is fastest when:

- it is windy,
- it is a dry day (the air is not humid),
- it is warm,
- it is a bright, sunny day.

TURNING FORCES

These are ***forces*** that make things turn, usually about an axle or a pivot.

The size of a turning force is its ***moment*** and will depend on the size of the force *and* the distance of the force from the pivot. When things are balanced on a sharp edge the pivot is sometimes called a fulcrum.

Levers, Moment, Principle of moments

TWINS

Twins are two babies that develop at the same time in the ***uterus***, and are born at the same time. There are two different types of twins, identical and non-identical.

Identical twins

These develop from the same ***zygote***.

At an early stage of development, it splits completely into two, and two separate individuals are formed.

Identical twins are always of the same sex, and have inherited exactly the same ***genes*** from their parents. They may grow up to look different, because of differences in their upbringing or lifestyle.

Sometimes the zygote does not completely divide, leading to identical twins who are joined together. These are called conjoined or Siamese twins, and this condition is very rare. Sometimes the twins can be separated by an operation after they have been born.

Non-identical twins

Non-identical twins are formed when two eggs are released from the ovary in the same month, and both are fertilized, so two embryos will start to develop inside the uterus.

Non-identical twins may both be of the same sex, or they may be different sexes. They might look alike, or might look completely different. In fact, non-identical twins are just like normal brothers and sisters, but they happen to have been born at the same time!

Of course, more than two embryos can develop in the uterus at once. If there are three embryos they are called triplets, and if there are four embryos they are called quads. There might even be five or six or seven! Unfortunately, when there are several embryos developing, each one will be smaller and lighter than an embryo developing on its own, so it is less likely that all the babies will survive.

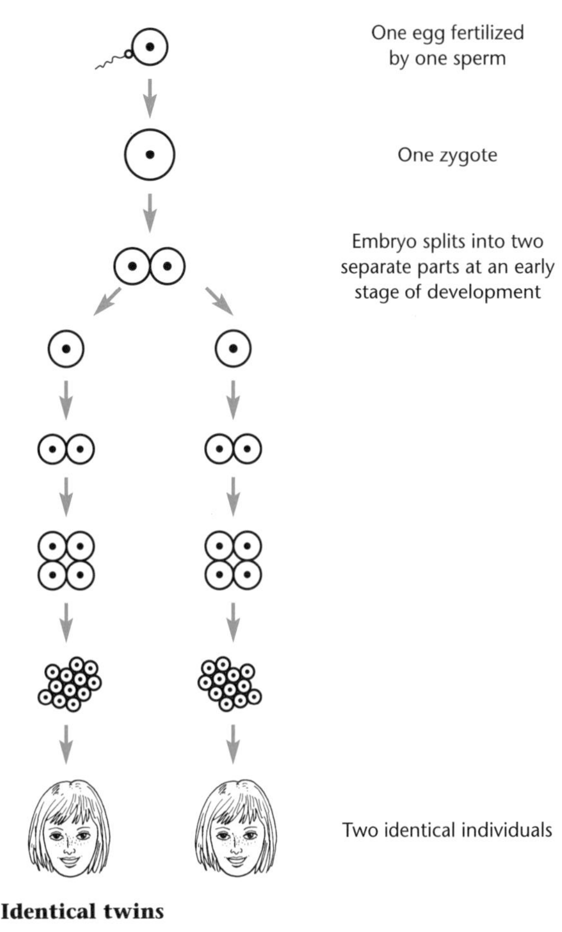
One egg fertilized by one sperm
One zygote
Embryo splits into two separate parts at an early stage of development
Two identical individuals

Identical twins

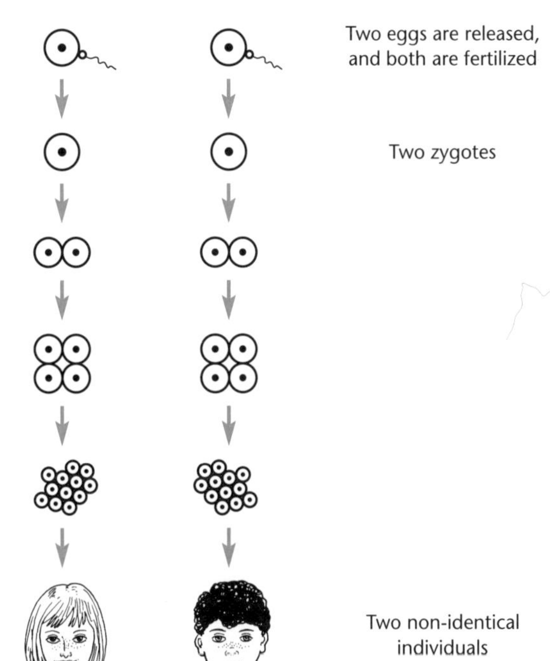
Two eggs are released, and both are fertilized
Two zygotes
Two non-identical individuals

Non-identical twins

Genes, Reproduction, Variation

Umbilical cord

This is a tube joining the ***foetus*** to the ***placenta*** during ***pregnancy***. It contains ***blood vessels*** (veins and an artery) that carry substances to and from the foetus. It is clamped and cut after birth.

✦ *Reproduction*

Universal indicator

✦ *Indicator*

Urea

This is a very poisonous substance made when ***proteins*** are broken down in the ***liver***. If it was allowed to build up, it would cause death. It travels in the ***blood*** to the ***kidneys***, and is removed from the body in ***urine***.

Urine

This is a pale yellow liquid excreted by the ***kidneys***. It contains water, salts and ***urea*** (waste products no longer needed by the body). It is stored in the ***bladder*** until it is excreted. It should never contain sugar or blood – these are signs that there is something wrong with the person's health.

An average person produces about one and a half litres of urine a day, but the exact amount depends on how much you drink, and how much you sweat.

Uterus

This is where the baby develops when a woman is pregnant. It has thick walls made of muscle to push the baby out during birth. It has a soft, blood-filled lining to nourish the ***embryo*** in the early stages of ***pregnancy***.

If a woman is not pregnant, this lining breaks up each month, causing a ***period***.

✦ *Menstrual cycle, Reproduction*

VACCINATION (IMMUNIZATION, INOCULATION)

This is a way of encouraging our ***white blood cells*** to make ***antibodies***, so that we do not catch a particular ***infectious disease***. There are four main steps:

1. The person is injected with a sample of the microbes that cause the disease. The microbes have been killed, or have been treated so they will not make the person ill.
2. White blood cells inside that person will start to make antibodies to destroy the microbes.
3. Even after the microbes have been destroyed, the white blood cells can 'remember' how to make the antibodies.
4. If the same type of microbes enter the body at any time in the future, white blood cells will make antibodies to destroy them immediately, so the person will not become ill.

Children in Britain are often vaccinated against the following infectious diseases:

diphtheria
polio
measles
mumps
rubella (german measles)
tetanus
whooping cough

Vaccination was first carried out successfully in Britain by Edward ***Jenner*** in 1796. He vaccinated a boy against smallpox, a fatal disease that has now been wiped out.

Defence against disease, Immune system

VACUOLE

This is a bubble of fluid (cell sap) found inside lots of plant cells. It is very important because it helps to keep the plant cell the right shape; if water is lost from the vacuoles, the plant wilts.

VACUUM FLASK

The vacuum flask was originally designed to keep liquids cold, but is good at stopping heat transfer both in and out and can be used equally well to keep things hot.

Conduction is reduced by the vacuum between the glass walls and by the stopper, which is usually plastic with a foam interior. ***Convection*** is also reduced by the surrounding vacuum and the stopper, which prevents convection currents between the contents and the air above the flask. ***Radiation*** is prevented by the silvering of both interior walls of the glass container. There will be slow heat transfer caused mainly by conduction through the walls of the glass container at the neck and conduction through the stopper.

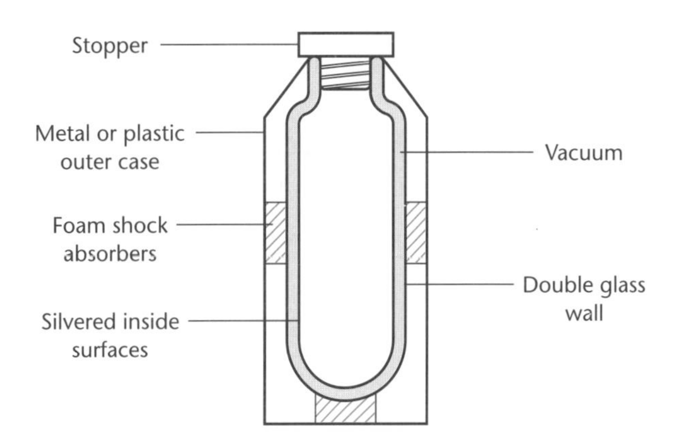

Vacuum flask

Conduction, Convention, Infra-red radiation

VAGINA

This is part of the female reproductive system. Sperm from the male are released here during ***sexual intercourse***, and they swim to the fallopian tubes where ***fertilization*** may take place. During ***birth***, the baby passes out of the woman's body through the vagina.

Reproduction

VARIABLE

This is something that you measure as it varies (changes) during an experiment. Usually you will choose one variable, called the *independent variable*, and change it in steps while you record what happens to a second variable, the *dependent variable*. In order to make a ***fair test*** you will only change one independent variable at a time and everything else must be kept the same.

For example: if you were investigating how fast magnesium reacts with hydrochloric acid you might change the concentration of the acid and measure the time taken for a 2 cm length of magnesium ribbon to completely react. The concentration of the acid is the independent variable, the time for the reaction is the dependent variable. All other factors like the temperature of the acid, the amount of magnesium, the volume of acid used must stay the same.

Fair test, Graph, Hypothesis

VARIABLE RESISTOR

This is a resistor made so that you can change its ***resistance***, usually by turning a control knob. If you make the resistance less, then more current will flow. If you turn it up, then less current gets through the resistor. A variable resistor like this can be used to make small bulbs brighter or dimmer. (A 'mains' bulb must have some other components as well!) With some other components it can be used as the volume (loudness) control or tone control on hi-fi.

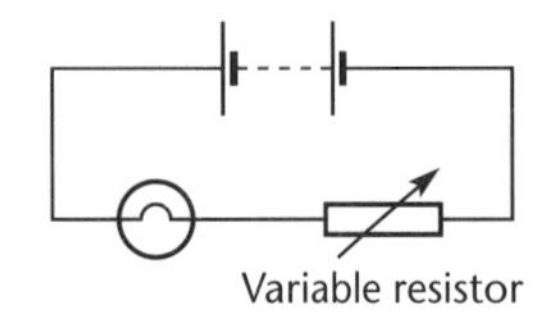

Making a torch bulb brighter or dimmer

Look at the figure above. The total ***voltage*** from the ***battery*** stays the same. When you turn up the resistance, less current flows through and the bulb gets dimmer. It will also take a larger share of the voltage to get the current through the variable resistor and there will be less left to drive current through the bulb. You can check that this is true if you put a ***voltmeter*** across the bulb and the vary the resistor.

Resistance, Resistor, Circuit

VARIATION

This means that living things are different to each other.

There is variation *between species*, e.g.

polar bears are different to brown bears,
whales are different to dolphins,
oak trees are different to daisies.

These differences are due to ***adaptations to the environment***.

There is a variation *within a species*, e.g.

all dogs are not identical,
all geranium plants are not identical,
all humans are not identical.

What causes variation within a species?

There are two main reasons why all members of a species are not identical:

1. They inherit different genes from their parents

If you look at the section on ***reproduction***, you will see that there are two types of reproduction:

a. ***asexual reproduction*** involves only one parent, and the offspring are identical to that parent. This is because they inherit all their ***genes*** from that parent.
b. ***sexual reproduction*** usually involves two parents, and the offspring are similar (but *not* identical) to both parents. This is because they inherit some genes from one parent, and some from the other.

Genes are instructions about features, e.g. eye colour, hair colour, height, blood group. If we inherit genes from both our parents, then we will inherit features from both our parents, so we cannot be *exactly* the same as either of them.

Every sperm cells carries 23 chromosomes, which is half of a full set of genes. Every ovum carries 23 chromosomes, which is half a full set of genes. It is a matter of luck which of the genes are inside any particular gamete.

Every time fertilization occurs, a new combination of genes is put together, so a unique individual is formed, i.e., there is a huge amount of variation within a species. The only exception to this is identical ***twins***, who both started life as the same zygote, so they have exactly the same genes!

Think about a typical family: the mother and father pass on features to their children through genes, but the children are not all exactly the same as each other.

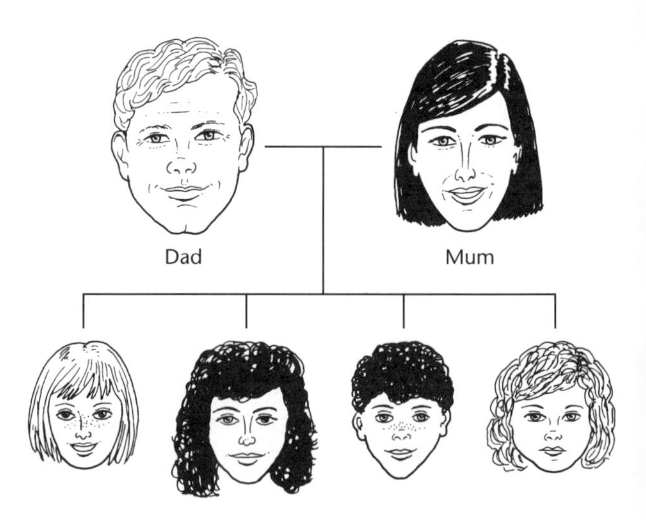

Family tree to show genetic variation

2. Things happen during their life which make them different

These are called environmental differences. Even if two organisms are genetically identical, they may develop very differently if they are brought up in different conditions, e.g. if one set of cress seeds is germinated and grown in the light, and another is germinated and grown in the dark.

Humans can be affected by environmental differences as well. If a child is not given a ***balanced diet*** with enough ***vitamins*** and ***minerals***, he or she will not grow properly, and may have lots of health problems.

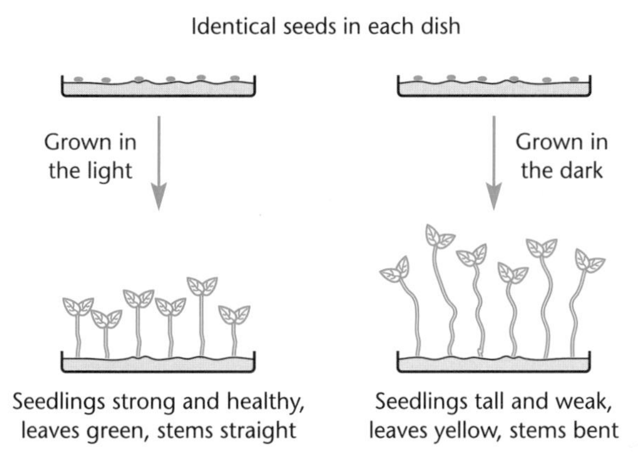

Cress seeds showing environmental variation

Some features, e.g. height and skin colour, are influenced by genes and the environment. For example, you inherit your skin colour from your parents (genetic) but it may become darker if it is exposed to strong sunlight (environmental).

Types of variation

If you try to find out about variation in your class, you will find that your data fits into one of two groups:

1. Continuous variation

There is a range of values from the smallest to the largest, e.g. height in humans, handspan in humans. When you display this data, you should use a histogram.

You will usually find that there are a small number of people at either end of the range, and most people are in the middle of the range.

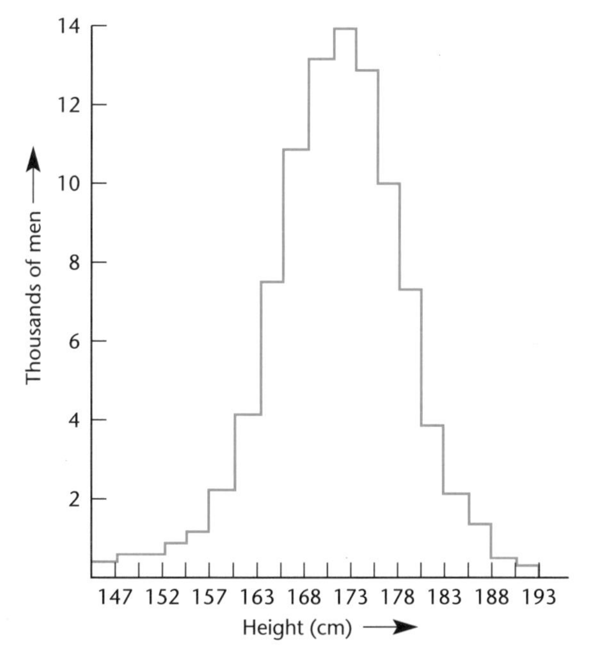

Continuous variation e.g., human height

2. Discontinuous variation

Organisms fit clearly into a particular group, and there are no intermediate values, e.g. eye colour in humans, blood group in humans. When you display this data, you should use a bar chart or pie chart.

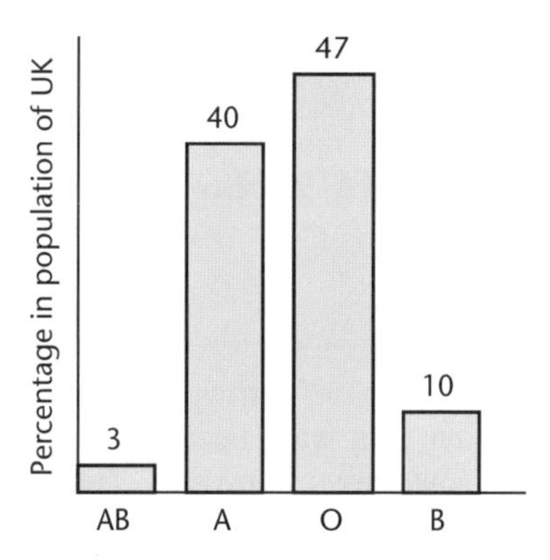

Discontinuous variation e.g., human blood groups

> *CHECKPOINT*
>
> Decide whether each of these features is controlled by genes or the environment:
>
> - flower colour in geraniums,
> - fingerprint type in humans,
> - number of leaves in geraniums,
> - blood group in humans,
> - being able to play the piano,
> - height in humans.

Breeds, Selective breeding, Species

VARIETIES

These are produced by ***selective breeding***. They are still members of the same ***species***, but they have very different characteristics. For example:

- all dogs are the same species, but different varieties include dalmatian, poodle, sheepdog, labrador, husky,
- all potatoes are the same species, but different varieties include King Edwards, Cara, Jersey royals, Desirée.

Varieties are sometimes called breeds.

> *CHECKPOINT*
>
> You should be able to think of different varieties of:
>
> 1. apples
> 2. cats
> 3. horses
>
> Why are hamsters and gerbils *not* an example of different varieties?

Variation

Vector

A vector is a measurement that has a direction as well as a size.

Forces will always be vectors because their direction will always be important.

Velocity is a vector. It is the speed in a particular direction.

Acceleration, Force, Velocity

Veins

This type of ***blood vessel*** carries ***blood*** towards the ***heart***. They have thin walls because blood travels slowly and at low pressure in veins. They have pocket valves to stop blood flowing the wrong way. You cannot feel a ***pulse*** in veins. The main vein of the body is called the vena cava.

Velocity

Velocity is the ***speed*** in a particular direction.

Sometimes the direction is just as important as the speed. This is an example of a ***vector*** quantity.

Speed

Vertebrates

These are ***animals*** that have an internal ***skeleton***. Vertebrates are classified into five groups, or classes:

1. fish,
2. amphibians,
3. reptiles,
4. birds,
5. mammals.

Fish, e.g. trout, shark, cod:

- body covered in damp scales,
- no legs,
- fins to move through water,
- breathe using gills,
- cold blooded,
- lay eggs in water (no shells).

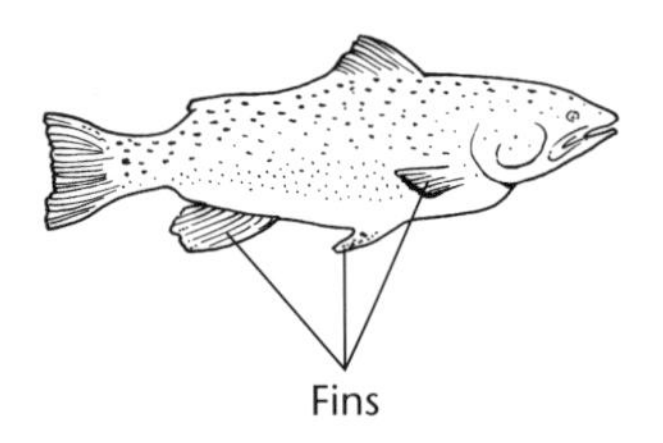

Amphibians, e.g. frogs, toads:

- body covered in damp skin (no scales),
- four legs,
- breathe through lungs and damp skin,
- cold blooded,
- lay eggs in water (no shells).

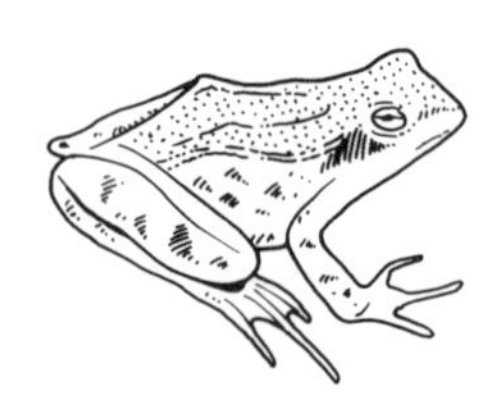

Reptiles, e.g. snake, lizard, crocodile:

- body covered in dry scales,
- most have four legs,
- breathe using lungs,
- cold blooded,
- most live on land, some feed in water,
- lay eggs on land (soft shells).

Birds, e.g. sparrow, crow, gull:

- body covered with feathers,
- two legs,
- one pair of wings,
- breathe using lungs,
- warm blooded,
- most live on land,
- lay eggs on land (hard shells).

Mammals, e.g. squirrels, humans, elephants:

- skin covered in *hair* or *fur*,
- most have four legs,

- breathe using lungs,
- warm blooded,
- most live on land,
- eggs develop *inside* the mother's body so babies are born alive,
- babies are fed on *milk* from the mother's mammary glands.

Classification

VILLUS

Food is absorbed from the gut into the blood in the ileum (*small* ***intestine***). The walls of the ileum are specially adapted for this because they are covered in thousands of tiny villi. Each villus is a tiny spike sticking into the lumen of the ileum. Together, they increase the surface area and make ***absorption*** very much more efficient. The villi have very thin walls to allow substances to pass through them easily, and each one contains ***capillaries*** so that the food is absorbed quickly.

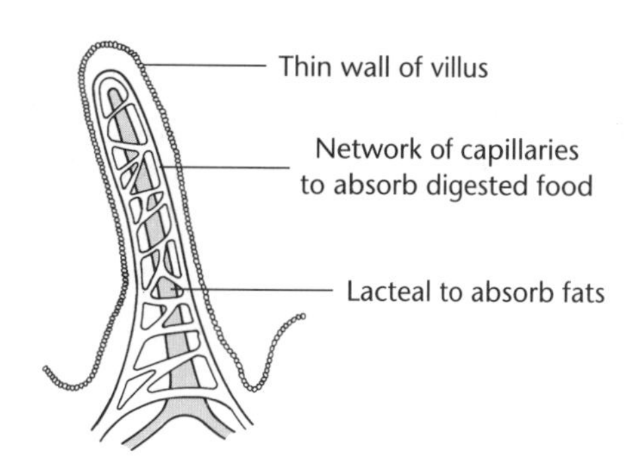

Structure of one villus

VIRUSES

Viruses are microscopic organisms that are completely different to all other living things. They are not included in the ***classification*** table, because scientists cannot agree where they should go.

Each virus is made up of a protein coat surrounding a piece of ***DNA*** or RNA. There is no cytoplasm and no nucleus. Viruses are much smaller than other microbes, about 0.0001mm across, so 10,000 viruses in a row would measure 1mm.

All viruses are ***parasites***: they live inside the cells of other organisms. They damage and destroy the cells they live in, causing disease. All viruses are harmful:

- some cause human ***diseases***, e.g. mumps, flu, german measles, colds, AIDS, hepatitis.
- some cause diseases in other animals and plants.

Table to summarize features of vertebrates

	Live in?	*Skin type?*	*Move with?*	*Breathe through?*	*Can control body temperature?*	*Eggs or live young?*
Fish	Water	Scales	Fins	Gills	No	Eggs laid in water (no shell)
Amphibians	Water when young, land when older. Go back to water to breed	Moist skin, no scales	Legs	Damp skin and lung	No	Eggs laid in water (no shell)
Reptiles	Some on land, e.g. tortoise, some in water, e.g. crocodile	Scaly skin	Most have four legs (snakes do not)	Lungs	No	Eggs laid on land (soft shell)
Birds	On land, in water	Skin covered with feathers	Legs and wings (most birds can fly)	Lungs	Yes	Eggs laid on land (hard shell)
Mammals	Some on land, e.g. humans, elephant, some in water, e.g. whales, dolphin	Skin covered with hair	Most have legs, bats also have wings,	Lungs	Yes	Give birth to live babies and feed them on milk

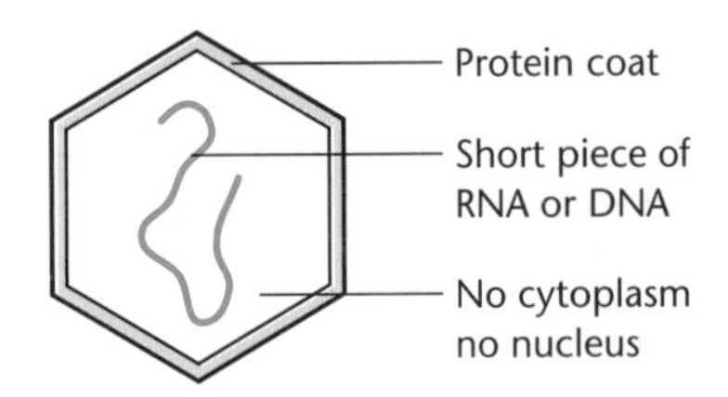

Inside a virus

Antibiotics will not kill viruses – they can only be killed by anti-viral drugs, but these often have bad side effects for the person who takes them.

Viruses do not reproduce like other organisms, but while they are inside host cells they make copies of themselves. When the host cell dies, it bursts open and hundreds of new viruses are released.

VITAMINS

These are nutrients needed in tiny amounts to keep the body healthy. They are usually given a letter name, e.g. Vitamin C, but often have a scientific name as well, e.g. Ascorbic acid. Vitamins are found in lots of fresh foods, e.g. fruits, vegetables, meat, milk, but are often damaged or destroyed by cooking or storage. Vitamins can also be obtained in vitamin tablets. If your diet does not contain enough of a particular vitamin, you might suffer from a ***deficiency disease***.

Table to show some of the main vitamins

Vitamin	*Found in...*	*Needed for...*	*Problems if you do not have enough*
A	Liver, cheese, milk, carrots	Healthy skin, good vision	Skin may break and bleed easily, problems seeing in dim light (night blindness)
B Vitamins e.g. B1, B2, B6, niacin, folic acid	Cereals, yeast	Obtaining energy from food	Skin diseases, e.g. pellagra, anaemia, beri-beri (muscle weakness and paralysis)
C	Citrus fruits, potatoes, green vegetables	Healthy skin and gums	Scurvy – skin breaks and bleeds easily, wounds take a time to heal, gums bleed and swell
D	Liver, eggs, made in skin	Healthy bones and teeth	Rickets – bones are too weak to support the body's weight, so they bend

Balanced diet

VOLT

This is the unit that you use when you measure ***emf*** or ***pd***.

Potential difference, Voltmeter

VOLTAGE

This is the number of volts measured across part of a circuit.

Potential difference, Voltmeter

VOLTMETER

A voltmeter is the meter that you use to measure ***potential difference*** or ***emf***. It must be connected *across* the part of the ***circuit*** where you wish to take the measurement. The measurement will be in ***volts***.

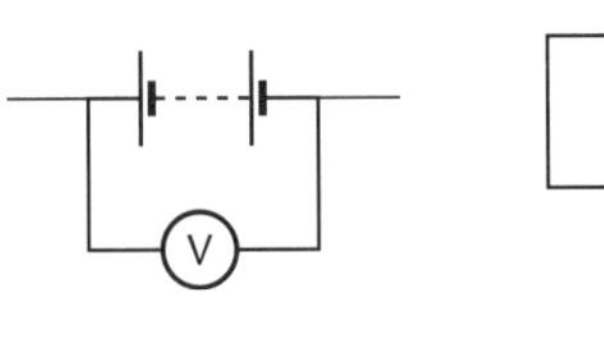

Measuring emf

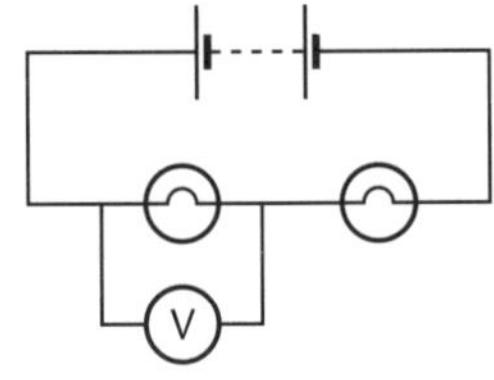

Measuring pd across a bulb

Voltmeter

The emf of a battery can be measured when *only* the voltmeter is connected across it.

Remember: The meter must always be connected across *the voltage to be measured.*

This means that the voltmeter must have a very high ***resistance*** or a ***current*** will use it to by-pass part of the circuit and may even change what is happening in the circuit.

> *CHECKPOINT*
>
> Use the standard circuit symbols to show how you would measure the voltage across one of two bulbs connected in series.

Potential difference

VOLUME

This is a measurement of the space that is occupied by a material. It is usually measured in m^3 or cm^3 but liquids and gases are often measured in litres.

It may sometimes help to remember that
1,000 litres = 1 m^3

There are a number of ways to measure volume:

Cube or rectangular solid

A simple cube or rectangular solid can have the volume calculated by:

$$\text{Volume} = \text{Length} \times \text{Width} \times \text{Height}$$

Liquid

The volume of a liquid can often be found by pouring it into a ***measuring cylinder***. It is important to use the cylinder with the smallest possible divisions on its scale so that you get the best possible answer.

Powder

A powder can be difficult to measure, especially a coarse one such as sand, because of the air that is trapped between the particles. Pouring it into a measuring cylinder will only give a very approximate answer. Put some water into a measuring cylinder and note the reading (fill it to a nice easy number!). Gently and slowly pour in the powder until it is all in the cylinder and then take the new reading. Subtract the first reading from the last and you have the volume of the powder. If the powder dissolves in water or reacts with it then you would need to use another liquid.

If you are using this as part of an experiment to find density then find the mass first, or the wet powder has to be dried before you can carry on!

Irregular objects

The volume of an irregularly shaped object, such as a stone, can be measured by displacing water. You can do this for a small object such as a marble by putting water into a measuring cylinder and noting the reading. Gently drop the marble into the cylinder and check that it is completely under the water. Take the new reading on the measuring cylinder and subtract the first one.

A larger object will need the water to be displaced from a eureka can (often called a displacement can.)

Fill the can above the level of the spout and the put it onto a level surface so that the excess water drains away. Put an empty measuring cylinder under the spout and then gently lower the object into the water. The volume of the object will be exactly the same as the volume of the water in the measuring cylinder.

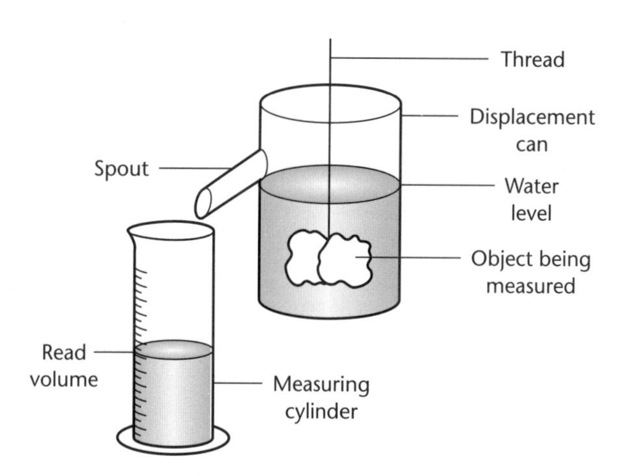

Using a displacement can

Remember: Use the measuring cylinder with the smallest possible divisions.

✦ *Density, Mass*

WATER

Water is a liquid, with a chemical formula of H_2O. This formula indicates that the water molecule is made up of two hydrogen atoms to every one oxygen atom. The water molecule has slight charges on each atom. These charges give water its unusual properties. Water freezes at 0°C and boils at 100°C. Water has its maximum density at 4°C while still liquid, rather than in its solid form as ice. This is why ice floats on water. Water can dissolve many different substances; it has been nicknamed 'the universal solvent'.

Test for water

Add water to white anhydrous copper sulphate and it turns blue, or dip blue cobalt chloride paper into water and it changes colour to very pale pink.

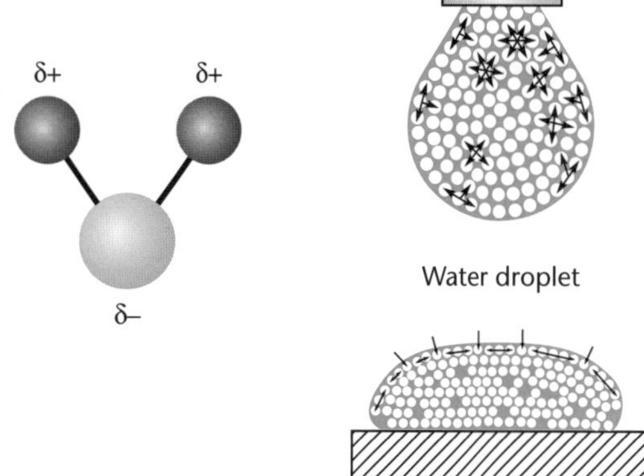

Water molecules

WATER IN PLANTS

Plants absorb water from the soil through ***root hair cells***. It is important to plants for many vital processes, e.g.

- it is needed for ***photosynthesis***,
- it is needed for cell sap – without this the plant will wilt,
- it is pumped to the leaves of the plant by the process of ***transpiration***.

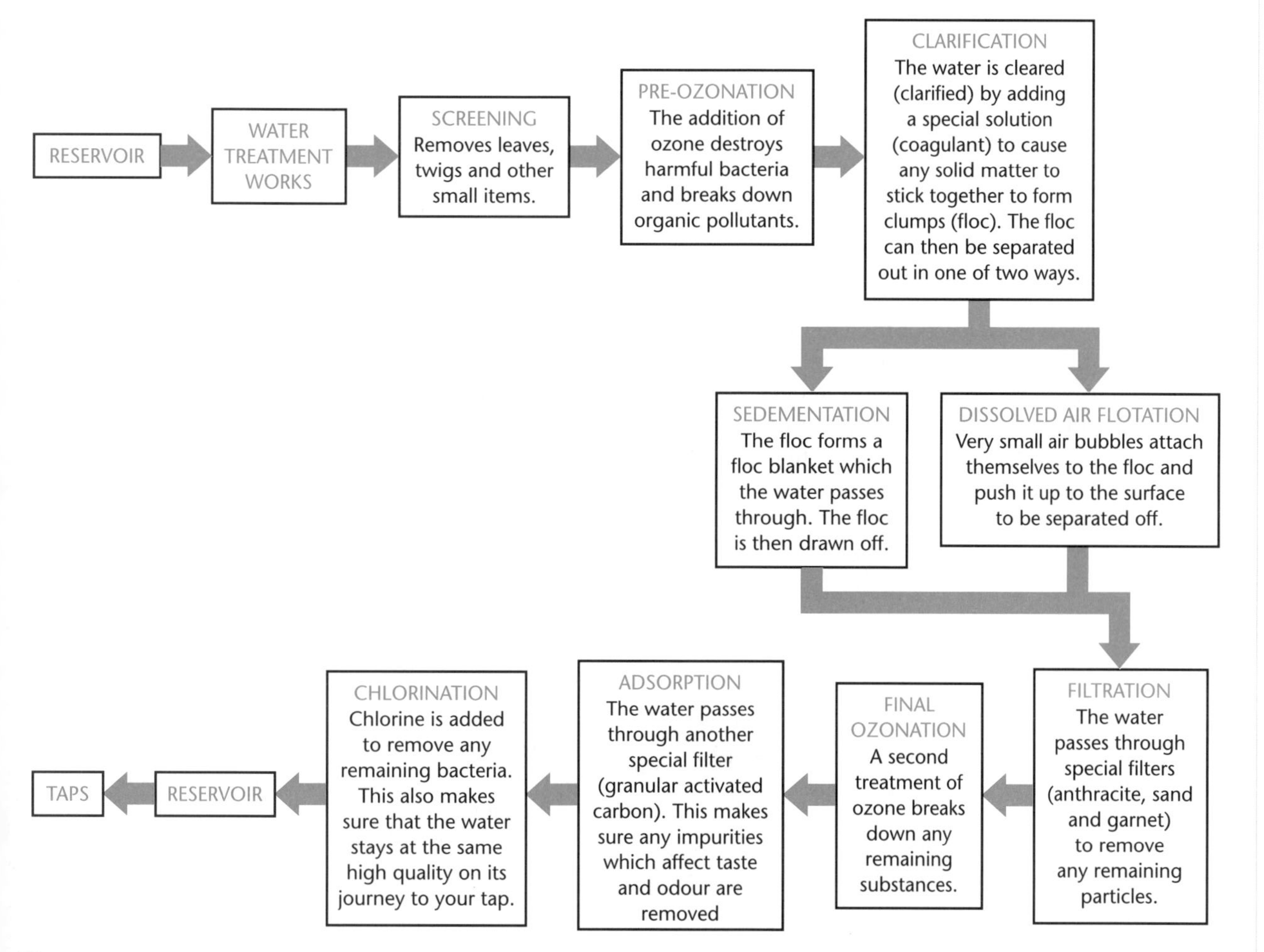

Water treatment

WATER TREATMENT

Water from reservoirs has to be treated before we can drink it. The figure on p. 163 shows how this process takes place.

WATSON (1928–)

James Watson is an American scientist who worked in the team which discovered the structure of ***DNA*** in 1953. He was awarded the Nobel Prize for this work.

WAVE

A wave is a vibration that travels out from its source carrying ***energy***. There are two main types of wave: transverse waves and longitudinal waves.

Transverse waves

In a transverse wave the vibration is across the direction of travel of the wave. (The direction of the wave and the vibration are at 90°.) Most waves are this type, including ripples on water, light waves, radio waves and waves such as X-rays and microwaves.

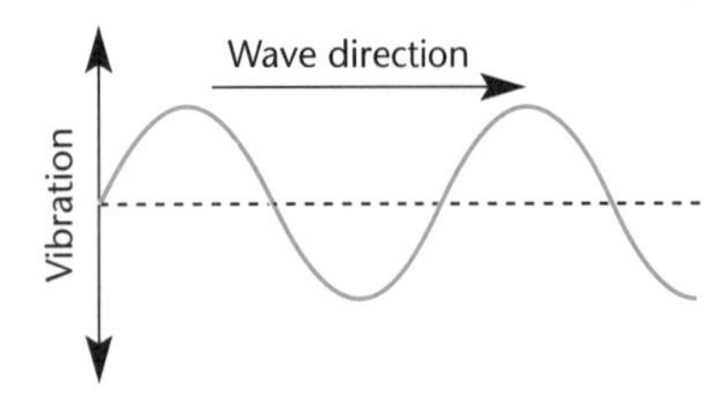

A transverse wave

Some of these waves are part of the electromagnetic ***spectrum***. In that case, there are no ***particles*** to vibrate and it is a magnetic and electric field that vibrates instead. Electromagnetic waves can travel through a vacuum because they do not need particles to vibrate.

You can make transverse waves by stretching out a piece of rope and vibrating one end. You can then see the sideways vibration travel along.

Longitudinal waves

In a longitudinal wave the vibration is forwards with the wave and then back against it. The backwards and forwards movements bunches the vibrating particles together into compressions. Halfway between the compressions the particles will be spread out lowering the pressure. Sound waves are this type of wave.

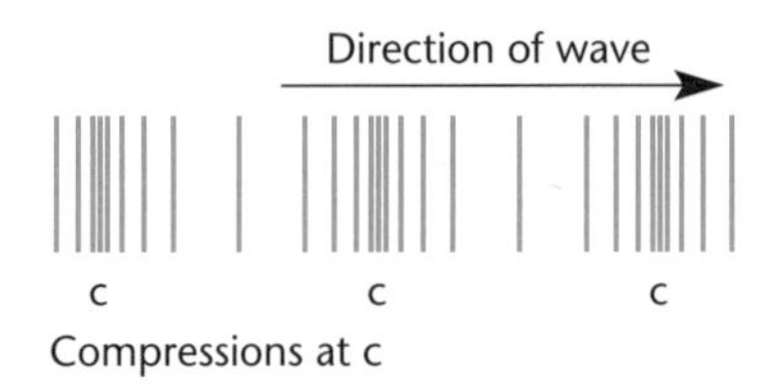

A longitudinal wave

This type of wave has to have particles that vibrate, so they cannot travel through a vacuum. This is why sound waves cannot travel through a vacuum such as space even though light waves can.

You can make longitudinal waves by stretching out a long spring. The ones sold as a toy called a 'slinky' are ideal. If you pull some of the coils together to make a compression and then let go you can see the compression travel along to the other end of the spring.

To describe a wave fully you would also need to know about its ***amplitude***, ***frequency*** and its ***wavelength***.

> CHECKPOINT
>
> Name the two main types of wave.
>
> Which way do the particles vibrate in each of these two types?
>
> Give an example of each type.

Frequency, Light, Sound, Wavelength

WAVELENGTH

This is the length of one complete wave and will be measured in m.

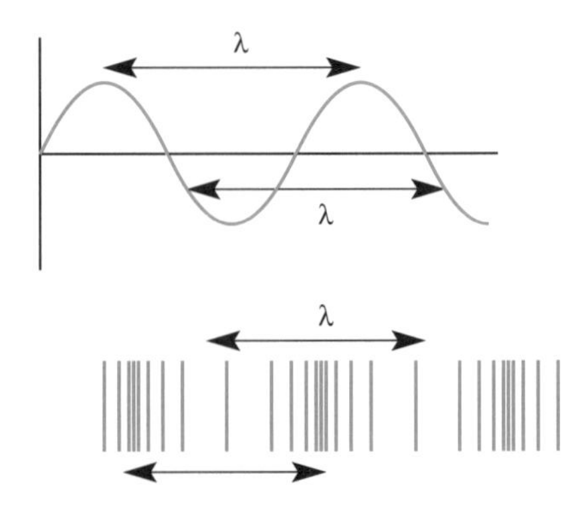

Wavelengths

The distance will be the distance between two peaks of a transverse wave or the distance between two compressions in a longitudinal wave.

The wavelength is often given the special symbol λ.

Amplitude, Frequency, Wave

WAVE POWER

Sea waves often carry large quantities of ***energy*** as a large mass of water is being moved up and down. To extract energy from waves involves strings of machines on the surface of the sea. As the waves go by they drive part of the machine up and down and this drives a hydraulic pump. The fluid driven by the pump in turn drives a generator. Another method uses the water to push air in and out through a wind turbine. The waves emerge smaller than before meeting the machine because they now have less energy. The main problems have been the large differences in size of the waves and the damage done by bad weather. A lot of machines are needed and suitable sites can be difficult to find. The original source of this energy is the Sun – NOT the moon which produces tidal energy! The Sun creates different temperatures and pressures in the air, and the winds that this produces makes the waves.

The advantage is that the energy will not run out.

The disadvantages are the problems in designing a machine that can survive at sea and that sometimes there are no waves.

Sources of energy

WEAK ACID

Weak acids have pH values of 3–6. Ethanoic and citric acids are examples.

pH scale

WEAK ALKALI

Weak alkalis have pH values of 8–11. Milk and soap are examples.

pH scale

WEATHERING

The process by which rocks are broken down is called weathering.

- Chemical weathering affects limestone quite badly. Rain water is slightly acidic and reacts with the calcium carbonate in the limestone. The soluble salt that is formed then drains away. The unusual scenery of caves and grikes in limestone karst country is due mainly to this type of weathering.
- Physical weathering is the other main method of breaking down rocks. Water percolates into fine cracks in the rock. When the water freezes, it then expands and cracks the rock.

WEIGHT

Weight is a ***force*** caused by ***gravity*** acting on a ***mass***. Any two objects that have mass will be attracted towards each other (even people!) but at least one of the objects must be *very* massive for the force to be large enough to matter. The force also gets less quickly as the distance between the objects increases. As weight is a force it *must* be measured in ***newtons***. Each 1kg of mass at the surface of the ***Earth*** will be attracted to the Earth with a force of about 10 N.

> *Remember: Objects have weight because of the gravitational attraction between them and the Earth.*

For example: a person of mass 60kg will have a weight of 600N. This is the force of attraction towards the Earth. The Earth is attracted towards the person with the same force but it is so massive that it is not going to move very far!

This means that, on Earth, the weight in N of a mass in kg is given by:

Weight = mass × 10
in N   in kg

It is important that you do not confuse weight with mass – a weightless object moving in space will still have mass.

If you find it difficult to imagine the size of 1 N, remember that a bag of sugar from the supermarket will weigh about 10 N. Sir Isaac Newton would also have been pleased to know that an average eating apple weighs about 1 N !

Weight will cause objects to accelerate 'downwards'. This ***acceleration*** should be the same for *all* objects because a larger force (weight) will be needed to accelerate a larger mass. If you drop a ball and a piece of paper together this seems not to be true, as the paper drifts gently downwards. If you screw the paper up into a ball to reduce its air resistance and try again you can see that they do fall together. The problem was caused by the extra force of the air resistance. A better version of this experiment was done by an American astronaut on the moon. He dropped an eagle feather and a hammer at the same time and they could be seen to fall together because there was no air resistance. They also accelerated more slowly than on Earth because the moon's smaller mass produces smaller weights that are only about $\frac{1}{6}$ of that on Earth.

> *Remember: In everyday speech we often mix up mass and weight because everything that is on Earth that has a mass also has weight. Do not mix the two in Science, the difference is sometimes very important.*

Acceleration, Force, Mass, Vector

WHITE BLOOD CELLS

These help to defend the body against disease (they are not involved in transporting substances).

There are two main types:

1. Phagocytes – surround and destroy germs (bacteria and viruses) in the body.
2. Lymphocytes – make chemicals called ***antibodies*** to destroy bacteria and viruses in the body.

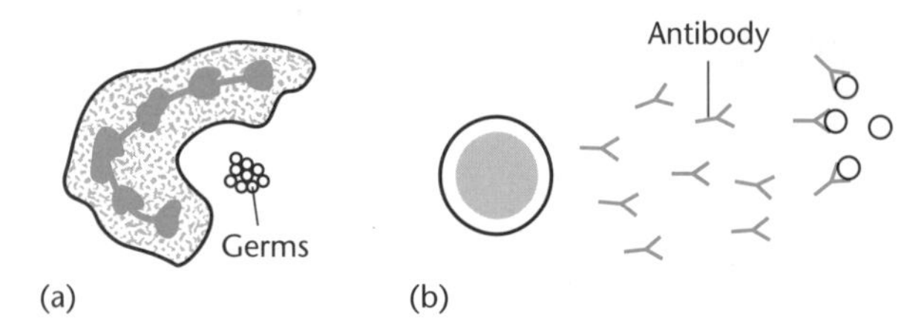

White blood cells: (a) Phagocytes, (b) Lymphocytes

Blood, Circulatory system, Defence against disease

WIND POWER

Wind power can be derived from modern windmills with rotors that are rather like the propellers of an aeroplane in shape. Large rotors can produce enough electricity by driving a generator to be economical but there are problems with lack of wind (or too much some of the time!) – and objections about the large unsightly structures in country areas. If these are to provide an ***alternative energy source*** on a large scale there will have to be many of them on westward facing hills and many people would find the effect on the landscape unacceptable. Modern wind generators vary from small ones that keep batteries recharged and are useful on remote farms and islands, up to large ones feeding the national grid which have rotors 25 m in length. The original source of energy is the Sun, which heats the air causing temperature and pressure differences and, therefore, wind as the air spirals into low pressure areas.

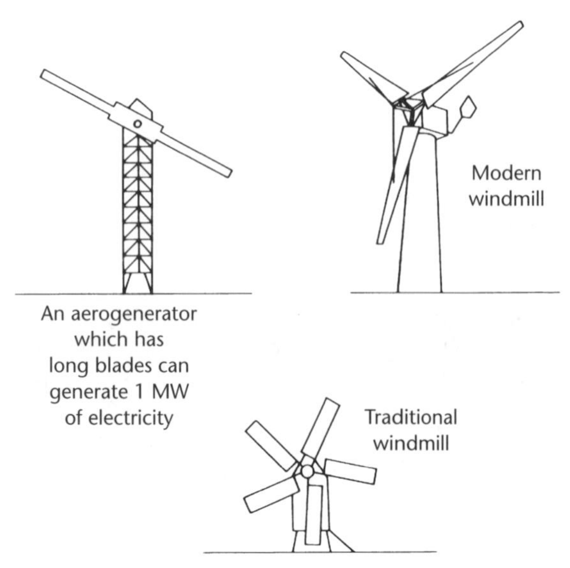

Using wind energy to generate electricity

Sources of energy

WORD EQUATION

This is a short way of writing down what happens when a ***chemical reaction*** takes place.

For example, it is much easier to write the word equation:

Magnesium + Oxygen ⟶ Magnesium oxide

rather than having to write in long hand:

'When magnesium is heated in air, it reacts with the active gas oxygen to produce a white powder magnesium oxide.'

WORK

Work is done when a ***force*** moves an object.

The amount of work done will depend on the size of the force and how far it moves.

If a force of one ***newton*** moves a distance of one metre then it does one ***joule*** of work.

Work done = Force × distance moved

You should also be able to see that when work is done the same amount of energy is being transferred from one form to another.

Remember: The work done does NOT depend on how long it takes. The equation only works when the force is in N and the distance is in m so that the work is in J.

For example: a man pushes a car with a force of 300 N and it moves forward by 5 m. How much work has he done and how much energy has he used?

Work done = Force × distance moved
= 300 × 5
= 1500 J

The energy used is the same as the work that is done: 1,500 J.

CHECKPOINT

How much work will you do if you lift 150 N from the floor onto your desk? (The desk will be about 0.75 m high.)

How much work would you do if you climbed up onto the desk?

Energy, Force

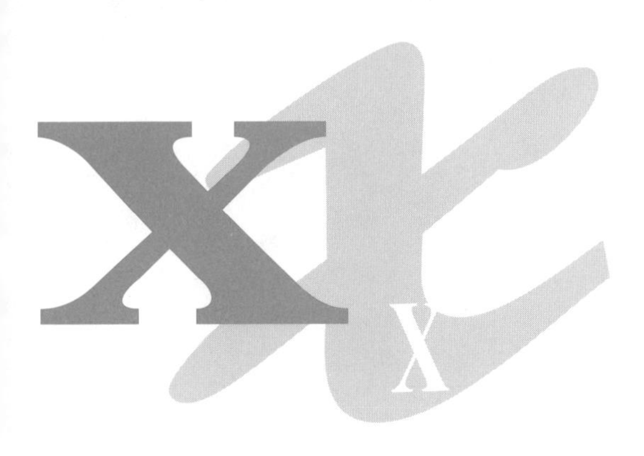

XYLEM VESSELS

These are tubes inside plants that carry water and minerals. They are found in the ***stem*** and ***roots***, and inside veins in leaves. Water always travels *upwards* in xylem vessels. It travels from the roots (where it is absorbed from the soil) to the leaves (where it is lost by ***transpiration***).

YEAST

Yeast is a microscopic fungus. It is single celled.

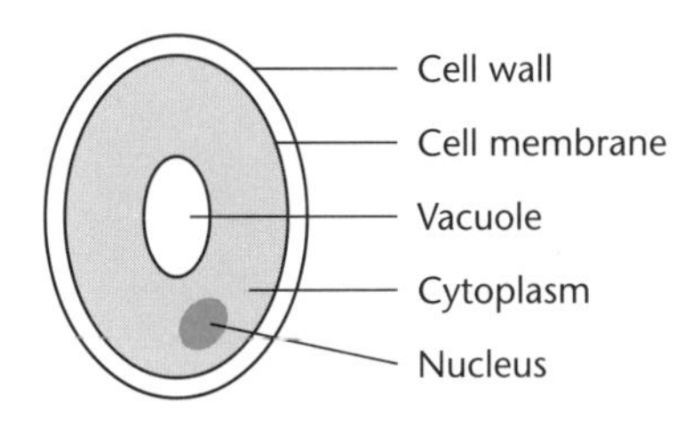

Yeast

It grows in soil and on fruit skins, but it is very important to humans in the processes of brewing and bread-making.

If yeast does not have enough oxygen, it carries out anaerobic ***respiration***. It uses ***glucose*** as a fuel to make energy, and the waste products in this reaction are alcohol and carbon dioxide.

This reaction is also called ***fermentation***:

Glucose ⟶ Energy + Alcohol + Carbon dioxide

Yeast in brewing

If yeast and sugar are added to fruit juice, or to malted barley, an alcoholic drink will be produced (wine, lager or beer, depending on the type of plant material you start with). Yeast feeds on the sugar making alcohol, and the flavour comes from the original plant material. In some drinks, the carbon dioxide is trapped, so the drink is fizzy.

Yeast in baking

Yeast and sugar are added to flour and water to make dough. As the yeast respires, bubbles of carbon dioxide gas are produced and the dough rises to almost double its original size. When the dough is baked, the dough 'sets'; the heat kills the yeast and evaporates the alcohol. This gives you light, open-textured bread.

Measuring the respiration rate in yeast

This is an experiment that is often done in schools. You can find the respiration rate by counting the number of bubbles of carbon dioxide produced in a set time, e.g. in two minutes.

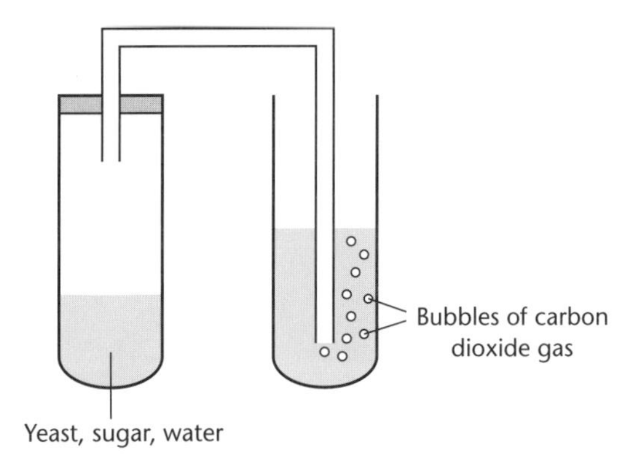

Measuring the respiration rate in yeast

You could investigate what happens if you change the following factors:

- amount of sugar,
- amount of yeast,
- temperature (by putting the apparatus in a water bath).

ZYGOTE

This is a single cell formed when a ***sperm*** joins to an ***ovum*** during ***fertilization***. It divides up to form all the cells (millions) making up a human being.

Just think, you were once a zygote!

✦ ***Reproduction***

APPENDIX 1

Doing an investigation

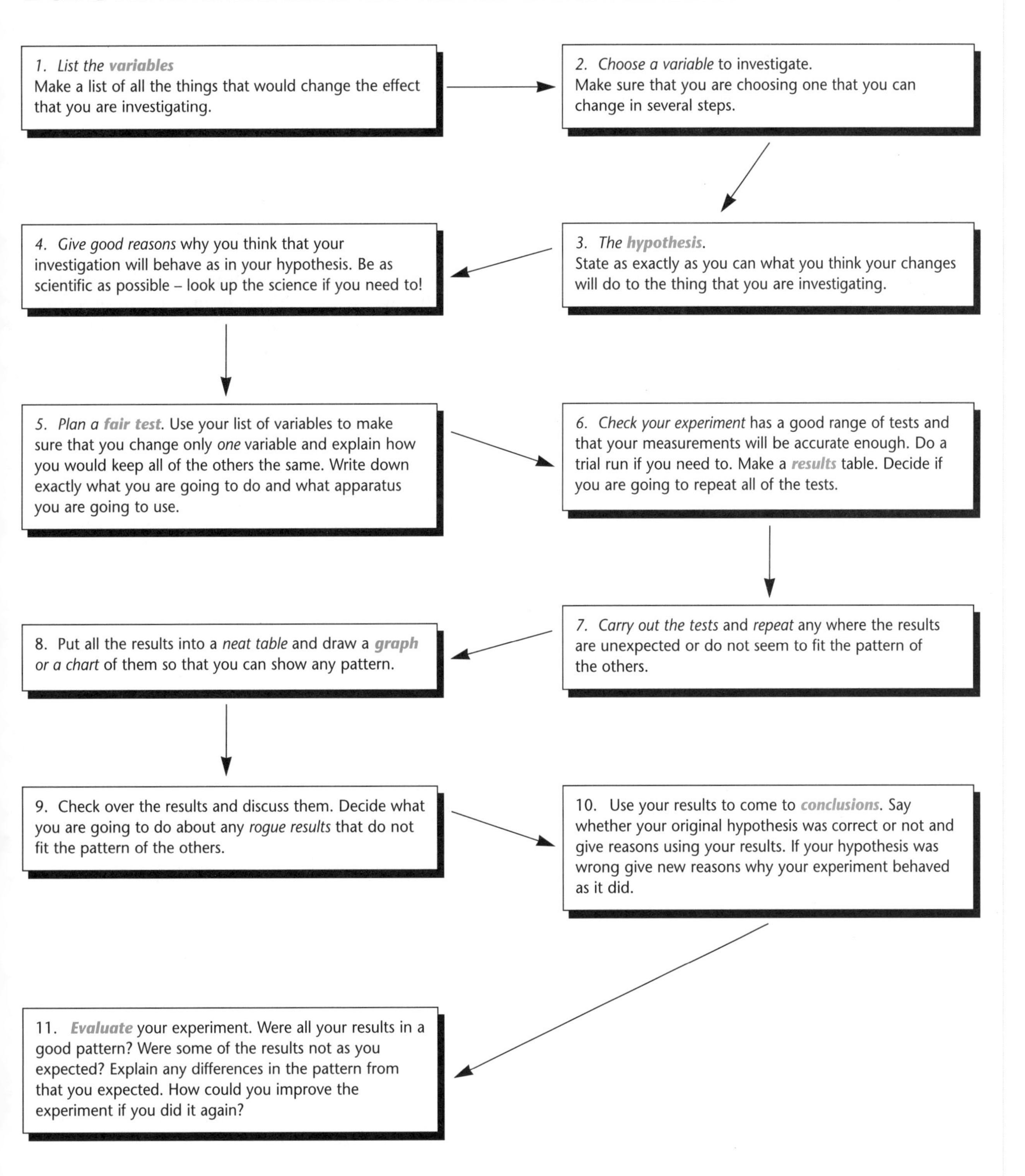

1. *List the* ***variables***
Make a list of all the things that would change the effect that you are investigating.
2. *Choose a variable* to investigate.
Make sure that you are choosing one that you can change in several steps.
3. *The* ***hypothesis***.
State as exactly as you can what you think your changes will do to the thing that you are investigating.
4. *Give good reasons* why you think that your investigation will behave as in your hypothesis. Be as scientific as possible – look up the science if you need to!
5. *Plan a* ***fair test***. Use your list of variables to make sure that you change only *one* variable and explain how you would keep all of the others the same. Write down exactly what you are going to do and what apparatus you are going to use.
6. *Check your experiment* has a good range of tests and that your measurements will be accurate enough. Do a trial run if you need to. Make a ***results*** table. Decide if you are going to repeat all of the tests.
7. *Carry out the tests* and *repeat* any where the results are unexpected or do not seem to fit the pattern of the others.
8. Put all the results into a *neat table* and draw a ***graph*** *or a chart* of them so that you can show any pattern.
9. Check over the results and discuss them. Decide what you are going to do about any *rogue results* that do not fit the pattern of the others.
10. Use your results to come to ***conclusions***. Say whether your original hypothesis was correct or not and give reasons using your results. If your hypothesis was wrong give new reasons why your experiment behaved as it did.
11. ***Evaluate*** your experiment. Were all your results in a good pattern? Were some of the results not as you expected? Explain any differences in the pattern from that you expected. How could you improve the experiment if you did it again?

CARS 'n' TRACKS

Here is an example of a short investigation and how you might approach it. You might like to have a look at the problem that is set and then use the flow diagram on the first page of this Appendix to try to solve it. They you can check your answers with the following ideas.

You are given a small toy car and a length of plastic track.

Investigate the factors that change how far the car will travel along the floor after you release it down the track.

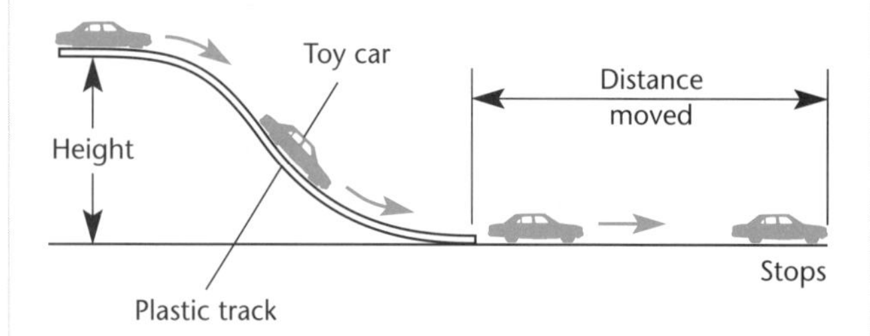

1. First list all of the variables

These should include:

- the height from which you release the car,
- the surface that the car runs along,
- the weight of the car,
- the 'streamlining' of the car and any others that you think might have an affect that you could investigate.

2. Choose one of the variables that looks interesting

I will choose the height that the car is released from. This can be done from a range of heights and is easy to measure and repeat. Changing the surface would be a poorer choice because there are a limited number if possibilities and you cannot do a range of values to see clear patterns and plot graphs. It is better to choose something that changes 'continuously'.

3. State a hypothesis – a prediction

I think that the car will go further along the floor when released from a greater height. I think that it will go twice as far if I double the height. (A *good* maths student might say that the distance will be proportional to the height!).

4. Give reasons

I could simply say that the car will speed up more from the bigger height and that makes if go further. I can be more scientific if I say that the car has more potential energy at a greater height and that this gets turned into kinetic energy. The car with more kinetic energy will go further against friction along the floor. Being more scientific gets better marks. Looks things up in books in your library or your notebooks if you need to.

5. Plan a fair test that keeps all of the other variables the same so they are 'controlled'

In my case this will mean always using the same car and the same stretch of the floor. The list of variables is useful here and you *must* write down what makes the test fair.

Choose a suitable range for the variable you have chosen. I will release the car from a height of 5 cm, 10 cm and then each 5 cm up to 40 cm. I will need to test two or three times at each height to check the results. I might decide to use the average distance travelled.

6. Do a trial run

I would need to know if my car worked at 5 cm and if it was too fast or too slow at 40 cm high. I can quickly do these and decide if I need to change the range – would it be better to go up in 10 cm stages? Would I get enough results if I did? (Remember that you need at least five results to plot a reasonable graph.) My results table would have the following headings:

Height above floor/cm	Distance travelled/cm 1	2	3	Average distance/cm
10				
15				
20				
25				
30				
35				
40				

7. Now the fun bit – do all the tests and record the results in your table

Repeat any results that are obviously a long way from the pattern of the others and do not include any rogue results in the averages.

8. Plot a graph of the results

Put the variable that you changed along the bottom and the measurements that you made up the side. In my case, the heights go along the bottom and the distances travelled go up the side. Check that each square on each axis increases by the same amount on the scale. Put the best curve or straight line that you can as near as you can to all the points – remember *not* to join the dots!

9. You can check again now to see that you have not included any rogue results

If your line is an odd shape make sure that you have plotted the points properly on a good scale.

10. Use your graph to see if your hypothesis was right

Explain again how the results fit in with your reasons. If your results show that your hypothesis was wrong then write down clearly what really happens and see if you can now explain what you found with good scientific reasons.

11. Now you have done the experiment you should be able to write down how someone else could do it and improve it

Was there a better way to measure the heights or the distances travelled? Was I careful in doing my measuring? I will know that my measuring was probably good enough if all my results were quite close to a good straight line or curve on the graph. If you are sure that your results do show that you were right but some so not quite seem to be exactly as you expected you should try to explain why not.

You will probably change the pattern of this and add things like a nice cover on the front, but make sure that you have not left anything out! I have just marked an investigation with a really wonderful front cover that must have taken hours to do but the student forgot to do a proper detailed conclusion and lost a lot of marks!

PHOTOSYNTHESIS IN PONDWEED

Photosynthesis is a very important chemical reaction occurring in the leaves of all plants. The equation is:

$$\text{Carbon dioxide} + \text{Water} \xrightarrow{\text{light}} \text{Sugar} + \text{Oxygen}$$

If you are investigating factors that change the rate of the reaction, you first have to think of a way to *measure* the rate.

In land plants this is difficult because you cannot easily measure the amount of sugar or oxygen that is made. In water plants it is quite easy because bubbles of oxygen gas are produced. This is why pondweed is usually used for this investigation.

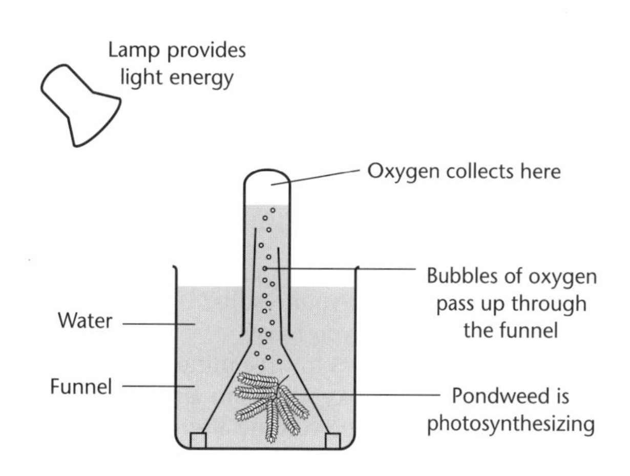

Which factors change the rate?

If you look at the equation, you might guess that

- amount of light,
- amount of carbon dioxide,

would affect the rate. Other things that you could investigate are:

- colour of light,
- temperature,
- amount of pondweed.

The factors that would change the rate are the ***variables***.

Choose a variable

If you choose one that you can change in small steps you will be able to plot a line ***graph***, e.g.,

- you could change the amount of light by moving the lamp closer,
- you could change the amount of carbon dioxide by adding sodium hydrogen carbonate to the water,
- you could change the temperature by adding warm water to the beaker.

This would help you to see a pattern in your ***results***. Choose one variable to investigate, e.g., ***temperature***.

The hypothesis

Say what you think will happen!

Use scientific reasons to explain why

If you look at the equation for photosynthesis you can see that ***light*** provides the energy for the reaction to occur, and ***carbon dioxide*** is a raw material in the reaction.

Why does temperature change the rate?

Photosynthesis is an enzyme-controlled reaction and enzymes work best when they are warm, but not too hot.

The plan

Think about which apparatus you need and how you will change your chosen variable

- Decide which temperatures you will test – it is best to use a range, e.g., 10°C, 20°C, 30°C, 40°C, etc.
- Decide how to collect your results
  How much time will you have?
  Will you count bubbles for five minutes?
  Will you collect the oxygen gas in a measuring cylinder and record the volume after one hour?

Make it a fair test

If you are changing the temperature, all the other variables must stay the same. This means:

- same amount of light (keep the lamp in the same place),
- same amount of carbon dioxide (put in the same amount of sodium hydrogen carbonate at the start of each experiment),
- same piece of pondweed.

Do the experiment

Collect your results and put them into a table. Do not forget to repeat the tests so that you can work out an average.

	Amount of oxygen produced			
Temp/°C	*1*	*2*	*3*	*Average*
10				
20				
30				
40				

If you have to change your plan, do not forget to write down what you actually did, and why you changed.

Draw a graph

This should be a line graph of your results, with temperature along the bottom (x axis) and amount of oxygen up the side (y axis). Join the points with a straight line or smooth curve. If any points are obviously wrong (i.e., they do not fit the pattern), do not join them up.

Write a conclusion

You should be able to write *one sentence* to say what you have found out. Does temperature affect the rate of photosynthesis? Does an increase in temperature cause an increase or decrease in rate?

Now *explain* your results. Was your prediction right? Were your reasons right? If you were wrong, try to explain your results now.

Evaluate your experiment

Where might you have made mistakes? If you had to start again, would you change your plan, or could you make any small improvements to it?

WHAT ARE THE CONDITIONS IN WHICH ACID RAIN HAS THE BIGGEST AFFECT ON BUILDING STONE?

Strand (i): Predicting and planning

At the highest level you could consider the following variables:

- rock type,
- concentration of acid,
- temperature.

You could predict that ***sandstone*** and ***limestone*** will react differently or that chalk, limestone and ***marble*** would react differently.

Another investigation could be to predict that more concentrated acid will react quicker or that sulphuric acid and nitric acid might react at different rates.

To get top marks, however, it is essential that you mention the ***chemical reaction*** between limestone and acid, or that you explain why chemical reactions are faster if acid is more concentrated.

Strand (ii): Observing and measuring

Remember it is important that you do not change more than one variable at a time. If you are going to compare results from two different experiments, it must be a fair test.

In this investigation it would be possible to measure how much ***carbon dioxide*** is produced or to measure the decrease in mass of the rock as the reaction progresses.

You need to make very accurate measurements. You also should repeat your experiment if you have time. If your teacher allows it, you could swop results with other groups in the class. Do remember, however, if the results are to be valid the other groups must have carried out exactly the same experiment.

Strand (iii): Recording results

Always record your results in a good clear table.

If you measure either the production of carbon dioxide gas or the decrease in mass of the rock, plot these points on a line graph.

Remember you need at least four points to produce a reasonable line graph. You can look for patterns in your graph. Always check your graph plot if some points look odd.

You should try to produce a line of best fit for a whole range of results.

Strand (iv): Concluding and evaluating

Do not just simply repeat your prediction.

Look very critically at your graph: are all the points on the line? If not, do you need to repeat these results?

Do the results show your prediction was wrong or were your experimental methods wrong?

If the sandstone did not react you need to explain that acids do not react with it. You must always draw on the scientific ideas you mentioned in the prediction stage of the investigation.

You can also suggest further investigations that can be done. For example, is acid rain only one type of acid?

PROMPT QUESTIONS FOR INVESTIGATIONS

The following questions should help you to improve from levels 5 to 8 in the 'Investigation of the effect of acid rain on different rocks'.

Strand (i): Predicting and planning

What ideas are you investigating in your experiment? Can you use scientific knowledge or theory to help you ask questions, suggest ideas and make predictions about what you think will happen in your investigation? (Remember you can use information from library books or the scientific books in the laboratory.)

Can you use scientific knowledge to:

- help you predict how one input variable (i.e., the thing you are deliberately varying to find out what effect it has, e.g., different types of rocks) will affect the outcome variable (i.e., the thing you are measuring).
- predict which input variable might affect the investigation the most?
- predict some of the likely measurements and outline the complete investigation?

Strand (ii): Observing and measuring

What input variables did you keep constant to make sure it was a fair test?
Can you handle and understand the effects of two or more input variables?
How did you make sure the measurements were accurate enough so that you could get sensible results? Could you have used any other measuring instruments?
Have you identified all the variables involved in the investigation, including the ones being controlled (i.e., the things you are keeping the same to make sure the investigation is a fair test) and made the measurements as accurate as possible?

Strand (iii): Recording results

Can you record your results in a variety of different ways?
Can you show your results clearly using tables, line graphs and bar charts where appropriate?
Have you chosen a good scale on the graph paper to show your results and can you draw a 'line of best fit'?

Strand (iv): Concluding and evaluating

Can you find any patterns that link your conclusions to your original predictions?
Can you criticize your results and understand when your results could have another meaning?
Can you use your results to explain:

- the relationship between your chosen variables using a scientific theory that explains the results?
- which of the input variables has the greatest effect and explain how your results might be partly true or could be improved?
- the part each stage of the investigation plays in getting results and conclusions?

APPENDIX 2

KEY STAGE 3 PROGRAMME OF STUDY

The requirements of the programmes of study apply across Experimental and Investigative Science, Life Processes and Living Things, Materials and their Properties and Physical Processes.

1. Systematic enquiry

Pupils should be given opportunities to:

a use practical tasks and investigations to acquire scientific knowledge, understanding and skills;

b use both first-hand experience and secondary sources of information, and to decide which sources to use;

c work quantitatively;

d choose ways of using IT to collect, store, retrieve and present scientific information.

2. Application of science

a relate scientific knowledge and understanding to familiar phenomena and to things that are used every day;

b consider how applications of science, including those related to health, influence the quality of their lives;

c relate scientific knowledge and understanding to the care of living things and of the environment;

d consider the benefits and drawbacks of scientific and technological developments in environmental and other contexts.

3. The nature of scientific ideas

a consider the importance of evidence and creative thought in the development of scientific theories;

b consider how scientific knowledge and understanding needs to be supported by empirical evidence;

c relate social and historical contexts to scientific ideas by studying how at least one scientific idea has changed over time.

4. Communication

Pupils should be taught to:

a use a wide range of scientific terms and symbols, and to consider why scientific and mathematical conventions are used;

b use SI units;

c present their ideas through the use of diagrams, graphs, tables and charts, using appropriate scientific and mathematical conventions.

5. Health and safety

a take responsibility for recognising hazards in a range of work with living things, materials and devices with which they are familiar;

b use appropriate information sources to assess risks, both immediate and cumulative;

c apply their knowledge and take action to control the risks to themselves and to others.

AT1 EXPERIMENTAL AND INVESTIGATIVE SCIENCE

Contexts derived from Life Processes and Living Things, Materials and their Properties and Physical Processes should be used to teach pupils about experimental and investigative methods. On some occasions, the whole process of investigating an idea should be carried out by pupils themselves.

1. Planning experimental procedures

Pupils should be taught:

a to use scientific knowledge and understanding to turn ideas suggested to them, and their own ideas, into a form that can be investigated;

b to carry out trial runs where appropriate;

c to make predictions where it is appropriate to do so;

d to consider, in simple contexts, key factors that need to be taken into account;

e to isolate the effect of changing one factor;

f to decide how many observations or measurements need to be made and what range they should cover;

g to consider contexts, *e.g. fieldwork*, where variables cannot readily be controlled, and to consider how evidence may be collected in these contexts;

h to select apparatus, equipment and techniques, taking account of safety requirements.

2. Obtaining evidence

a to use a range of apparatus and equipment safely and with skill;

b to make observations and measurements to a degree of precision appropriate to the context;

c to make sufficient relevant observations and measurements for reliable evidence;

d to repeat measurements and observations when appropriate;

e to record evidence clearly and appropriately as they carry out the work.

3. Analysing evidence and drawing conclusions

Pupils should be taught:

a to present qualitative and quantitative data clearly;

b to use graphs appropriate to the results obtained;

c to use lines of best fit where appropriate;

d to identify trends or patterns in results;

e to use results to draw conclusions;

f to decide whether the results support the original prediction when one has been made;

g to try to explain conclusions in the light of their knowledge and understanding of science.

4. Considering the strength of the evidence

a to consider whether the evidence is sufficient to enable firm conclusions to be drawn;

b to consider anomalies in observations or measurements and explain them where possible;

c to consider improvements to the methods that have been used.

AT2 LIFE PROCESSES AND LIVING THINGS

Work on life processes should be related to pupils' knowledge and understanding of the structures of the systems through which these processes take place. Work on variation within an environment should be related to adaptation, feeding relationships and competition.

1. Life processes and cell activity

Pupils should be taught:

a that many animals and plants have organs that enable life processes, *e.g. reproduction*, to take place;

b that animals and plants are made up of cells;

c the functions of the cell membrane, cytoplasm and nucleus in plant and animal cells;

d the functions of chloroplasts and cell walls in plant cells;

e ways in which some cells, including ciliated epithelial cells, sperm, ova, palisade cells and root hair cells, are adapted to their functions.

2. Humans as organisms

Nutrition

a that balanced diets contain carbohydrates, proteins, fats, minerals, vitamins, fibre and water;

b some sources of the main food components in the diet;

c that food is used as a fuel during respiration to maintain the body's activity and as a raw material for growth and repair;

d the principles of digestion, including the role of enzymes;

e that the products of digestion are absorbed and waste material is egested;

Circulation

f how blood acts as a transport medium and about the exchange of substances at the capillaries;

Movement

g the role of the skeleton, joints and muscles in movement;

h the principle of antagonistic muscle pairs, *e.g. biceps and triceps*;

Reproduction

i about the physical and emotional changes that take place during adolescence;

j the human reproductive system, including the menstrual cycle and fertilisation;

k how the foetus develops in the uterus, including the role of the placenta;

Breathing

l how lung structure enables gas exchange to take place;

m how smoking affects lung structure and gas exchange;

Respiration

n that aerobic respiration involves the reaction in cells between oxygen and food used as a fuel;

o that during aerobic respiration glucose is broken down to carbon dioxide and water;

p to summarise aerobic respiration in a word equation;

Health

Pupils should be taught:

q that the abuse of alcohol, solvents and other drugs affects health;

r that bacteria and viruses can affect health;

s that the body's natural defences may be enhanced by immunisation and medicines.

3. Green plants as organisms

Nutrition and growth

a that photosynthesis produces biomass and oxygen;

b that plants need carbon dioxide, water and light for photosynthesis;

c to summarise photosynthesis in a word equation;

d that nitrogen and other elements in addition to carbon, oxygen and hydrogen are required for plant growth;

e that root hairs absorb water and minerals from the soil;

Reproduction

f how sexual reproduction occurs in flowering plants, including fertilisation and see formation;

Respiration

g that plants carry out aerobic respiration.

4. Variation, classification and inheritance

Variation

a that there is variation within species and between species;

b that variation within a species can have both environmental and inherited causes;

Classification

c how keys can be used to identify animals and plants;

d to classify living things into the major taxonomic groups;

Inheritance

e that selective breeding can lead to new varieties.

5. Living things in their environment

Adaptation

a that different habitats support different plants and animals;

b how some organisms are adapted to survive daily and seasonal changes in their habitats, *e.g. light intensity, temperature*;

Feeding relationships

c how food chains may be quantified using pyramids of numbers;

d that in food webs there are several food chains with species in common;

e how toxic materials may accumulate in food chains;

Competition

f factors affecting the size of populations, including predation and competition for resources;

g that organisms successfully competing in their environment contribute relatively more offspring to the next generation.

AT3 MATERIALS AND THEIR PROPERTIES

Work on the classification of materials, the ways in which materials can be changed and the separation of mixtures should be related to pupils' knowledge about particles as constituents of matter. Work on chemical reactions should emphasise patterns of reaction and the importance of chemical change in making new substances.

Pupils should be taught:

1. Classifying materials

Solids, liquids and gases

a to recognise differences between solids, liquids and gases, in terms of properties, *e.g. density, compressibility, ease of flow, maintenance of shape and volume*;

b a simple model of solids, liquids and gases, in terms of the arrangement and movement of particles;

c how the particle theory of matter can be used to explain the properties of solids, liquids and gases, including changes of state, gas pressure and diffusion;

Elements

d that elements consist of atoms and that all atoms of the same element contain the same number of protons;

e that elements can be represented by symbols and that the periodic table shows all the elements;

Compounds

f how some elements combine through chemical reactions to form compounds, *e.g. water, carbon dioxide, magnesium oxide, sodium chloride*;

g that compounds have a definite composition, and to represent compounds by formulae;

Mixtures

h that mixtures, *e.g. air, sea water*, contain constituents that are not combined;

i about methods, including filtration, distillation and chromatography, that can be used to separate mixtures into their constituents;

Metals and non-metals

j that most metallic elements are shiny solids at room temperature, that most are good thermal and electrical conductors, and that a few are magnetic;

k that non-metallic elements vary widely in their physical properties, that many are gases at room temperature, and that most are poor thermal and electrical conductors;

l to use these properties to classify elements as metals or non-metals.

2. Changing materials

Physical changes

a that when physical changes, *e.g. changes of state, formation of solutions*, take place, mass is conserved;

b that solutes have different solubilities in different solvents and at different temperatures;

c that different materials change state at different temperatures;

d to relate changes of state to energy transfers;

e how materials expand and contract with changes in temperature, and that the forces that result are sometimes considerable;

Geological changes

f how rocks are weathered by expansion and contraction and by the freezing of water;

g that the rock cycle involves sedimentary, metamorphic and igneous processes that take place over different timescales;

h that rocks are classified as sedimentary, metamorphic or igneous on the basis of their processes of formation, and that these processes affect their texture and the minerals they contain;

Chemical reactions

i that when chemical reactions take place, mass is conserved;

j that virtually all materials, including those in living systems, are made through chemical reactions;

k to represent chemical reactions by word equations;

l that there are different types of reaction, including oxidation and thermal decomposition;

m that useful products can be made from chemical reactions, including the production of metals from metal oxides;

n about chemical reactions, *e.g. corrosion of iron, spoiling of food*, that are generally not useful;

o that energy transfers that accompany chemical reaction, including the burning of fuels, can be controlled and used;

p about possible effects of burning fossil fuels on the environment.

3. Patterns of behaviour

Metals

a the reactions of metals with oxygen, water and acid;

b the displacement reactions that take place between metals and solutions of salts of other metals;

c how a reactivity series of metals can be determined by considering these reactions;

d how this reactivity series can be used to make predictions about other reactions;

Acids and bases

e that pH is a measure of the acidity of a solution;

f to use indicators to classify solutions as acidic, neutral or alkaline;

g the reactions of acids with metals and bases, including carbonates, to form salts;

h some everyday applications of neutralisation, *e.g. the treatment of indigestion, the treatment of acid soil;*

i how acids in the atmosphere can lead to corrosion of metal and chemical weathering of rock.

AT4 PHYSICAL PROCESSES

The links between electricity and magnetism and between forces and motion should be made clear. Work on energy transfer should be related to pupils' knowledge of electricity, light and sound. Work on energy resources should be related to pupils' knowledge about nutrition and chemical reactions. Work on the solar system should be related to pupils' knowledge of forces and motion and the behaviour of light.

Pupils should be taught:

1. Electricity and magnetism

Static charge

a that an insulating material can be charged by friction;

b that there are forces of attraction between positive and negative charges, and forces of repulsion between like charges;

Current in circuits

c how to measure current in series and parallel circuits;

d that the current in a series circuit depends on the number of cells and the number and nature of other components;

e that current is not 'used up' by components in circuits;

f that current is a flow of charge;

Magnetic fields

g about magnetic fields as regions of space where magnetic materials experience forces;

h the field pattern produced by a bar magnet;

Electromagnets

i that a current in a coil produces a magnetic field pattern;

j how electromagnets are constructed and used in devices, *e.g. electric bells, relays.*

2. Forces and motion

Force and linear motion

a how to determine the speed of a moving object;

b the quantitative relationship between speed, distance and time;

c that unbalanced forces change the speed and/or direction of moving objects;

d that balanced forces produce no change in the movement of an object;

e ways in which frictional forces, including air resistance, affect motion, *e.g. the effect of air resistance on a descending parachute, the effect of friction between a tyre and a road;*

Force and rotation

f that forces can cause objects to turn about a pivot;

g the principle of moments and its application to situation involving one pivot;

Force and pressure

h the quantitative relationship between the force acting normally per unit are on a surface and the pressure on that surface;

i some applications of this relationship, *e.g. the use of snow shoes, the effect of sharp blades.*

3. Light and sound

The behaviour of light

a that, in a uniform medium, light travels in a straight line at a finite speed;

b how shadows are formed;

c that light travels much faster than sound;

d that non-luminous objects are seen because light scattered from then enters the eye;

e how light is reflected at plane surfaces;

f how light is refracted at the boundary between two different materials;

g that white light can be dispersed to give a range of colours;

h the effect of colour filters on white light;

i how coloured objects appear in white light and in other colours of light;

Hearing

j that sound waves cause the ear drum to vibrate and that different people have different audible ranges;

k the effects of loud sound on the ear;

Vibration and sound

l that sound waves cannot travel through a vacuum;

m the link between the loudness of a sound and the amplitude of the vibration causing it;

n the link between the pitch of a sound and the frequency of the vibration causing it.

4. The Earth and beyond

The solar system

a that the apparent daily and annual movement of the Sun and other stars is caused by the movement of the Earth;

b the relative positions of the Earth, Sun and planets in the solar system;

c the gravitational forces determine the movements of planets around the Sun;

d that the Sun and other stars are light sources and that the planets and other bodies are seen by reflected light;

e that artificial satellites can be used to observe the Earth and to explore the solar system.

5. Energy resources and energy transfer

Energy resources

a that there is a variety of energy resources, including oil, gas, coal, biomass, food, wind, waves and batteries;

b that the Sun is the ultimate source of most of the Earth's energy resources;

c that electricity is generated using a variety of energy resources;

d that some of the Earth's energy resources are renewable and some are not;

Conservation of energy

e the distinction between temperature and the total energy contained in a body;

f that energy can be transferred and stored;

g that energy is conserved;

h that although energy is always conserved, it may be dissipated, reducing its availability as a resource.

CHECKPOINT ANSWERS

Checkpoint answers, other than those listed below, can be found in the text preceding the checkpoint.

Acceleration acceleration, m/s², accelerate, force

Ammeter

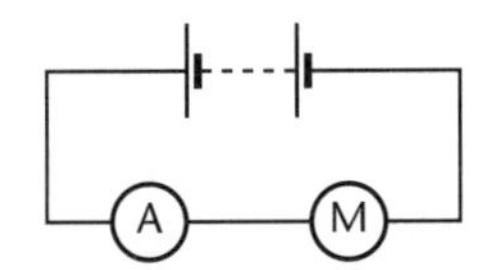

Blast furnace

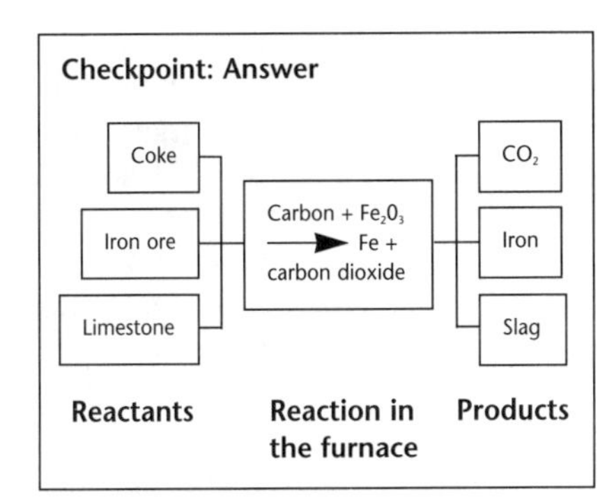

Breathing
bell jar = rib-cage
balloons = lungs
tubing = trachea and bronchi
rubber sheet = diaphragm
If the rubber sheet was pushed up, the balloons would deflate, because the volume inside the bell jar would decrease, so pressure in the bell jar would increase, forcing air to move from the balloons through the tubing.

Cell (electrical) A secondary cell can be recharged but a primary cell cannot. Primary – dry cell, secondary – lead-acid cell. Cost, can always have a cell available, etc.

Changes of state

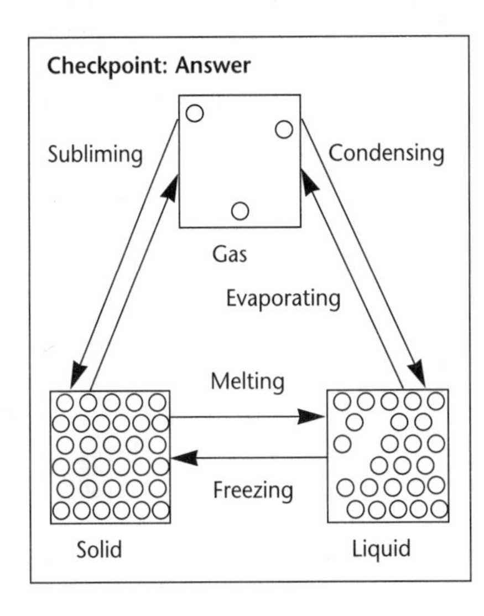

Compost Holes allow air to circulate. Decomposers need the oxygen in air to stay alive. Decomposers need water to stay alive. Earthworms will feed on the waste material, and will break it up into smaller pieces. They will also mix the layers in the compost bin, so that decomposers come into contact with more waste material. Decomposers are feeding on the waste material, and then using the food for respiration, to make energy. All respiring organisms give out heat.

Conduction of heat Metals, partly by passing vibrations along between layers of atoms and partly by free electrons carrying energy along. To make pans, the pipes inside boilers, the tubes of radiators.

Conductor (electricity) Metals, carbon.

Compounds

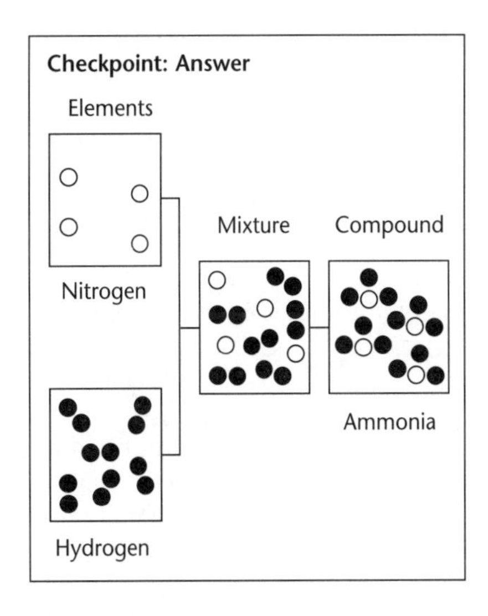

Iron and oxygen. Sodium, sulphur and oxygen. Magnesium, hydrogen and oxygen.

Counter forces Air resistance, rolling resistance, friction in bearings, weight when going uphill, wind.

Current The ammeter will gave the same reading in both places.

Dalton Magnesia (magnesium oxide), lime (calcium oxide), soda (sodium carbonate), potash (potassium carbonate), barytes (barium sulphate).

Density $\text{Density} = \frac{\text{mass}}{\text{volume}}$, 920kg/m³.

Dispersal of seeds
(a) Sycamore – wind
(b) Cleavers – carried on outside of animal

(c) Thistle – wind
(d) Stock – self-dispersal
(e) Balsam – self-dispersal
(f) Blackberry – eaten by animals
(g) Acorn – eaten by animals

Division of labour

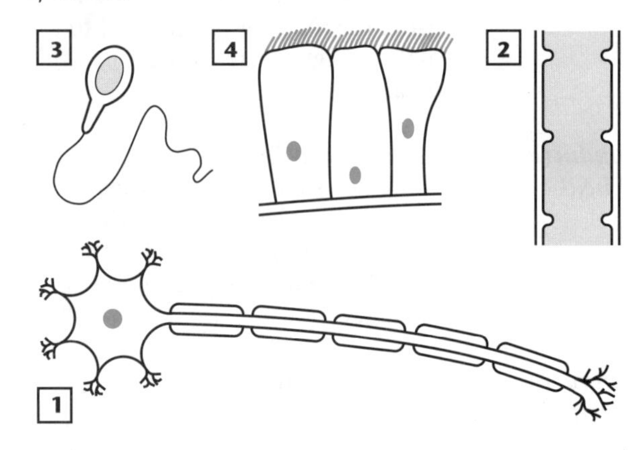

Energy Coal, oil, gas, wind, wave, water (in hydroelectric) solar, etc. Energy is not created or destroyed, the total remains the same.

Energy chains and arrows Electricity, light, heat.

Energy in food Energy = volume of water × rise in temperature × 4.2
= 20 × 42 × 4.2
= 3528 J
The peanut had a mass of 2g, so 100g of peanut would contain 3528 × 50 = 176400 J of energy. This is 176.4 kJ

Energy and food chains As energy is passed along a food chain, some is lost at each stage. If humans eat crops, they are the second organism in the chain, so they will receive more of the energy from the plants. If humans eat animals, they are the third or fourth organisms in the chain, and more energy will have been lost, so they receive less of the original energy from the plants.

Expansion Cracks in bridges, bending of railway lines – leave gaps. Breaking of oil pipelines – make in zig-zags, not straight, etc. Thermostat, fitting bearings to axles, etc. – see text for details.

Filter Blue, black, only blue light gets through blue filter and this is absorbed by the red filter – when no light passes it appears black.

Food chains plant, photosynthesis, producer, herbivore/primary consumer, carnivore/secondary consumer, consumer, top carnivore, decomposer.

Food webs: ***(See note on p. 59.)***

(a) Owls would decrease, because foxes will be eating more squirrels and voles, so they have less food.
(b) Sparrows would increase, because they would have more food.
(c) Voles would decrease, because the larger number of sparrows would lead to an increase in the numbers of owls (because they have more food). If there are more owls, they will eat more voles.
(d) Voles would decrease, because owls and foxes would not be able to eat squirrels, so more voles would be eaten.

Gas exchange B would change colour first, because the air you breathe out contains more carbon dioxide than the air you breathe in (it is made in the body during respiration).

Germination
A – no, no water
B – yes, it has water, air and warmth
C – no, no air
D – yes, it has water, air and warmth, and light is not needed for germination
E – no, it is too cold

Insulator (heat) Their particles are widely spaced and they do not have free electrons. Trap it into small pockets or layers to stop convection. Loft insulation, cavity wall insulation, double glazing, carpets.

Kelvin 400K, 727°C

Keys
(a) River crowfoot
(b) Perforated pondweed
(c) Ivy leaved crowfoot
(d) Curled pondweed
(e) Round leaved crowfoot
(f) Water soldier

Kinetic Energy Moving, speed, mass, speed.

Magnets Repel, attract, it will repel the N pole of a compass or point N if freely suspended.

Menstruation Menstruation is another word for a period (when the uterus lining breaks up and passes out of the vagina). It lasts about five days. The menstrual cycle is all the changes happening in a woman's reproductive system each month. It lasts about 28 days.

Moment Turning force. Force, distance. Moment = force × distance of force from pivot.

Parallel New bulb will be the same brightness. Current will be doubled.

Potential difference Voltmeter. Resistance.

Predator – prey relationships
A – Slugs decrease because the number of frogs is rising, so more slugs are being eaten.
B – Frogs decrease because there are not enough slugs for them to eat.
C – The number of frogs will increase (because there are lots of slugs to eat). The number of slugs will start to decrease (more are being eaten by frogs). The number of plants will increase (there are less slugs to eat them).

Pressure Pressure, greater.

$$\text{Pressure} = \frac{\text{force}}{\text{area}}, \text{ pascal (Pa)}$$

Principle of moments 12.5g

Quadrat Average number of daisy plants $= \frac{37}{10} = 3.7$

Total number of daisy plants in the whole garden: If the quadrat has an area of 0.25 m^2, and the garden has an area of 100 m^2, the gardren is 40 times bigger than the quadrat $\left(\frac{100}{0.25} = 40\right)$

There is an average of 3.7 plants per quadrat, so the number on the whole garden will be 3.7 × 40 = 148.

Refraction Less, towards, normal.

Relay Any two examples where the relay switches a larger current or voltage.

Resistance Larger, faster.

Salts Zinc nitrate, potassium sulphate, sodium chloride and water.

Series Both bulbs on and same brightness but dimmer than the single bulb was (assuming that the bulbs are identical). Current become smaller. Increase current to same as it was before by using a bigger voltage.

Smoking Tar causes cancer. Nicotine is addictive (makes you depend on cigarettes). Carbon monoxide affects the growth of the foetus when a pregnant woman smokes. Nicotine increases the risk of heat attacks. Smoke particles and tar damage cilia.

Sound Longitudinal. Reflected sound. See text for a suitable method. Time will be hardest to measure because it will be short. Because there will be no particles to vibrate.

Sources of energy Coal, oil, gas. Wind, wave, tidal, geothermal, solar, biomass, hydroelectric. Nuclear – from atoms and being split into smaller pieces. Geothermal – hot rocks in Earth's centre.

Speed

$$\text{Speed} = \frac{\text{Distance moved}}{\text{Time taken}}$$

2.5 m/s

Static electric charge Dust attracted to polished surfaces – especially plastic. Clothing becoming charges so that it 'clings'. Spraying paint or week killer. Removing dust/dirt/smoke from chimneys. Follow the explanations in the text and show what happens to the charges. Remember that it is only the negative electrons that move.

Temperature scale Two, fixed. Celsius, 0, °C, –183°C (boiling point of oxygen), 15 million °C (in Sun).

Variation
flower colour – genetic
fingerprint type – genetic
number of leaves – environmental
blood group – genetic ability to play piano – environmental
height in humans – both (you will inherit genes for height from your parents, but will not grow properly

if you do not have a balanced diet, or suffer from some illnesses).

Varieties

1. apples – Golden delicious, Cox's, Braeburn, Granny Smiths, Russett, Bramley
2. cats – Persian, Manx, Siamese, Burmese, Cornish rex, Japanese bob-tail
3. horses – Palomino, Shire-horse, Shetland pony, Cleveland bay, Welsh cob, race-horse, Suffolk

Hamsters and gerbils are different species – they could not breed together.

Voltage

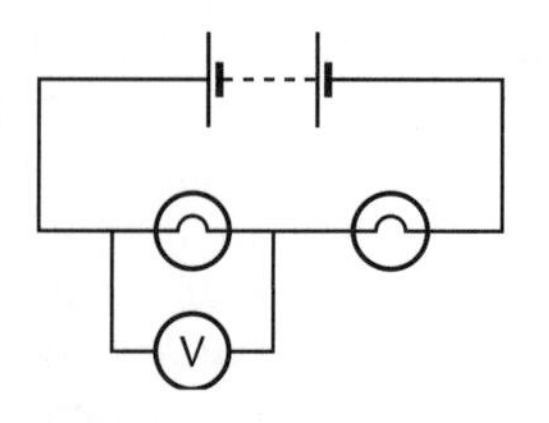

Wave

Transverse, longitudinal. Transverse vibration is across the direction of travel as in a water ripple or light. Longitudinal vibration is to and fro in the direction of travel as in a sound wave so that compressions travel along.

Work

112.5 J
The answer will be 0.75 × your weight (remember that your weight will be 10 × your mass in kg.)